442795

KT-520-817

Oil Paintings in Public Ownership in the National Trust for Scotland

The *Oil Paintings in Public Ownership* series of catalogues is an extraordinary work in progress. Published by The Public Catalogue Foundation, it is the result of the determined efforts of a small team of administrative staff, researchers and photographers spread across the United Kingdom.

Our national collection of oil paintings in public ownership is probably one of the finest anywhere in the world. It is held not just by our museums and galleries but is also to be found in hospitals, universities and other civic buildings throughout the United Kingdom. A large proportion of these paintings are not on display and many have never before been reproduced.

This series of books for the first time allows the public to see an entire photographic record of these works – a collection likely to number some 200,000 in total. In doing so, these volumes provide a unique insight into our nation's artistic and cultural history.

As Patron of The Public Catalogue Foundation, my visits to collections across the country have highlighted to me not only the desire of curators to publicise their paintings, but also the limited resources at their disposal. The Foundation's work goes a long way towards helping to create access to these collections, while at the same time giving the British public the opportunity to see and enjoy *all* the paintings that they own.

I wish The Public Catalogue Foundation every success in its continuing endeavours.

Camilla

Agnes Murray Kynynmond.
Daughter of Hugh Dalrymple Murray Kynynmond.
Wife of the Right Hon. Sir Gilbert Elliot of Minto
Bart. M.P.

Oil Paintings in Public Ownership

in the

National Trust for Scotland

Funding Patron
The Mercers' Company

Coordinator: Dr Laura Walters

The Public Catalogue Foundation
Patron
HRH The Duchess of Cornwall

Contents

Image opposite HRH The Duchess of Cornwall's statement: Raeburn, Henry, 1756–1823, *Mrs James Gregory, née Isobella Macleod (1770–1847)* (p. 96)

Facing page: Batoni, Pompeo, 1708–1787, *George Gordon, Lord Haddo*, 1775, The National Trust for Scotland, Haddo House (p. 33)

Image opposite title page: Ramsay, Allan, 1713–1784, *Agnes Murray Kynynmond, Daughter of Hugh Dalrymple Murray Kynynmond, Wife of the Right Honourable Sir Gilbert Elliot of Minto, Bt, MP*, 1739, The National Trust for Scotland, Newhailes (p. 143)

Preface

As Chief Executive, I warmly welcome the successful publication of the catalogue of paintings held by the National Trust for Scotland, in association with the Public Catalogue Foundation. This work is an exciting step in opening our collections to wider access, study and understanding.

Covering just over 1,900 paintings on display across Scotland, this catalogue reveals the incredible richness and diversity of one of the country's finest picture collections. Ranging from exceptional portraits such as Raeburn's *Isobella Macleod* and Ramsay's *Agnes Murray Kynynmond* to affectionate sketches of pets by their owners, we are immensely proud to care for these works on behalf of the Nation.

We aspire to present these pictures within the rooms for which they were commissioned or acquired. Many of our historic objects are set amongst the original decorative interiors of our houses – alongside the textiles, furniture and ceramics that survive *in situ*. By preserving the integrity of these displays we are brought closer to the people who lived and worked in the castles, great houses, homes and cottages we care for, and it is this insight which makes a visit to a Trust house or castle so intimate and revealing.

Kate Mavor, Chief Executive, National Trust for Scotland

Image opposite HRH The Duchess of Cornwall's statement: Raeburn, Henry, 1756–1823, *Sir General William Maxwell (1754–1837), 6th Bt of Calderwood,* The National Trust for Scotland, Fyvie Castle (p. 96)

Foreword

In recent years, it has seemed at times that the future for the National Trust for Scotland has looked bleak. Setting the Trust back on a safe path, securing the Future for our Past as the Trust now expresses its objective, has been a brave but brutally valid path that has had to be followed. Securing its National Heritage is vital not just for Scotland, socially and economically, but also for the British Isles as a whole, the Scottish diaspora and all those corners of our world that have been touched by it.

The Trust, as guardian for the Scottish Nation of 26 of the country's greatest buildings and 76,000 hectares of its finest land amongst many other assets, has an essential role to play in this fight. Its Chairman, Sir Kenneth Calman, in his annual report for the past year, said that "the cost to the Nation and to the World if we don't succeed....will be measured in far more than monetary terms". And he is right.

All of us at The Foundation wish him and his team every success in their great endeavour and are pleased to be able to play a role, however minor, in protecting the important collection of paintings that rest in their care and which is now recorded in full in this volume.

Fred Hohler, Founder

The Public Catalogue Foundation: People Involved

Catalogue Scope and Organisation

Medium and Support

The principal focus of this series is oil paintings. However, tempera and acrylic are also included as well as mixed media, where oil is the predominant constituent. Paintings on all forms of support (e.g. canvas, panel, etc.) are included as long as the support is portable. The principal exclusions are miniatures, hatchments or other purely heraldic paintings and wall paintings *in situ*.

Public Ownership

Public ownership has been taken to mean any paintings that are directly owned by the public purse, made accessible to the public by means of public subsidy or generally perceived to be in public ownership. The term 'public' refers to both central government and local government. Paintings held by national museums, local authority museums, English Heritage and independent museums, where there is at least some form of public subsidy, are included. Paintings held in civic buildings such as local government offices, town halls, guildhalls, public libraries, universities, hospitals, crematoria, fire stations and police stations are also included.

Geographical Boundaries of Catalogues

The geographical boundary of each county is the 'ceremonial county' boundary. This county definition includes all unitary authorities. Counties that have a particularly large number of paintings are divided between two or more catalogues on a geographical basis.

Criteria for Inclusion

As long as paintings meet the requirements above, all paintings are included irrespective of their condition and perceived quality. However, painting reproductions can only be included with the agreement of the participating collections and, where appropriate, the relevant copyright owner. It is rare that a collection forbids the inclusion of its paintings. Where this is the case and it is possible to obtain a list of paintings, this list is given in the Paintings Without Reproductions section. Where copyright consent is refused, the paintings are also listed in the Paintings Without Reproductions section. All paintings in collections' stacks and stores are included, as well as those on display. Paintings which have been lent to other institutions, whether for short-term exhibition or long-term loan, are listed under the owner collection. In addition, paintings on long-term loan are also included under the borrowing institution when they are likely to remain there for at least another five years from the date of publication of this catalogue. Information relating to owners and borrowers is listed in the Further Information section.

Layout

Collections are grouped together under their home town. These locations are listed in alphabetical order. In some cases collections that are spread over a number of locations are included under a single owner collection. A number of collections, principally the larger ones, are preceded by curatorial forewords. Within each collection paintings are listed in order of artist surname. Where there is more than one painting by the same artist, the paintings are listed chronologically, according to their execution date.

The few paintings that are not accompanied by photographs are listed in the Paintings Without Reproductions section.

There is additional reference material in the Further Information section at the back of the catalogue. This gives the full names of artists, titles and media if it has not been possible to include these in full in the main section. It also provides acquisition credit lines and information about loans in and out, as well as copyright and photographic credits for each painting. Finally, there is an index of artists' surnames.

Key to Painting Information

Almost all paintings are reproduced in the catalogue. Where this is not the case they are listed in the Paintings Without Reproductions section. Where paintings are missing or have been stolen, the best possible photograph on record has been reproduced. In some cases this may be black and white. Paintings that have been stolen are highlighted with a red border. Some paintings are shown with conservation tissue attached to parts of the painting surface.

Adam, Patrick William 1854–1929
Interior, Rutland Lodge: Vista through Open Doors 1920
oil on canvas 67.3 × 45.7
LEEAG.PA.1925.0671.LACF ❋

Artist name This is shown with the surname first. Where the artist is listed on the Getty Union List of Artist Names (ULAN), ULAN's preferred presentation of the name is given. In a number of cases the name may not be a firm attribution and this is made clear. Where the artist name is not known, a school may be given instead. Where the school is not known, the painter name is listed as *unknown artist*. If the artist name is too long for the space, as much of the name is given as possible followed by (…). This indicates the full name is given at the rear of the catalogue in the Further Information section.

Painting title A painting title followed by *(?)* indicates that the title is in doubt. Where the alternative title to the painting is considered to be better known than the original, the alternative title is given in parentheses. Where the collection has not given a painting a title, the publisher does so instead and marks this with an asterisk. If the title is too long for the space, as much of the title is given as possible followed by *(…)* and the full title is given in the Further Information section.

Execution date In some cases the precise year of execution may not be known for certain. Instead an approximate date will be given or no date at all.

Artist dates Where known, the years of birth and death of the artist are given. In some cases one or both dates may not be known with certainty, and this is marked. No date indicates that even an approximate date is not known. Where only the period in which the artist was active is known, these dates are given and preceded with the word *active*.

Medium and support Where the precise material used in the support is known, this is given.

Dimensions All measurements refer to the unframed painting and are given in cm with up to one decimal point. In all cases the height is shown before the width. An (E) indicates where a painting has not been measured and its size has been calculated by sight only. If the painting is circular, the single dimension is the diameter. If the painting is oval, the dimensions are height and width.

Collection inventory number In the case of paintings owned by museums, this number will always be the accession number. In all other cases it will be a unique inventory number of the owner institution. (P) indicates that a painting is a private loan. Details can be found in the Further Information section. Accession numbers preceded by 'PCF' indicate that the collection did not have an accession number at the time of catalogue production and therefore the number given has been temporarily allocated by The Public Catalogue Foundation. The ❋ symbol indicates that the reproduction is based on a Bridgeman Art Library transparency (go to www.bridgemanart.com) or that Bridgeman administers the copyright for that artist.

Facing page: Cadell, Francis Campbell Boileau, 1883–1937, *The Steading, Strachur*, The National Trust for Scotland, Hermiston Quay (p. 152)

THE PAINTINGS

The National Trust for Scotland, Craigievar Castle

Craigievar Castle is situated in the foothills of the Grampian mountains, 26 miles west of Aberdeen. It is located in an area rich with castles and, together with Castle Fraser, Crathes, Fyvie and Midmar, forms part of a distinctive group of castles, the Castles of Mar.

Craigievar Castle was built in the first quarter of the seventeenth century, after William Forbes purchased its lands from the Mortimer family. Forbes was a successful merchant in the Baltic and has been known as 'Danzig Willie' and Craigievar was designed to be a statement of his success. The property was passed down through the Forbes/Forbes-Sempill family and was used mainly as a holiday residence from 1829, when Fintray House, near Aberdeen, was established as the main family home. Craigievar became the family home again after the Second World War.

The Forbes family (later Forbes-Sempill) continued to live in the castle when a group of benefactors (including members of the family) bought the castle and presented it to The National Trust for Scotland, and it came complete with the vast majority of the contents, collected and lovingly preserved over the centuries by the family. The original furniture, namely the hall table and chairs, which date back to the completion of the castle, is extremely rare. The majority of the rest of the collections reflect the lives of the Forbes-Sempill family and help to tell the story of the castle and family. This is particularly true of the family portraits; the most important of which are the portraits of Sir William Forbes, 5th Baronet, and the Honourable Sarah Sempill by Sir Henry Raeburn. The artist's bill of 1788 is displayed alongside these important works, which are among Raeburn's earliest documented portraits. Family portraits by the father of Scottish portraiture, George Jamesone (c.1588–c.1644), are also present.

First and foremost, Craigievar was a home and it is the special family atmosphere that endears it to so many visitors and which the Trust has tried to preserve. Surrounding the castle are extensive parkland grounds. There is also a small Victorian kitchen garden and a Scottish glen garden.

The castle and grounds were bought from the Forbes-Sempill family by a consortium of benefactors and presented to The National Trust for Scotland in 1963.

British (Scottish) School
Sir John Forbes (1636–1703), 2nd Bt of Craigievar 1678
oil on canvas 66.7 x 53.3
63.500.1

British (Scottish) School
Margaret (d.1683), Wife of Sir John Forbes, Daughter of Peter Young of Auldbar 1678
oil on canvas 67.3 x 53.3
63.500.2

British (Scottish) School
Sir William Forbes (1660–1723), 3rd Bt of Craigievar c.1720
oil on canvas 74.3 x 62.2
63.500.14

British (Scottish) School
Portrait of an Officer 1775
oil on canvas 73 x 62.2
63.500.17

British (Scottish) School
Dr John Forbes of Corse (1593–1648)
oil on canvas 66.7 x 53.3
63.500.3

British (Scottish) School
Sir William Forbes (d.1648), 1st Bt of Craigievar
oil on canvas 66.7 x 52.7
63.500.6

Gordon, John Watson 1788–1864
Charlotte Elizabeth (1801–1883), Wife of Sir John Forbes, 7th Bt of Craigievar, Daughter of the 18th Lord Forbes 1850
oil on canvas 74.9 x 62.2
63.500.8

Gordon, John Watson 1788–1864
Sir John Forbes (1785–1846), 7th Bt of Craigievar
oil on canvas 74.9 x 62.2
63.500.7

Jamesone, George 1588–1644
Patrick Forbes of Corse (1564–1635), Bishop of Aberdeen
oil on canvas 62.2 x 49.5
63.500.4

Jamesone, George 1588–1644
William Forbes of Menie and Craigievar (1566–1627)
oil on canvas 66.7 x 50.7
63.500.5

Lawrence, Thomas (after) 1769–1830
Elizabeth (1775–1830), Wife of the 17th Lord Forbes
oil on canvas 73.7 x 62.2
63.500.20

Lawrence, Thomas (after) 1769–1830
James Ochonochar (1765–1843), 17th Lord Forbes (?)
oil on canvas 73.7 x 62.2
63.500.19

Raeburn, Henry 1756–1823
Sir William Forbes (1755–1816), 5th Bt of Craigievar 1788
oil on canvas 74.3 x 60.3
63.500.11

Raeburn, Henry 1756–1823
Sarah (1762–1799), Wife of Sir William Forbes, Daughter of John, 13th Lord Sempill 1788
oil on canvas 74.3 x 60.3
63.500.12

Raeburn, Henry 1756–1823
The Honourable Janet Sempill of Craigievar
oil on canvas 73 x 60
205.1 (P)

Ramsay, Allan (follower of) 1713–1784
Sir Arthur Forbes (1709–1773), 4th Bt of Craigievar
oil on canvas 74.3 x 60.9
63.500.16

Scougall, David 1610–1680
Sir John Forbes (1636–1703), 2nd Bt of Craigievar 1668
oil on canvas 74.9 x 61.6
63.500.15

Stuart, Gilbert 1755–1828
Sir Arthur Forbes (1784–1823), 6th Bt of Craigievar
oil on canvas 71.1 x 59.7
63.500.9

unknown artist
Icon of the Virgin Mary
oil on panel 27.5 x 21.5
T3253

unknown artist
Icon of the Virgin Mary
oil on panel 31.5 x 24.7
T3254

unknown artist
Portrait of a Lady with a White Ruff
oil on canvas 33.2 x 29
T3256

unknown artist
Portrait of a Man in Armour
oil on canvas 65.8 x 51.6
T3257

unknown artist
Woman Seated on a Chair
oil on canvas 22.4 x 26.6
T3255

Wild, Frank Percy 1861–1950
Portrait of a Young Girl 1912
oil on canvas 110 x 84.4
T3258

Wild, Frank Percy 1861–1950
Sir John Forbes (1863–1934), 9th Bt of Craigievar and 18th Lord Sempill 1912
oil on canvas 73.7 x 60.9
63.500.10

The National Trust for Scotland, Crathes Castle, Garden & Estate

Crathes Castle, Gardens and Estate in the north east of Scotland is one of the most beautiful and best-preserved castles in Scotland. Standing against a background of rolling hills and set in its own glorious gardens, this magical turreted castle is a favourite destination of fans of Scottish history, gardeners and romantics.

King Robert the Bruce gave the present estate, which once formed part of the much larger Land of Leys, to the Burnett family in 1323. Sir James Burnett the 13th Baronet of Leys bequeathed the property, and an endowment, to the National Trust for Scotland in 1951. The family connections remain strong as James Burnett of Leys (grandson of the donor) and his family continue to live on the property. Crathes is a diverse and very busy property of 595 acres. As well as the Castle and Gardens, the property comprises mainly of mixed woodlands, farmland, ponds and burns, and includes the majority of the designed landscape.

Crathes Castle is one of the internationally renowned 'Castles of Mar'. Associated with the Bel family of master masons, the Castle was finished by 1595, although changes and additions continued to be made over the subsequent 350 years of Burnett occupation, some of which are still in evidence today. Also visible are important remnants of late sixteenth and early seventeenth century decoration, much of which was restored during the Victorian period, a critical era in the property's evolution. In addition a series of decorative schemes have been carried out, with the post-1876 work being of outstanding significance in Scotland as an early example of Scottish antiquarianism.

The Castle also contains an important collection of its original furniture (including a dated bed and seat furniture), portraits of the family alongside many exotic and highly unusual objects, such as the Italian (Louis XIV) prie-dieu and the famous Horn of Leys.

Borsseler, Pieter (style of) active 1664–1687
Gilbert Burnett (1643–1715), Bishop of Salisbury
oil on canvas 126 x 99
51.918 (P)

Brekelenkam, Quiringh van (circle of) 1627–1674
A Girl Embroidering and a Youth Eating in an Interior c.1800
oil on panel 50.5 x 42.5
51.922

British (Scottish) School
Robert (1661–1694), 3rd Viscount Arbuthnott, Brother of Dame Margaret Arbuthnott c.1690
oil on canvas 74 x 62
51.914

British (Scottish) School
Sir Alexander Burnett of Leys (1679–1758), 4th Bt and 16th Laird c.1720
oil on canvas 67.5 x 57
51.955

British (Scottish) School
William Burnett of Criggie (1638–1747), Son of Sir Thomas Burnett of Leys, 3rd Bt c.1736
oil on canvas 74.9 x 58.4
51.912

British (Scottish) School
Sir Thomas Burnett of Leys (1759–1783), 6th Bt and 18th Laird
oil on canvas 89 x 76
51.953

Dutch School
Topers in an Interior
oil on panel 66 x 52
88.133.2

Fraser, Alec C.
Sir Thomas Burnett (b.1586)
oil on canvas 60.9 x 58.4
51.946

Grixoni, Mario 1879–1946
Sybil Crozier Smith (d.1960), Wife of Major General Sir James Lauderdale Gilbert Burnett of Leys, 13th Bt 1929
oil on canvas 140.9 x 93.9
51.905

Holbein the younger, Hans (after) 1497–1543
Erasmus (1466–1536) 19th C
oil on metal 17 x 14.2
51.954.1

Holbein the younger, Hans (after) 1497–1543
Thomas Cromwell (c.1485–1540) 19th C
oil on metal 19.5 x 17
51.954.2

Horsburgh, John A. 1835–1924
Elizabeth Bannerman Burnett (1839–1877) 1877
oil on canvas 76 x 63.5
51.93

Italian School
Quartet Dancing Outside an Inn
oil on glass 40.5 x 49
51.935

Jamesone, George 1588–1644
Alexander Skene of Skene (b.1590)
oil on panel 71.1 x 58.4
51.91

Jamesone, George 1588–1644
Janet Burnett, Sister of Sir Thomas Burnett of Leys, 1st Bt, and Wife of Alexander Skene of Skene
oil on panel 71.1 x 57.2
51.911

Jamesone, George 1588–1644
Sir Thomas Burnett of Leys (1619–1653), 1st Bt and 13th Laird
oil on panel 71.1 x 54.3
51.919

Jamesone, George (circle of) 1588–1644
Jean Burnett, Daughter of Sir Thomas Burnett of Leys and Wife of Sir William Forbes of Monymusk, Bt, and Robert Comyne of Altyre
oil on panel 72.4 x 58.4
51.913

Jamesone, George (circle of) 1588–1644
Sir William Forbes of Monymusk (d.1654), Bt, Husband of Jane Burnett
oil on panel 71.1 x 55.9
51.916

Kneller, Godfrey (circle of) 1646–1723
Gilbert Burnett (1643–1715), Bishop of Salisbury
oil on canvas 125 x 99
51.96 (P)

Lander, John Saint-Helier 1869–1944
Major General Sir James Lauderdale Gilbert Burnett of Leys (1886–1953), 13th Bt 1919
oil on canvas 90.1 x 70
51.903

Moir, John 1776–1857
Margaret Dalrymple Horn Elphinstone (1764–1849), Daughter of General Robert Dalrymple Horn Elphinstone of Logie (...)
oil on canvas 73.7 x 60.9
51.951

Scougal, John 1645–1737
Sir Thomas Burnett of Leys (c.1656–1714), 3rd Bt and 15th Laird
oil on canvas 73.7 x 60.9
51.915

Above: Peploe, Samuel John, 1871–1935, *Anemones in a Brown Jar*, The National Trust for Scotland, Greenbank Garden (p. 205)

The National Trust for Scotland, Mar Lodge Estate

Located in the heart of the Cairngorms National Park, the 72,598-acre estate takes in fifteen Munros (mountains over 3,000 feet). Mar Lodge itself, restored following a fire in 1991, is still an impressive building, with a notable Bavarian influence in style, and of some architectural value. Its associations with the Fife family and Victorian royalty give added historical interest.

Mar Lodge was built in 1895 for the Duke and Duchess of Fife, following the destruction by fire of a previous building, Corriemulzie Cottage. The foundation stone was laid by Queen Victoria, grandmother of the Duchess. The architect, A. Marshall Mackenzie, was the leading architect in Aberdeen during this period. The Duchess had an interest in art and has been credited with the unusual butterfly plan of the Lodge, which floods it with light and opens it up to the forest and the landscape. Although most of the interiors, such as the Dining Room and Billiard Room, reflect the native timbers and taxidermy of Corriemulzie Cottage, the Duchess's private rooms were in the international Adam revival style, much of which was executed in papier maché. Much of this was removed in a later 1930s modernisation along with the introduction of eighteenth-century furniture from other family houses.

The Lodge originally had a tree-trunk veranda running around the house, but now only the porch survives. After the fire in 1991, what the visitor sees now is a brilliant re-instatement of the original internal designs based on the original architectural drawings and photographs. Although the pine-panelling has been re-instated, the fire-proofing required today gives it a different surface texture in comparison with the doors of the original rooms, which survived the fire, along with much of the original furniture, being stored at the time in the detached Ballroom.

Parts of the ground and first floor of the Lodge have been converted into holiday flats, but many of the grand features of the Lodge in its heyday as a hunting lodge are retained. The principal rooms reflect something of their original appearance, furnished with many of the original pieces acquired by The National Trust for Scotland.

Mar Lodge was purchased by the National Trust for Scotland in 1995.

Adams, A. Denovan active 1870s
Homeward Bound, Glenlochy 19th C
oil on canvas 31.5 x 60.2
96.59.2

Adams, A. Denovan active 1870s
The Rivals 19th C
oil on canvas 38.2 x 59.3
96.59.1

Alexander, Cosmo 1724–1772
Elizabeth of York
oil on canvas 74.7 x 62.4
56.682

Alexander, Robert L. 1840–1923
Head of a Deerhound 1907
oil on board 34 x 25.5
98.214

Alexander, Robert L. 1840–1923
A Bay Pony Sheltering
oil on panel 19.5 x 24.3
98.216

Alexander, Robert L. 1840–1923
A St Bernard Dog
oil on canvas 56.5 x 43.5
98.212

Anderson, Charles Goldsborough 1865–1936
Portrait of a Gentleman with a Dog 1918 (?)
oil on canvas 125 x 88.2
2012.117

Ashton, G. A.
A Spanish Girl (after Bartolomé Esteban Murillo)
oil on canvas 59.3 x 43.2
205.35

Barry, W.
A Tower House by a Loch 1885/1886
oil on panel 29.7 x 37.5
200.297.1

Barry, W.
Ailsa Craig with Fishing Boats at Dusk
oil on panel 18.2 x 26.5
200.297.2

British (English) School
Fishing Boats and Activities on Shore
oil on canvas 26.3 x 36.7
200.293

British (Scottish) School
A Gentleman in a Black Coat Holding an Open Letter
oil on canvas 90.5 x 69.5
94.76.6

Facing page: Neri, Pietro Martire, c.1601–1661, *Portrait of a Clerk*, The National Trust for Scotland, Haddo House (p. 47)

British (Scottish) School
Portrait of a Woman in a Black Dress Holding a Book
oil on canvas 90.5 x 69.8
94.76.5

Craig, H. T. M.
Evening Cloud
oil on board 59 x 90
98.427

Dozeman, Roelof b.1924
The South of France
oil on canvas 74.8 x 59.6
56.1503

Dyck, Anthony van (style of) 1599–1641
James Skene 1635
oil on canvas 62.3 x 48.5
56.696

Evans, Treyer Meredith 1889–1958
Miss D. Walker
oil on board 34.7 x 25.3
98.193

Ewan, Frances 1891–1944
Isobel (Portrait of a Young Girl) 1913
oil on canvas 42 x 32.2
94.57.1

Fergusson, D.
Cliad Beach, Isle of Coll c.1960
oil on board 24.2 x 35
56.169

Ferneley I, John E. 1782–1860
The Game Keeper's Larder 1836
oil on canvas 74.4 x 61.5
56.1753.1

Ferneley I, John E. 1782–1860
The Game Keeper's Larder 1836
oil on canvas 74.7 x 62
56.1753.2

Ferneley I, John E. 1782–1860
Solomon, Out of King David
oil on canvas 49.8 x 67
98.155

Giles, James 1801–1870
The Honourable Mrs Gordon of Fyvie 1822
oil on canvas 238.5 x 147
84.2

Gino
Beached Fishing Boats 1967 (?)
oil on board 24.3 x 62
98.43

Guarguetta (possibly)
Mexican Window Scene 1979
oil on canvas 25.2 x 20.2
200.289

H., W.
A Lady Seated Wearing a Red Dress and Crocheting by Candlelight
oil on canvas 26 x 22.3
98.159

Hansford, Audrey Peagram active 1974–1979
Mar Lodge Estate with the Dalvorer Ruins 1974
oil on canvas 38.5 x 74.4
56.12

Hansford, Audrey Peagram active 1974–1979
Mar Lodge Estate with the River Lui and Derry 1974
oil on canvas 38 x 76
56.15

Hansford, Audrey Peagram active 1974–1979
Mar Lodge Estate with the River Lui and Fairy Glen 1974
oil on canvas 38.2 x 74
56.11

Hansford, Audrey Peagram active 1974–1979
Mar Lodge Estate, the River Geldie 1974
oil on canvas 39 x 76.5
56.14

Hansford, Audrey Peagram active 1974–1979
Mar Lodge Estate, Bridge over the River Geldie 1977
oil on canvas 39 x 75
56.13

Hansford, Audrey Peagram active 1974–1979
Mar Lodge Estate, the River Geldie Looking East 1979
oil on canvas 39 x 75
56.16

Hinchcliffe, P.
Culross Houses
oil on board 39.5 x 49
99.1624

Inglis, R.
Landscape
oil on board 23.4 x 33.6
96.202

Italian School
Travellers Resting in a Landscape
oil on panel 32.5 x 27.7
98.219

Law, Jean
Dahlias and Gladioli in a Stoneware Jug
oil on canvas 49.5 x 39.5
99.195

Leemput, Remi van (after) 1607–1675
George Skene, of that Ilk, Aged 30
oil on canvas 70.9 x 61
56.683

Loose, Basile de 1809–1885
The Connoisseur
oil on panel 62.4 x 52.2
98.153

Lucas, Henry Frederick Lucas 1848–1943
'Minting', a Bay Chaser
oil on panel 21.8 x 29.7
98.168

McCulloch, Horatio 1805–1867
Landscape
oil on canvas 49.7 x 74.8
2012.112

Miereveld, Michiel Jansz. van (after) 1567–1641
Alexander Skene
oil on canvas 62.5 x 57.1
56.698

Nicholson, Jim 1924–1996
The Hills of Harris from Lusk
oil on board 49 x 54.5
56.1501

Peddie, George
A Village Landscape with Trees
oil on canvas 26.2 x 36.6
56.159

Pruser
Roses in a Pottery Vase
oil on canvas 39.4 x 49.5
97.55

Ramsay, Hugh 1877–1906
Roses
oil on canvas 49 x 60
97.179

Ritchie, C. S.
Lady Stewart
oil on canvas 97 x 77.5
207.165

Robb, Lena 1891–1980
White Rhododendrons in a Vase
oil on board 29.4 x 24
97.164

Roe, Robert Henry (attributed to) 1793–1880
Brighton Rivière, a Collie in a Highland Landscape
oil on canvas 73.5 x 94.2
56.2

Shirreff, J. B.
Portrait of a Gentleman (said to be Stewart of Banchory)
oil on canvas 126.5 x 100.5
207.166

unknown artist
Beatrix Gordon 1620
oil on canvas 61.5 x 48
56.679

unknown artist
Mrs Sayle c.1810
oil on canvas 54.5 x 44.5
96.46

unknown artist
Captain Gordon, Master of the 'Queen Charlotte', off Algiers 1816
oil on canvas 75.3 x 62.5
95.35.1

unknown artist
Portrait of a Gentleman of the Gordon of Abergeldie Family c.1830
oil on canvas 74.3 x 61.5
95.35.2

unknown artist
Portrait of a Seated Man (said to be Sir Stewart) c.1888
oil on canvas 90.5 x 70
207.160.1

unknown artist
A Vase of Summer Flowers
oil on board 51.5 x 29
97.175

unknown artist
Lady Castlehill, Wife of Sir John, 4th Bt
oil on canvas 125.5 x 99
207.161

unknown artist
Landscape (River Estuary)
oil on canvas 29.5 x 44.8
94.76.2

unknown artist
Madonna della sedia (after a sixteenth-century Italian original)
oil on ivory 10 x 10.1
98.16

unknown artist
Portrait of a Gentleman
oil on canvas 103 x 83
2012.116

unknown artist
Portrait of a Gentleman in Morning Dress
oil on canvas 125.3 x 100
2012.118

unknown artist
Portrait of a Seated Man at a Desk with Papers
oil on canvas 49 x 59.5
207.164

unknown artist
Portrait of a Woman (said to be Lady Stewart)
oil on canvas 89.5 x 70
207.160.2

unknown artist
Portrait of a Woman with a Bonnet
oil on canvas 73.4 x 61
T4479

unknown artist
Portrait of the Daughter of Lady Mary Kerr
oil on canvas 125.2 x 100
73.688

unknown artist
Sir Robert Sinclair, 9th Bt of Stevenson and Caithness
oil on canvas 58 x 51.5
2012.111

unknown artist
Skene of Skene
oil on canvas 72.6 x 60
56.697

unknown artist
The Brodie of Brodie with a Dog
oil on canvas 140.4 x 110
2012.12

unknown artist
The Mongols (Battlescene)
oil on canvas 154 x 198
45.78

unknown artist
Wooded Landscape
oil on canvas 44 x 29
94.76.4

Weiler, Lina von 1830–1890
William Forbes-Sempill, 17th Lord Sempill 1857
oil on canvas 202 x 138
63.1

Wheeler, Alfred 1851–1932
'Bendigo' with Jockey 1887
oil on canvas board 29.5 x 27.5
98.169

Wheeler, John Arnold 1821–1903
An Irish Setter, 'Dan'
oil on canvas 44.5 x 34.3
98.157

Whiteford
Coast
acrylic on paper 38.2 x 47
98.446

Witz, Johannes van Pritzel
Girl with a Lace Shawl 1880
oil on panel 43.1 x 32.5
98.167

Wyllie, Aileen
Mrs Mona Grogan c.1960
oil on canvas 76 x 60.5
98.614

Facing page: Opie, John, 1761–1807, *Courtship in the Park*, The National Trust for Scotland, Fyvie Castle (p. 93)

The National Trust for Scotland, Drum Castle, Garden & Estate

Drum Castle, Garden and Estate are the last remnant of the once extensive estate of the Irvines of Drum. It is situated on a ridge above open country, 10 miles from the centre of Aberdeen. Drum Castle, a composite structure, is set around a courtyard and comprises a thirteenth-century tower, a Jacobean mansion and Victorian additions, remnants of parkland, a walled garden with later ornamental planting, an arboretum and lawns.

The most significant component of the property is the tower: it is one of the three oldest towers in Scotland and, of these, the most intact. Its early date (probably before 1286), lack of later alterations and associations with Robert the Bruce makes it of outstanding national importance. This, and its ownership by one family over 21 generations, together with the survival of the family archive, including the original Bruce Charters, makes the property unique in The National Trust for Scotland and an important resource both nationally and regionally.

The alterations undertaken by David and John Bryce in 1876 included a very thorough refit of the interiors of the mansion, and intended to harmonise with the old whilst giving it an air of antiquity. The creation of the library in the tower is of particular historical note as a pioneering piece of Scots Baronial antiquarianism, and its origins may lie in the taste of the patron rather than the advice of the architect. The collections are an important relic of the Irvine's occupancy of the castle for, despite some dispersal in the eighteenth century, they still include much that came from the family, particularly paintings. These paintings, under the influence of Hugh Irvine and Anna Forbes Irvine, are, as a collection, of national significance.

Drum Castle was bequeathed to The National Trust for Scotland by Mr H. Q. Forbes Irvine of Drum in 1976.

Alexander, Cosmo 1724–1772
Alexander Irvine (d.1761), 17th Laird of Drum 1756
oil on canvas 74.7 x 61.4
2010.1775

Alexander, Cosmo 1724–1772
James Irvine of Altamford 1756
oil on canvas 74.3 x 61.5
2010.1774

Alexander, Cosmo 1724–1772
Mary Ogilvie, Wife of Alexander Irvine, 17th Laird of Drum 1756
oil on canvas 74.1 x 61.5
2010.1769

Alexander, Cosmo 1724–1772
Alexander Irvine (possibly 10th, 11th or 12th Laird of Drum) 1757
oil on canvas 74.4 x 61.2
2010.1791

Alexander, Cosmo 1724–1772
Charles Irvine, Brother of Alexander Irvine, 16th Laird of Drum 1760
oil on canvas 77.2 x 63.1
2010.1773

Alexander, Cosmo 1724–1772
Mrs James Irvine of Altamford
oil on canvas 74.5 x 62
2010.1768

Bough, Samuel 1822–1878
Mountain Valley with a Drover 1874
oil on unidentified support 17.4 x 24.3
2010.1002

Brandon, Louis E. active 1953–1958
Henry Quentin Forbes Irvine (1908–1975), 24th Laird of Drum 1953
oil on canvas 59.3 x 49.1
2010.179

British (Scottish) School
Portrait of a Gentleman in Armour (possibly one of the Campbell of Glenlyon family) c.1680
oil on canvas 73.8 x 61.5
2010.1047

British (Scottish) School
Portrait of a Gentleman in Armour (possibly John Campbell, 1636–1717, 1st Earl of Breadalbane) c.1680
oil on canvas 74.8 x 62
2010.1048

British (Scottish) School
Portrait of a Gentleman in Armour c.1680
oil on canvas 73.5 x 61.5
2010.177

British (Scottish) School
Portrait of a Gentleman in Armour and a White Stock c.1680
oil on canvas 73.8 x 61
2010.1788

British (Scottish) School
Captain Robert Campbell of Glenlyon (1630–1696) (copy after a seventeenth-century original) c.1700
oil on canvas 74.7 x 62
2010.1803

British (Scottish) School
Portrait of a Gentleman in a Dark Red Coat c.1700
oil on canvas 77 x 61.2
2010.18

British (Scottish) School
Portrait of a Lady in a Red Dress c.1700
oil on canvas 72.4 x 61.5
2010.1772

British (Scottish) School
Portrait of a Lady in a Red Dress c.1700
oil on canvas 74.5 x 61.8
2010.1777

British (Scottish) School
Bathia Forbes, Wife of Gutcher c.1720
oil on canvas 74.8 x 62
2010.1056

British (Scottish) School
Lady Egidia Keith c.1730
oil on canvas 122 x 99.1
2010.1783

British (Scottish) School
Robert Campbell, 3rd Earl of Breadalbane c.1730
oil on canvas 73.4 x 61.2
2010.1049

British (Scottish) School
Jean Grant, Daughter of Sir Francis Grant c.1750
oil on canvas 73.8 x 61.5
2010.1052

British (Scottish) School
Mr Burnett of Elrick and Dalgety c.1780
oil on canvas 74.3 x 61.5
2010.1054

British (Scottish) School
Alexander Gordon, MP for Aberdeenshire
oil on canvas 78.8 x 61.8
2010.105

British (Scottish) School
John Campbell of Glenlyon
oil on canvas 75 x 62.3
2010.1051

British (Scottish) School
View of Drum Castle with Cattle
oil on canvas 43.5 x 64.2
2010.1779

British School
Mrs Penelope Garden of Dalgety and Her Son c.1790
oil on canvas 208.3 x 146.7
2010.1053

British School
Margaret Hamilton (d.1855), Wife of Alexander Irvine, 19th Laird of Drum c.1840
oil on unidentified support 10.7 x 10.7
2010.1123

British School
A Girl with a Rake over Her Shoulder c.1900
oil on unidentified support 49.5 x 29.2
2010.1098

Carmichael, John Wilson (circle of) 1799–1868
Dutch Vessels and a Man-of-War at Sea
oil on canvas 83.5 x 130
2010.1764

Chalmers, George 1720–1791
Mary Irvine, Sister of Alexander Irvine, 16th Laird of Drum 1766
oil on canvas 75 x 62.5
2010.1785

De Noter, Pierre-François 1779–1843
A Canal in a Town 1826
oil on panel 44.2 x 62
2010.178

Downes, Thomas Price active 1835–1887
Mary Agnes Ramsay (b.1858), Daughter of John Ramsay of Banna and Wife of Francis Hugh Forbes Irvine, 21st Laird of Drum
oil on canvas 59.5 x 49.5
2010.1794

Dubois, Louis 1821–1869
A Poser
oil on panel 20.4 x 25.4
2010.1767.2

Dubois, Louis 1821–1869
An Interesting Letter
oil on panel 20.4 x 26.2
2010.1767.1

Dyck, Anthony van (circle of) 1599–1641
Charles I (1600–1649), in Armour
oil on canvas 72 x 63.5
2010.1797

Giles, James (attributed to) 1801–1870
Alexander Forbes Irvine (1777–1861), 19th Laird of Drum
oil on canvas 73.3 x 62.1
2010.1771

Graham-Gilbert, John 1794–1866
James Irvine (d.1831) 1826
oil on canvas 61.7 x 50
2010.1798

Graham-Gilbert, John 1794–1866
Ann Margaret Forbes Leslie, Wife of Alexander Forbes Irvine, 20th Laird of Drum
oil on canvas 122 x 99.1
2010.1796

Graham-Gilbert, John (attributed to) 1794–1866
Alexander Forbes Irvine (1818–1892), 20th Laird of Drum
oil on canvas 124.4 x 98.3
2010.925

Hamilton, Gavin (circle of) 1723–1798
Woman with a Lyre
oil on canvas 149.8 x 183.5
2010.1765

Hollis, Charles T. 1855–1925
Distant View of Windsor 1907
oil on canvas 39.8 x 29.8
2010.1003

Howard, Henry 1769–1847
Charles Irvine
oil on canvas 74.7 x 61.4
2010.1776

Howard, Henry 1769–1847
Hugh Irvine, Son of Alexander Irvine, 16th Laird of Drum
oil on canvas 74.8 x 61.5
2010.1793

Irvine, Hugh 1783–1829
Castle Gate, Aberdeen 1812
oil on canvas 43.2 x 63.7
2010.1781

Irvine, Hugh 1783–1829
Archangel Gabriel
oil on canvas 124.4 x 98.3
2010.922

Irvine, James (attributed to) –1703
Portrait of a Man (said to be James Irvine of Drum) 1700
oil on canvas 75.8 x 61.1
2010.1795

Kettle, Tilly (circle of) 1735–1786
Francis Garden (1721–1793), Lord Gardenstone
oil on canvas 74.8 x 62
2010.1055

Kettle, Tilly (circle of) 1735–1786
Francis Garden (1721–1793), Lord Gardenstone, 5th of Troup, in His Kilt and Plaid
oil on canvas 124.5 x 99.2
2010.1985

Leslie, George Dunlop 1835–1921
Washington Irving (1783–1859) (after Charles Robert Leslie) 1857
oil on board 22.8 x 16.8
2010.1792

Meder
Fruit Being Given to Children
oil on panel 99 x 130
2010.1804

Moir, John 1776–1857
Christina Irvine, Daughter of Alexander Irvine, 18th Laird of Drum
oil on canvas 74 x 61.1
2010.1784

Morland, George (style of) 1763–1804
A Pastiche c.1860
oil on canvas 49 x 39.8
2010.1184

Mosman, William d.1771
Erminia after Imperiali with a View of Culter House in the Background
oil on canvas 248.9 x 392.4
92.101 (P)

Nasmyth, Alexander 1758–1840
Stirling Castle
oil on panel 28 x 38.5
2010.1801

Nasmyth, Alexander (circle of) 1758–1840
Loch Katrine
oil on canvas 44.8 x 59.6
2010.1782

Nattier, Jean-Marc (after) 1685–1766
Prince Charles Edward Stuart (1720–1788), in Armour
oil on canvas 58.8 x 48.6
2010.1763

Peters, Matthew William (circle of) 1742–1814
Miss Bianca
oil on canvas 74.8 x 61.6
2010.1786

Raeburn, Henry 1756–1823
James Hamilton
oil on canvas 74.2 x 61.5
2010.1799

Raeburn, Henry 1756–1823
Mary Irvine, Daughter of Alexander Irvine, 16th Laird of Drum
oil on canvas 75 x 62.5
2010.1787

Raeburn, Henry (circle of) 1756–1823
Francis Garden (1721–1793), Lord Gardenstone
oil on canvas 142.5 x 110.1
2010.1057

unknown artist
Landscape with a Large House
oil on canvas on board 19 x 29.9
2010.1006

unknown artist
Portrait of a Lady
oil on unidentified support 9.6 x 8
2010.1124

unknown artist
Portrait of a Lady
oil on unidentified support 9.9 x 7.8
2010.1176

unknown artist
Portrait of a Man with a White Stock
oil on canvas 74.8 x 61
2010.1778

unknown artist
Portrait of a Seated Lady
oil on panel 25 x 20.8
2010.1005

unknown artist
Portrait of an Old Lady Spinning
oil on canvas 51.2 x 61.5
2010.1802

Verboeckhoven, Charles Louis 1802–1889
Belgian Vessels in a Stiff Breeze 1835
oil on canvas 58 x 71.2
2010.1766

W., F.
Woman with a Snowball 1887
oil on canvas 73.5 x 44.5
2010.1046

Wright, John Michael (attributed to) 1617–1694
Alexander or William, 11th Lord Forbes
oil on canvas 116.7 x 96.7
2010.1789

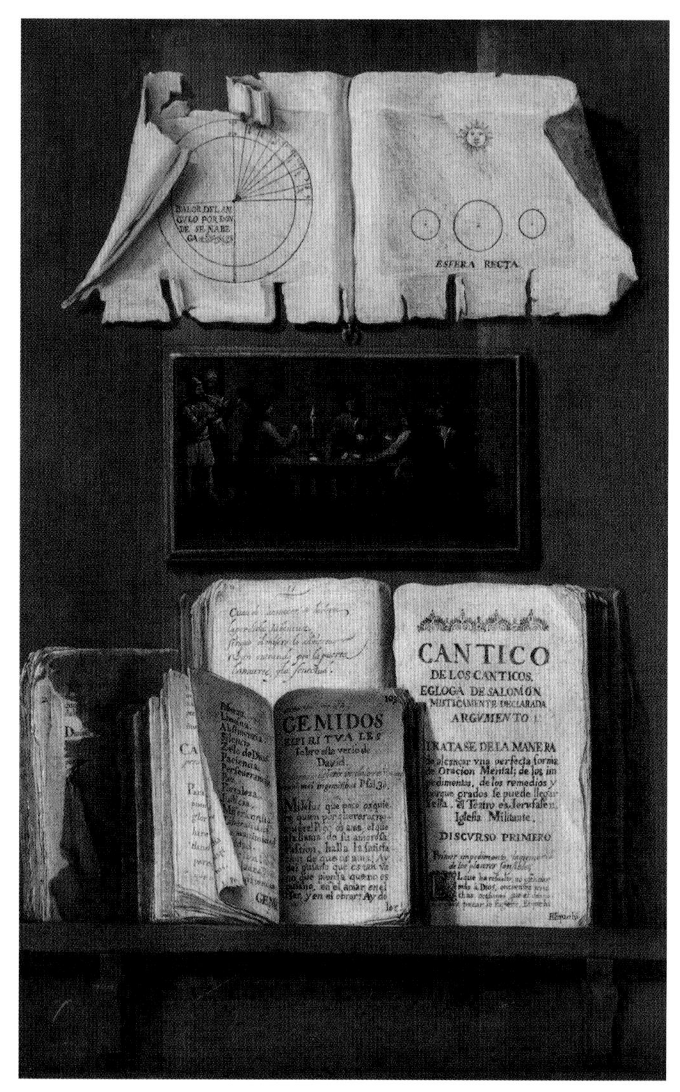

Above: Morales, Juan Francisco, active 17th C, *Trompe L'oeil*, both The National Trust for Scotland, Haddo House (p. 46)

The National Trust for Scotland, Haddo House

Haddo House, once the epicentre of one of the most important country estates in the north east of Scotland derives much of its significance from its architectural history, interior design, and garden design and development, as physical expressions of the social, cultural, and historical context of the Gordon family as key aristocratic landowners in Scotland for more than 500 years. Many generations of the family were significant players in both local and national affairs and this was recognised by the creation of the 3rd Baronet, Sir George Gordon as the Earl of Aberdeen in 1682 and then in 1915 the elevation of the 7th Earl to Marquess of Aberdeen and Temair. Commensurate with their rise in status was the acquisition and expansion of their estates and fortune, the estate reaching at its greatest extent, around 75,000 acres.

At the heart of the property is Haddo House designed by William Adam, regarded at the time as 'the pre-eminent Scottish architect of his generation' and today as the 'dominant architectural figure of his time'. Adam's design for the 2nd Earl, a mansion house in the Palladian style was in stark contrast to anything that had been seen in the north east of Scotland before, a region characterised by tower houses and castles.

Over the years, Adam's house was modified by the subsequent involvement of other nationally recognised architects: Archibald Simpson, John Smith, G. E. Street and Wardrop & Reid. Their involvement is in itself an expression of the Gordon family's perception of their own place as leading landowners, politicians and socialites throughout the eighteenth to twentieth centuries. The interior of the mansion is increasingly recognised by design historians as being of national importance through the rare survival of extensive furnishings and fittings supplied by the eminent London interior design firm of the late nineteenth century, Wright & Mansfield. The interior they created in the second quarter of the nineteenth century is of particular significance to Haddo as it gave a framework which both guided and framed the later developments. Their interior was the most visible; however a number of other design schemes were executed en suite with major building phases. Little development of the mansion took place during the twentieth century, except for some decorative work immediately after World War II, thus preserving a good deal of the earlier schemes intact.

Despite a number of sales in the nineteenth and early twentieth centuries, Haddo's art collection retains a nationally important collection of portraits, including key figures in the Gordon family. Of other works in the collection, the series of topographical watercolours and oil paintings executed by James Giles (1801–1870) is one the treasures of the Trust.

Alexander, John 1686–1766
Portrait of a Lady (said to be the Countess of Aberdeen, Mother of George, 4th Earl of Aberdeen) 1761
oil on canvas 88.9 x 68.6
79.63

Allan, William 1782–1850
Sir Walter Scott Dictating to His Daughter, Anne, in the Armoury at Abbotsford 1844
oil on panel 114.3 x 88.9
79.81

Anglo/Dutch School & Monnoyer, Jean-Baptiste (1636-1699)
Sir William Lockhard of Lee
oil on canvas 86.4 x 67.3, 86.4 x 67.3
79.148.1

Anglo/Dutch School & Monnoyer, Jean-Baptiste (1636-1699)
Lady Lockhart c.1699
oil on canvas 86.4 x 67.3, 86.4 x 67.3
79.148.2

Aubrey, John 1909–1985
June, Marchioness of Aberdeen 1974
oil on canvas 100.9 x 74.9
79.118 (P)

Aubrey, John 1909–1985
Saint John the Baptist with a Kneeling Knight of the Order of Saint John 1978
acrylic on board 172.7 x 62.2
79.252

Barnekow, Elizabeth
John, 1st Marquess of Aberdeen and Temair 1934
oil on canvas 254 x 142.2
79.108

Barnekow, Elizabeth
John, 1st Marquess of Aberdeen and Temair
oil on canvas 67.3 x 53.3
79.109

Barnekow, Elizabeth
The Honourable Ishbel Marjoribanks, Later Wife of the 7th Earl of Aberdeen and 1st Marquess of Aberdeen (...) (after A. E. Ellis)
oil on canvas 119.4 x 66
79.105

Batoni, Pompeo 1708–1787
George Gordon, Lord Haddo 1775
oil on canvas 259 x 170.2
79.6

British (English) School
David, Earl of Devon c.1700
oil on canvas 71.1 x 60.9
79.152

British (Scottish) School
William, 2nd Earl of Aberdeen c.1740
oil on canvas 73.7 x 63.5
79.92

British (Scottish) School
Lady Anne Gordon, 3rd Wife of the 2nd Earl of Aberdeen, with Her Son, Alexander, Lord Rockville c.1760
oil on canvas 152.4 x 127
79.7

British (Scottish) School
Lady Anne Gordon c.1780
oil on canvas 73.7 x 60.9
88.107.4 (P)

British (Scottish) School
Lady Jean Gordon, Aged 14
oil on canvas 73.7 x 62.2
88.107.2 (P)

British School
Portrait of a Man, Aged 57 (said to be James VI and I) 1623
oil on panel 90.2 x 71.1
79.8

British School
Cecile Elizabeth Gordon
oil on canvas 99 x 73.6
79.107

Brooke, Bryan active 1958–1979
Stella Hamilton 1958
oil on canvas 49 x 38.5
2011.347

Canziani, Louisa Starr 1845–1909
Two Little Home Rulers: The Honourable Dudley Gladstone Gordon and the Honourable Archie Gordon 1890
oil on canvas 131.4 x 162.6
79.11

Carpenter, Margaret Sarah 1793–1872
Lady Harriet Hamilton 1840
oil on canvas 56.7 x 44.4
79.95

Carpenter, Margaret Sarah 1793–1872
Mary, Lady Haddo
oil on canvas 73.7 x 63.5
79.82

Carpenter, Margaret Sarah 1793–1872
The Honourable and Reverend Douglas Gordon
oil on canvas 59.7 x 45.7
79.84

Childers, Milly 1866–1922
Dudley Gordon 1886
oil on canvas 49.5 x 39.4
79.218

Custodis, Hieronymus (circle of) active c.1585–1598
Portrait of a Gentleman, Aged 26 1580
oil on panel 72.4 x 58.4
79.101

Delaroche, Paul 1797–1856
Francois-Pierre-Guillaume Guizot 1847
oil on canvas 74.9 x 62.2
79.18

Domenichino (circle of) 1581–1641
David with the Head of Goliath
oil on canvas 104.1 x 74.9
79.72

Donaldson, Gordon
David, 4th Marquess of Aberdeen
oil on canvas 125.7 x 100.3
79.97

Dughet, Gaspard 1615–1675
A Classical Landscape
oil on canvas 73.7 x 96.5
79.147

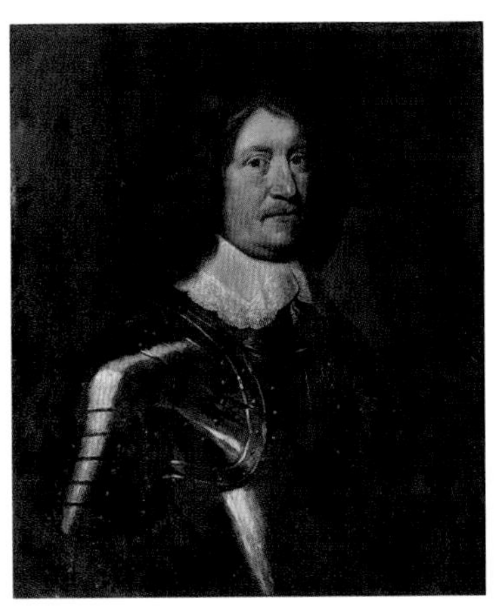

Dutch (The Hague) School
Portrait of an Officer
oil on panel 73.7 x 60.9
79.103

Dutch School
Portrait of a Gentleman
oil on copper 15.2 x 11.4
79.173.1

Dutch School
Portrait of a Lady
oil on copper 15.2 x 11.4
79.173.2

Dyck, Anthony van 1599–1641
Head of a Bearded Old Man (style of Paolo Veronese)
oil on panel 47 x 38.1
79.75

Dyck, Anthony van (circle of) 1599–1641
Charles I (1600–1649)
oil on canvas 73.7 x 58.4
79.68.1

Dyck, Anthony van (circle of) 1599–1641
Henrietta Maria
oil on canvas 73.7 x 58.4
79.68.2

Eastman, Frank S. 1878–1964
June, Marchioness of Aberdeen
oil on canvas 90.2 x 68.6
79.106

Eaton, Wyatt 1849–1896
Lady Marjorie Gordon 1894
oil on canvas 81.3 x 63.5
79.3

Eaton, Wyatt 1849–1896
The Honourable Archie Gordon
oil on canvas 180.1 x 127
79.79

Evans, Robert
Arthur Wellesley, 1st Duke of Wellington (after Thomas Lawrence)
oil on canvas 73.7 x 60.9
79.19

Fink, Wilhelm
Lady Marjorie Gordon 1898
oil on canvas 50.8 x 40.6
79.219

Ford, Emily
Saint Christopher 1963
acrylic on metal 172.7 x 62.2
79.251

Gascars, Henri 1634–1701
Portrait of a Woman c.1678
oil on canvas 88.9 x 71.1
79.85

Giles, James 1801–1870
The Interior of the Drawing Room at Haddo 1836
oil on board 35.6 x 69.2
79.42

Giles, James 1801–1870
Woodland Path with Figures 1837
oil on board 59.7 x 49.5
79.120.3

Giles, James 1801–1870
Moorland Landscape with Sportsman and Setter 1843
oil on board
79.143

Giles, James 1801–1870
Bridge over a River c.1845
oil on board 24.8 x 37.4
79.212.2

Giles, James 1801–1870
Castle by a River c.1845
oil on board 24.7 x 37.5
79.212.1

Giles, James 1801–1870
Deer Forest c.1845
oil on board 25 x 39.5
79.212.5

Giles, James 1801–1870
Hagberry Pot, River Ythan c.1845
oil on board 24.5 x 37.5
79.212.4

Giles, James 1801–1870
Stalking c.1845
oil on board 24.5 x 39.5
79.212.3

Giles, James 1801–1870
Landscape 1847
oil on board 32 x 45.6
79.338

Giles, James 1801–1870
Buchanness 1851
oil on board 44.4 x 59.7
79.214

Giles, James 1801–1870
The Monarch of the Glen 1861
oil on canvas 59.7 x 49.5
79.116

Giles, James 1801–1870
A Gun Room with George, 4th Earl of Aberdeen
oil on panel 49.5 x 69.9
79.113

Giles, James 1801–1870
A Lake at Haddo
oil on panel 34.3 x 50.2
79.225

Giles, James 1801–1870
Aberdeen from the South, with the Bridge of Dee
oil on panel 101.6 x 139.7
79.323

Giles, James 1801–1870
An Interior
oil on panel 47 x 95.2
79.165

Giles, James 1801–1870
An Interior at Haddo with George, 4th Earl of Aberdeen, Reading
oil on board 23.5 x 34.3
79.38

Giles, James 1801–1870
Baillie George Hendry of Aberdeen
oil on canvas 90.1 x 69.8
90.116

Giles, James 1801–1870
Castle of Gight
oil on canvas 86.4 x 124.5
79.83

Giles, James 1801–1870
Evening on the Findhorn
oil on board 60.9 x 91.4
79.39.1

Giles, James 1801–1870
Gight, from below
oil on board 59.7 x 49.5
79.120.4

Giles, James 1801–1870
Haddo: The Park Seen through the Open Drawing Room Door
oil on board 24.1 x 34.3
79.41

Giles, James 1801–1870
On Deeside
oil on panel 62.2 x 86.4
79.77.1

Facing page: Fildes, Luke, 1843–1927, *The Honourable Ethel Louise Forbes-Leith (1872–1930), Lady Forbes Leith,* 1906, The National Trust for Scotland, Fyvie Castle (p. 88)

Giles, James 1801–1870
Quarrying: Peterhead Quarry with a Lighthouse in the Background
oil on board 101.6 x 139.7
79.324

Giles, James 1801–1870
The Findhorn from Heronry
oil on board 60.9 x 91.4
79.39.2

Giles, James 1801–1870
Tolquhon Castle
oil on board 59.7 x 49.5
79.120.1

Giles, James 1801–1870
Tolquhon Castle
oil on board 59.7 x 49.5
79.120.2

Giles, James 1801–1870
View of a Scottish Castle
oil on panel 88.7 x 111.1
79.77.2

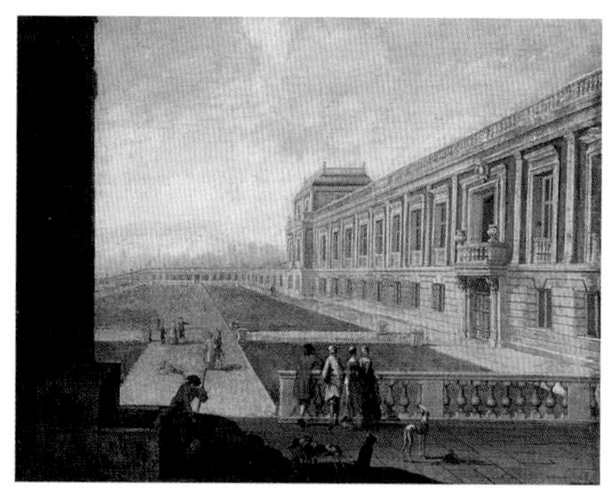

Giles, James (after) 1801–1870
Figures by a Palace
oil on canvas 69.8 x 49.7
T3366

Giles, James (attributed to) 1801–1870
A Sketch of Lord Haddo's Terrace
oil on board 32.2 x 46.4
79.37

Giles, James (attributed to) 1801–1870
Landscape
oil on board 49.4 x 59.5
2011.344

Gordon, John Watson 1788–1864
George, 4th Earl of Aberdeen
oil on canvas 236.2 x 146
79.89

Grainger
Farmyard Scene 1944
oil on canvas 35.4 x 50.5
2011.348

Haddo, George 1816–1864
A Stormy Landscape with Classical Figures (after Gaspard Dughet) 1841
oil on canvas 55 x 84
79.172

Haddo, George 1816–1864
Lady Haddo 1841
oil on canvas 58.4 x 48.3
79.169

Haddo, George 1816–1864
View from St Leonard's Park 1843
oil on board 34 x 44
79.168

Haddo, George 1816–1864
Windsor Castle 1843
oil on canvas 60.9 x 78.7
79.166

Haddo, George 1816–1864
A Cathedral
oil on board 24.1 x 16.5
79.167.3

Haddo, George 1816–1864
A Piebald Pheasant
oil on canvas 60.9 x 83.8
79.31

Haddo, George 1816–1864
Hagar and the Angel (after Claude Lorrain)
oil on canvas 51 x 41
79.17

Haddo, George 1816–1864
Mediterranean Coastal Landscape
oil on board 13.3 x 19
79.167.5

Haddo, George 1816–1864
Sailing Barges
oil on board 16.5 x 24.1
79.167.2

Haddo, George 1816–1864
Seascape from a Pillared Terrace
oil on board 24.7 x 17.1
79.167.1

Hambling, Harry 1902–1998
The Blacksmith's Shop 1972
oil on board 35.6 x 50.2
79.309.4

Hambling, Maggi b.1945
Archibald, 5th Marquess of Aberdeen and Temair
oil on canvas 91.4 x 91.4
79.246

Hambling, Maggi b.1945
River Scene
oil on canvas 38 x 29.4
2011.349

Harris, Robert 1849–1919
John, 7th Earl of Aberdeen, Later 1st Marquess, Montreal 1895
oil on canvas 210.8 x 119.4
79.13

Harwood, Lucy 1893–1972
Still Life, Fruit and Flowers on a Kitchen Table c.1948
oil on canvas 60.9 x 50.8
79.238.3

Haynes, Edward Travanyon 1840–1922
Gladstone
oil on board 75 x 62
2012.41

Hayter, George 1792–1871
Ladies Alice, Jane and Caroline Gordon 1815
oil on canvas 175.3 x 213.4
79.8

Hayter, George 1792–1871
George John James, 5th Earl of Aberdeen
oil on panel 31.5 x 26.5
79.104

Hayter, George 1792–1871
Lady Alice Gordon
oil on canvas 60.9 x 49.5
79.93

Hayter, George 1792–1871
Lady Caroline Gordon
oil on canvas 60.9 x 49.5
79.91

Hayter, George 1792–1871
Lady Jane Gordon
oil on canvas 58.4 x 48.3
79.32

Heyl, Daniel
The Fire of London
oil on canvas 73.7 x 79.8
79.4

Hutchison, William Oliphant 1889–1970
George, 2nd Marquis of Aberdeen 1959
oil on canvas 139.7 x 114.3
79.35

Innocenzo Francucci da Imola 1485–1548
The Virgin
oil on panel 51.4 x 34.3
79.76

Jangers, N.
Lady Marjorie Gordon 1898
oil on canvas 45 x 31
79.221

Jangers, N.
'Monarch': Head of a Terrier
oil on unidentified support 38.1 x 33
79.29

Janssens van Ceulen, Cornelis (attributed to) 1593–1661
Charles I (1600–1649)
oil on canvas 54.6 x 45.7
79.1 (P)

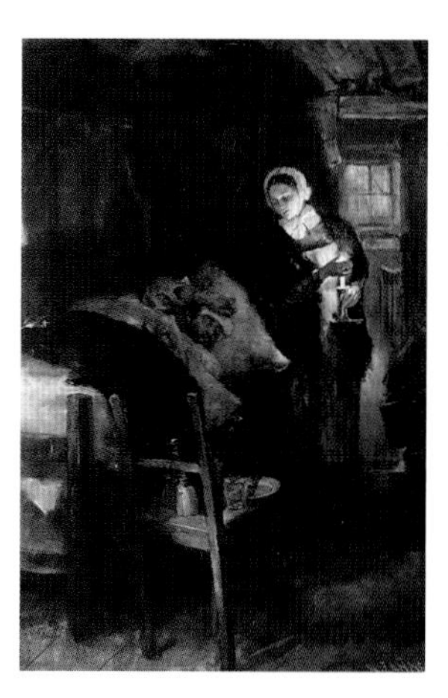

Jehme, W.
A Nurse at a Sickbed 1897
oil on board 67.3 x 45.7
79.112

Lawrence, Thomas (after) 1769–1830
George, 4th Earl of Aberdeen
oil on canvas 74.3 x 58.4
79.15.1

Lawrence, Thomas (after) 1769–1830
Harriet, 2nd Wife of the 4th Earl of Aberdeen
oil on canvas 72.4 x 62.2
79.64

Lawrence, Thomas (after) 1769–1830
Lady Maria Hamilton
oil on canvas 71.1 x 60.9
79.7

Lawrence, Thomas (circle of) 1769–1830
John James Stewart, 1st Marquess of Abercorn
oil on canvas
79.33

Lawrence, Thomas (circle of) 1769–1830
Philip Kemble
oil on canvas 140.9 x 87.6
79.87

Lee, Frederick Richard 1798–1879
On the Lochy, near Killin
oil on canvas 90.2 x 121.9
79.65

Lely, Peter (studio of) 1618–1680
Charles II (1630–1685)
oil on canvas 73.7 x 53.3
79.102

Leslie, Charles Robert 1794–1859
Dominie Sampson
oil on panel 25.4 x 17.8
79.24

Lilley, E.
Country Scene
oil on board 43 x 46.3
2011.352

Lockwood, Lucy active 1896–1934
'Monarch': A Terrier 1896
oil on canvas 27.9 x 35.6
79.224

Lorrain, Claude (attributed to) 1604–1682
A Pastoral River Landscape with Fishermen
oil on canvas 43.2 x 58.4
79.73

Lucas, John 1807–1874
The Honourable Arthur Gordon as a Boy
oil on canvas 58.4 x 45.7
79.69

Maratta, Carlo (circle of) 1625–1713
Portrait of a Gentleman
oil on canvas 66.7 x 57.2
79.2

Marsh, Edward
Dudley, 3rd Marquess of Aberdeen 1939
oil on canvas 127 x 91.4
79.9

Medina, John (circle of) 1720–1796
George, 1st Earl of Aberdeen c.1720
oil on canvas 78.7 x 60.9
79.94

Medina, John (circle of) 1720–1796
John Murray, Duke of Atholl c.1724
oil on canvas 73.7 x 60.9
79.99

Miereveld, Michiel Jansz. van (circle of) 1567–1641
Earl of Southampton
oil on canvas 90.2 x 69.9
79.78

Morales, Juan Francisco active 17th C
Trompe L'oeil
oil on canvas 66 x 45.7
79.88.1

Morales, Juan Francisco active 17th C
Trompe l'oeil
oil on canvas 66 x 45.7
79.88.2

Morris
Rural Cottage
oil on canvas
79.339

Morris, Cedric Lockwood 1889–1982
Coconut Gatherers 1965
oil on canvas 76.2 x 50.2
79.241.3

Morris, Cedric Lockwood 1889–1982
Lord Archie Gordon, Later 5th Marquess of Aberdeen 1974
oil on canvas 80 x 54.9
79.240.3

Mosman, William 1700–1771
Ann (1713–1791), Countess of Aberdeen, with Her Eldest Son, William 1741
oil on canvas 124.5 x 99.1
79.1515

Mosman, William 1700–1771
Catherine, Wife of George, Lord Haddo, Later 3rd Earl of Aberdeen 1741
oil on canvas 72.4 x 60.9
79.96.2

Mosman, William 1700–1771
George, Lord Haddo, Later 3rd Earl of Aberdeen
oil on canvas 72.4 x 60.9
79.96.1

Murillo, Bartolomé Esteban (circle of) 1617–1682
The Good Shepherd
oil on canvas 47 x 58.4
79.74

Neri, Pietro Martire 1596–1661
Portrait of a Clerk
oil on canvas 71.1 x 60.9
79.151

Norie, James 1684–1757
Landscape with a Bridge 1740s
oil on panel 137 x 95
T3367

Norie, James 1684–1757
Landscape with Cattle 1740s
oil on panel 105.3 x 61
T3368

Norie, James 1684–1757
*Figures by a River**
oil on panel
79.139.4

Norie, James 1684–1757
*Fortified Building with Trees and Figures**
oil on board
79.139.1

Norie, James 1684–1757
*Kneeling Figure by a Road**
oil on panel
79.139.2

Norie, James 1684–1757
*Landscape with a Lake and Building**
oil on board
79.139.5.1

Norie, James 1684–1757
*Landscape with a River and a Building**
oil on board
79.139.5.2

Norie, James 1684–1757
*Town by a River**
oil on panel 60.5 x
79.139.3

Panini, Giovanni Paolo (circle of) 1691–1765
A Prison Interior
oil on canvas 59.7 x 86.4
79.4

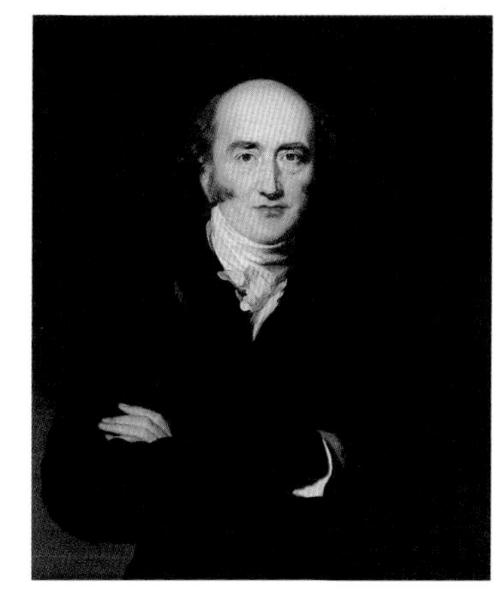

Patten, George 1801–1865
George Canning (after Thomas Lawrence)
oil on canvas 73.7 x 60.9
79.86

Patten, George 1801–1865
Henry, 3rd Earl of Bathurst
oil on canvas 74.9 x 60.9
79.17

Patten, George 1801–1865
Robert Stewart, Earl of Castlereagh
oil on canvas 73.7 x 63.5
79.2

Patten, George 1801–1865
Sir Robert Peel, 2nd Bt (after Thomas Lawrence)
oil on canvas 73.7 x 60.9
79.14

Patten, George 1801–1865
William Pitt the Younger (after Thomas Lawrence)
oil on canvas 73.7 x 62.2
79.16

Phillips, Thomas 1770–1845
General the Honourable Sir Alexander Hamilton Gordon
oil on canvas 69.9 x 59.7
79.66

Puligo, Domenico 1492–1527
Young Woman: La Fornarina
oil on canvas 40.6 x 31.7
79.36

Facing page: Delaroche, Paul, 1797–1856, *Francois-Pierre-Guillaume Guizot,* 1847, National Trust for Scotland, Haddo House (p. 34)

R., E. T.
Landscape with Trees
oil on canvas 34 x 44.2
T3365

Raeburn, Henry 1756–1823
Jean Christie, 2nd Wife of the 4th Duke of Gordon
oil on canvas 73.7 x 60.9
88.107.1 (P)

Reid, George 1841–1913
William Cosmo Gordon of Fyvie, 2nd Earl of Aberdeen 1878
oil on canvas 76.2 x 54.6
79.12

Reid, George 1841–1913
Alexander Henry Gordon of Fyvie 1881
oil on canvas
79.13.1

Reni, Guido (circle of) 1575–1642
The Virgin Sewing
oil on copper 27.9 x 21.6
79.25

Romagnoli, Angiolo 1826–1896
The Visitation (after Mariotto Albertinelli)
oil on canvas 121.9 x 78.7
79.21

Rosa, Salvator 1615–1673
Vanitas
oil on panel 36.8 x 69.8
79.5

Russell, John Bucknell 1819–1893
The Bear and the Beehives
oil on canvas 149.2 x 73.5
79.1.2

Russell, John Bucknell 1819–1893
The Cat and the Mice
oil on canvas 146.5 x 71.5
79.1.6

Russell, John Bucknell 1819–1893
The Crow and the Pot
oil on canvas 146.8 x 64.6
79.1.4

Russell, John Bucknell 1819–1893
The Dog and the Piece of Flesh
oil on canvas 150 x 92.5
79.1.3

Russell, John Bucknell 1819–1893
The Fighting Cocks and the Partridge
oil on canvas 146.5 x 71.7
79.1.7

Russell, John Bucknell 1819–1893
The Fox and the Grapes
oil on canvas 146 x 91.4
79.1.1

Russell, John Bucknell 1819–1893
The Goat and the Well
oil on canvas 148.8 x 73.2
79.1.10

Russell, John Bucknell 1819–1893
The Parliament of Birds
oil on canvas 146.3 x 72.2
79.1.11

Russell, John Bucknell 1819–1893
The Stag Looking into the Water
oil on canvas 149.6 x 92.3
79.1.9

Russell, John Bucknell 1819–1893
The Tortoise and the Hare
oil on canvas 146.7 x 72.2
79.1.8

Russell, John Bucknell 1819–1893
The Wolf and the Lamb
oil on canvas 146.8 x 72.2
79.1.5

Sant, George active 1856–1879
Ishbel, Countess of Aberdeen 1879
oil on canvas 210.8 x 119.4
79.131

Sant, George active 1856–1879
John, 7th Earl of Aberdeen
oil on canvas 210.8 x 119.4
79.3

Smith-Burnet
Lady Catherine Gordon (after Henry Raeburn) c.1760
oil on canvas 73.7 x 60.9
88.107.3 (P)

Smith-Burnet
Alexander, 4th Duke of Gordon (after Henry Raeburn)
oil on canvas 73 x 61
88.107.5 (P)

Somer I, Paulus van (circle of) 1576–1621
James VI and I (1566–1625)
oil on canvas 77.5 x 54.6
79.1

Steel, Gourlay 1819–1894
Old Pets at Haddo 1891
oil on canvas 68.6 x 90.2
79.215

Syme, J. T.
Seascape
oil on board 25.3 x 32.5
2011.353

Thomson, John 1778–1840
A Lake among Mountains with a Castle
oil on canvas 72.4 x 104.1
79.15

unknown artist
Portrait of a Woman 1837
oil on panel 17.6 x 15.1
2011.357

unknown artist
Corner of Terrace at Haddo 1937
oil on canvas 17 x 11.5
79.121.5

unknown artist
Charles II (1630–1685)
oil on panel 31.1 x 26.7
79.9 (P)

unknown artist
Cornish Coastal Scene
oil on board 7 x 15.2
79.228

unknown artist
Dianthus with Butterfly
oil on glass 36 x 25.7
79.111

unknown artist
Heron Wading
oil on board 38.7 x 52.3
79.235.4

unknown artist
Landscape, River Scene
oil on canvas 39.5 x 60.2
2011.346

unknown artist
Parrots in a Forest Scene
oil on canvas 62.8 x 75.2
2011.345

unknown artist
Portrait of a Man
oil on panel 25.6 x 21
2011.355

unknown artist
Portrait of a Priest
oil on panel 20.4 x 17.2
2011.356

unknown artist
Rachel Emily Shaw Lefevre
oil on board 52.1 x 41.3
79.226

unknown artist
The Coast at Boddam
oil on canvas 44.5 x 59.7
79.115

unknown artist
Two Birds on Branches
oil on canvas 29 x 43.8
2011.25

unknown artist
Woman Reading by a Window
oil on canvas 15 x 22
2011.358

Veronese, Paolo (after) 1528–1588
The Adoration of the Shepherds
oil on canvas 93.9 x 116.8
79.13.2

Vlieger, Simon de 1601–1653
A Boat off Shore
oil on panel 53.3 x 76.2
79.71

Vlieger, Simon de 1601–1653
Fishing Boats off a Jetty
oil on panel 45.7 x 69.8
79.67

Voet, Jakob Ferdinand (style of) 1639–1700
Portrait of a Nobleman
oil on canvas 73.7 x 59.7
79.98

W., D.
Wood Anemones
oil on canvas 22.9 x 30.5
79.242.1

Waldorp, Antonie W. 1803–1866
A Canal near The Hague
oil on canvas 71.1 x 100.3
79.34

Ward, Edwin Arthur 1859–1933
John, 7th Earl of Aberdeen, 1st Marquess
c.1870
oil on canvas 49.5 x 59.7
79.222

Wells, Henry Tanworth 1828–1903
Katherine, Wife of the 6th Lord Burleigh 1877
oil on canvas 132.1 x 95.3
79.22

Wilson, Derek
Willy Lot's Cottage, Drockwaters 1940
oil on board 27 x 35.6
79.309.1

Wissing, Willem (circle of) 1656–1687
Queen Mary
oil on canvas 124.5 x 100.3
79.23

Wissing, Willem (studio of) 1656–1687
Portrait of a Woman
oil on canvas 73.7 x 60.9
79.149

The National Trust for Scotland, Pitmedden Garden

In 1952, Pitmedden House, Garden and Estate were presented to The National Trust for Scotland by Major James Keith, CBE. In addition, Major Keith donated furniture, furnishings and paintings, some of which still remain in the house. Adjacent to the garden is the Museum of Farming Life containing the Cook Collection of farming artefacts, donated to the Trust by Aberdeenshire farmer William Cook in 1978. Since that time, the collection has been augmented by further gifts from generous benefactors.

The present house is believed to be the third on this site, built around 1860. However it does incorporate elements that are older: the north and west wings are eighteenth-century with some seventeenth-century work, whilst the south wing contains much re-used stone from structures of a similar date. Through the use and re-use of core structural fabric it is possible to chart the continuing use of the site and the development of the individual buildings and their uses. All these structures add significantly to our appreciation and understanding of the history and aesthetics of the property, its form and design, and the status of its owners through time.

The Trust was fortunate also to receive Major Keith's furniture and furnishings as part of his gift in 1952. It is a small collection and includes some furnishings with a strong colonial air from the 1920s and 1930s. However, its relative completeness and quality make it an important collection, particularly for the Trust, which has little in its fine art or furniture collection from this period. Of considerable interest within the collection is the art deco bedroom furniture and, of high significance, the two John Duncan paintings, both from the early twentieth century. The Seton family connection has been renewed recently, with the permanent loan of two chests together with family china and documents by a descendant of the Seton family. One of the chests is of particular interest having been made from wood taken from the house following the fire of 1818.

The property was gifted by Major James Keith in 1952. The collection of the Museum of Farming Life was given by the Trustees of William Cook of Little Meldrum, Tarves in 1978.

Facing page: Gainsborough, Thomas, 1727–1788, *Major William Tennant (d.1803), of Needwood House, Staffordshire,* The National Trust for Scotland, Fyvie Castle (p. 88)

Adam, Joseph Denovan 1841–1896
Highland Cattle on a Moorland 1895
oil on canvas 74.9 x 125.7
78.5

Anrooy, Anton Abraham van 1870–1949
An Interior with a Woman Reading c.1930
oil on canvas 73 x 57.2
78.2

Borthwick, Alfred Edward 1871–1955
The Fugitive 1929
oil on canvas 101 x 63.5
78.4

British (Scottish) School
Lake Scene
oil on canvas 19.3 x 29.2
78.34

British (Scottish) School
Portrait of a Lady in a Black Dress
oil on canvas 75 x 62.2
78.1529

Elwell, Frederick William 1870–1958
Beverley Minster from the Hall Garth c.1900
oil on canvas 61.6 x 73.7
78.6

Munro, Charles Binning 1840–1910
Catterline from Dunnottar 19th C
oil on canvas 66 x 58.4
78.3

Reid, Archibald David 1844–1908
The Ythan Estuary 1873
oil on canvas 77.5 x 120
78.1

Reid, Stephen 1873–1948
The Letter 1936
oil on canvas 59 x 43.2
78.1558

unknown artist
Portrait of a Gentleman c.1900
oil on canvas 36.8 x 28.6
78.35

Wright, E.
An East Coast Fishing Village 1885
oil on canvas 36.2 x 66.3
78.29

The National Trust for Scotland, The Hill House

The Hill House is situated in the town of Helensburgh, approximately 20 miles north-west of Glasgow. The house was designed in 1902 by the renowned architect and designer Charles Rennie Mackintosh for his client Walter M. Blackie, a Glasgow publisher. The building was completed with some alterations to the original design, being handed over to Blackie in 1904. The Hill House remained the family home of the Blackies until 1953.

The Hill House is internationally important, being a complete expression of Mackintosh's design philosophy of integrating architecture, decoration and furniture. Mackintosh's striking, modern style was influential in continental Europe during his lifetime and he contributed to the 8th Vienna Secession and participated in international exhibitions in Turin, Moscow and elsewhere. The Hill House offers visitors a unique opportunity to see a Mackintosh building and the style that has become synonymous with him and indeed the Glasgow area. His distinctive style is revered across the world and as a result, The Hill House is one of the Trust's most recognisable properties to those in Scotland and abroad.

The Hill House is regarded as one of the finest buildings in Charles Rennie Mackintosh's small portfolio, possibly only bettered by the Glasgow School of Art. It is his most significant domestic commission, encompassing all of his best features. The overriding importance comes from the totality of the design. The building, interior and collections were all designed by Mackintosh in unity down to the smallest detail. The shape and space of rooms, decoration of the walls, lights and light fittings, the furniture, including built-in furniture down to the smallest fitments were all carefully designed to serve both practical and aesthetic functions. This is typical of Mackintosh's design philosophy and the building also contains many of his recognisable motifs and details. The influence of Mackintosh's wife, Margaret Macdonald is also evident at The Hill House.

The Hill House was offered to The National Trust for Scotland in 1982 to ensure its permanent conservation.

Fergusson, John Duncan 1874–1961
Elizabeth Dryden
oil on board 74 x 63.4
91.67

Henry, George 1858–1943
Mrs Younger 1902/1903
oil on canvas 104.8 x 90
T4460

Mackintosh, Margaret Macdonald 1864–1933
Sleeping Princess 1908
oil & gesso on panel 54.2 x 105
T4459

Raeburn, Henry 1756–1823
Walter Graham c.1815
oil on canvas 74.8 x 62.3
89.123

Strain, Hilary 1884–1960
Walter Blackie 1928
oil on canvas 101.5 x 111
2.77.1 (P)

Torrance, James 1859–1916
Mr Younger
oil on canvas 83.2 x 71
T4461

The National Trust for Scotland, Leith Hall Garden & Estate

Leith Hall, situated in Kennethmont in Aberdeenshire, has been in the possession of The National Trust for Scotland for almost 60 years, having been gifted to the Trust by the Honourable Louisa Henrietta Valdevia Leith-Hay in 1946. Leith Hall, garden and estate is a fascinating and diverse property, which over the last three and a half centuries has grown and developed to suit the changing needs and aspirations of generations of the Leith-Hay family. It is important as an example of a house retaining a relatively complete setting of gardens and parkland.

Built in stages from 1650 to the early twentieth century, Leith Hall is a compact quadrangular country house set around a central courtyard. It was very much a practical house: one that was lived in, used, and altered to meet the family's needs and this is reflected in the hall's interiors and much of the collections, so much of which the Trust was fortunate to acquire.

The interiors include several original features of considerable historical and decorative value, for example the mid-nineteenth century wallpaper in the Music Room and tapestry corridor, a rare and remarkably complete, surviving example from this era. The contents are of great interest and importance as they provide more of an insight into the Leith-Hay family, particularly the many personal items that relate to the family's military exploits and as such are of outstanding historical and decorative value. With so many items relating to this aspect of their lives, the entire house must once have resembled a military museum, with the family living amongst the 'trophies of war' and memorabilia of military campaigns, on a day to day basis.

Aiken, John MacDonald 1880–1961
Charles O'Neill Leith-Hay of Rannes, Aged 14
1932
oil on canvas 63.5 x 49.5
2011.828

Aiken, John MacDonald 1880–1961
The Honourable Henrietta O'Neill (d.1965), Wife of Charles Leith-Hay
oil on canvas 125 x 99
2011.777

Anglo/Indian School
Nawab of Oudh c.1850
oil on enamel 15 x 10 (E)
T 3372

Anglo/Indian School
Sir Stapleton Cotton, Lord Combermere, Commander-in-Chief, India (1825–1830)
oil on enamel 15 x 10 (E)
T 3373

Barclay, John MacLaren 1811–1886
Colonel Alexander Sebastian Leith-Hay (1818–1900) 1868
oil on canvas 279 x 187.5
2011.412

Bassano II, Francesco 1549–1592
The Element of Water
oil on canvas 95.4 x 131
77.1

Berchem, Nicolaes Pietersz 1620–1683
An Italianate Landscape with Herdsmen
oil on canvas 37.5 x 49
2011.452

Bird, William
Children in a Landscape
oil on board 39.4 x 34.3
2011.458.1

Bird, William
Children in a Landscape
oil on board 39.4 x 34.3
2011.458.2

Breun, John Ernest 1862–1921
Charles Edward Norman Leith-Hay (1858–1939), of Leith Hall 1905
oil on canvas 140.5 x 114.8
2011.78

British (English) School
Captain, Lord Cochrane (1775–1860), Later 10th Earl of Dundonald 1801
oil on panel 58.2 x 39.8
2011.71

British (English) School
Captain, Later Rear-Admiral, John Leith-Hay (1788–1854), RN
oil on canvas 75 x 62.3
2011.7

British (English) School
Fishing Boats in Rough Seas
oil on panel 21.5 x 27.3
2011.544

British (English) School
John Leith of Leith Hall (c.1698–1736)
oil on canvas 124 x 101.5
2011.542.2

British (English) School
Mary Hay of Rannes (c.1698–1736)
oil on canvas 124 x 101.5
2011.542.1

British (Scottish) School
George Ross of Clachan and Colp c.1680
oil on canvas 73.7 x 62
2011.785

British (Scottish) School
Portrait of a Lady c.1780
oil on canvas 76.1 x 63.5
2011.783

British (Scottish) School
Chess Players c.1820
oil on copper
2011.414

British (Scottish) School
Nicola Arbuthnot (1823–1874) c.1850
oil on canvas 126 x 100.5
2011.799

British (Scottish) School
Elspeth Robertson, Wife of George Ross of Clachan and Colp c.1860
oil on canvas 68 x 58
2011.79

British (Scottish) School
Alexander Leith of Freefield
oil on canvas 76.1 x 63.5
2011.805

British (Scottish) School
Christina Howieson (d.1705)
oil on canvas 59.5 x 43.8
2011.788

British (Scottish) School
Classical Ruins with a Rotunda
oil on canvas 57 x 72.5
2011.451

British (Scottish) School
Elizabeth Leith-Ross, Wife of David Souter Robertson, with Her Son Thomas Robertson
oil on canvas 160.7 x 111
77.13

British (Scottish) School
Elizabeth Young of Bourtie (1782–1852)
oil on canvas 125 x 100.5
2011.8

British (Scottish) School
John Ross of Arnage (1707–1789)
oil on canvas 72.2 x 59.5
2011.794

British (Scottish) School
John Ross of Arnage (1707–1789)
oil on canvas 73.6 x 61
2011.797

British (Scottish) School
John Ross of Clachan and Colp
oil on canvas 66.8 x 56
2011.793

British (Scottish) School
Lawrence Begg, a Cook
oil on canvas 50.8 x 45.7
2011.798

British (Scottish) School
Portrait of a Lady of Mar
oil on canvas 76.7 x 62
2011.442

British (Scottish) School
Portrait of a Man (said to be Lord Nisbet)
oil on canvas 74.8 x 62
2011.66

British (Scottish) School
Ross John Leith (1777–1839)
oil on canvas 73.6 x 61
2011.795

British (Scottish) School
Walter Robertson
oil on canvas 71.1 x 58.4
2011.792

British (Scottish) School
William Stuart of Loanhead
oil on canvas 63.3 x 53.3
2011.787

British (Scottish) School
Woman with a Candle
oil on panel 27.2 x 22.3
2011.74

British School
Portrait of a Gentleman
oil on canvas 73 x 62
2011.781

Cameron, J. D. Beauchamp
John Leith Ross
oil on canvas 59 x 48.5
2011.803

Cameron, J. D. Beauchamp
John Leith Ross
oil on canvas
2011.804

Chandler, John Westbrooke 1764–1807
General Alexander Leith-Hay of Rannes and Leith Hay (1758–1838)
oil on canvas 150 x 121.8
2011.538

Chandler, John Westbrooke 1764–1807
Mary Forbes of Ballogie (d.1824), Wife of General Leith-Hay
oil on canvas 152.2 x 124
2011.539

Crespi, Giovanni Battista 1575–1632
The Flight into Egypt
oil on canvas 156.2 x 126
2011.464

Dighton, Denis 1792–1827
The Storming of San Sebastian
oil on canvas 177.5 x 300
2011.782

Dutch School
A Woman and Children in a Yard
oil on panel 41.5 x 35
2011.75

French School
Romulus and Remus
oil on canvas on panel 46.8 x 45
2011.784

Hay, J. E.
View of Leith Hall from the South East 1907
oil on canvas 38.5 x 55.2
2011.779

Hayter, George 1792–1871
Sir Andrew Leith-Hay, MP
oil on canvas 34.3 x 29.2
2011.72

Henry, John
Christian Leith-Ross
oil on canvas 88.9 x 73.6
2011.789

Howe, James 1780–1836
John Anderson, Falconer to the Flemings of Barochan
oil on canvas 35.5 x 27
2011.541

Hughes, Edward Robert 1851–1914
Charles Edward Leith-Hay Clark (1858–1939)
oil on canvas 59 x 49
77.16

Italian School
Saint Peter
oil on canvas 76.2 x 55.8
2011.463

Italian School
The Adoration of the Shepherds
oil on canvas 106.6 x 78.8
2011.46

Kneller, Godfrey (circle of) 1646–1723
Jean Ross (1683–1717), Wife of Sir David Ogilvie, 3rd Bt of Barras
oil on canvas 120.5 x 100
2011.791

Kneller, Godfrey (circle of) 1646–1723
Portrait of a Man in Armour
oil on canvas 76.5 x 63.5
2011.536

Lawrence, Thomas 1769–1830
Head of a Boy
oil on canvas 43.2 x 33
2011.45

Maes, Dirk (follower of) 1659–1717
A Cavalry Skirmish
oil on canvas 46.4 x 61.5
2011.73

Medina, John 1720–1796
John Ross (1664–1714)
oil on canvas 76.1 x 63.5
2011.786

Moir, John 1776–1857
Harriot Christian Leith-Hay (d.1830), Wife of Sir Harry N. Lumsden, Bt
oil on canvas 76.2 x 63.5
2011.69

Mosman, William 1700–1771
Mary Hay of Rannes (d.1736), Wife of John Leith
oil on canvas 76.3 x 63.5
2011.543

Mura, Francesco de (circle of) 1696–1782
Madonna and Child
oil on canvas 44.5 x 33
2011.449

Northcote, James 1746–1831
Mary Margaret Clarke (d.1859), Wife of Sir Andrew Leith-Hay
oil on canvas 124 x 99
2011.68

Northern Italian School
The Holy Family with Saint Elizabeth and the Infant Saint John the Baptist
oil on canvas 40.5 x 38.7
2011.461

Opie, John 1761–1807
A Girl with a Basket of Flowers
oil on canvas 127 x 101.6
2011.453

Raeburn, Henry 1756–1823
Alexander Leith of Freeland
oil on canvas 88.9 x 68.5
2011.796

Ramsay, Allan 1713–1784
Jean, Lady Banff 1747
oil on canvas 74 x 61.2
2011.447

Ramsay, Allan 1713–1784
Jane Nisbet, Lady Dirleton 1748
oil on canvas 76.5 x 63.5
2011.446

Smith, Arthur 1814–1882
A Frigate off a Rocky Coast 1857
oil on panel 27 x 43
2011.545

Facing page: Hayter, John, 1800–1891, *Lady Augusta FitzClarence Kennedy-Erskine (d.1860), Natural Daughter of King William IV and Wife of the Honourable John Erskine, with Her Children, Wiliam Henry, Wilhelmina and Millicent Ann Mary*, The National Trust for Scotland, House of Dun (p. 108)

Smith, W.
Andrew Hay of Rannes (b.1713) (after Henry Raeburn)
oil on canvas 73.8 x 61
2011.67

Smith, W.
John Leigh of Leith Hall (1731–1763)
oil on canvas 120 x 97
2011.537

Smith, W. H.
Harriot Steuart of Auchlunchart, Wife of John Leith
oil on canvas 73.5 x 58.5
2011.54

Spanish School
A Praying Saint with Cherubim above c.1620
oil on canvas 71.1 x 54.5
2011.462

Stuart, Gilbert 1755–1828
William Abercromby of Glasgow
oil on canvas 76.2 x 61.5
2011.776

Teniers II, David (attributed to) 1610–1690
Peasants Merrymaking in a Courtyard c.1620–c.1660
oil on canvas 82 x 154.5
2011.778

unknown artist
Portrait of a Boy 1832
oil on canvas 58.5 x 45.7
2011.448

unknown artist
Admiral R. MacAlpine
oil on canvas 59.8 x 50.8
2011.111

unknown artist
Funerary Monument
oil on canvas 64 x 47
2011.806

unknown artist
Portrait of a Small Child
oil on board (?) 10.5 x 8.5
2011.802

unknown artist
The Lute Player
oil
2011.807

unknown artist
William Leith Ross
oil on canvas 75 x 62
2011.801

Varley I, John 1778–1842
View with Leith Hall
oil on board 40.1 x 56.7
2011.485

Watson, George (after) 1767–1837
Alexander Leith of Freefield
oil on canvas 88.9 x 68.5
2011.615

Weigall, Henry 1829–1925
Christina Grace Agnes Hamilton (d.1897), Wife of Colonel Alexander Leith-Hay 1861
oil on canvas 63.5 x 50.8
2011.413

Westmacott I, Richard 1775–1856
Colonel Sir Andrew Leith-Hay (1785–1862), MP
oil on canvas 126.5 x 101
2011.65

Wouwerman, Philips 1619–1668
Landscape with a Woodman Loading a Horse
oil on canvas 31 x 39
2011.455

Zuccarelli, Francesco 1702–1788
Landscape with a Mill
oil on canvas 62 x 74
2011.456

The National Trust for Scotland, Castle Fraser, Garden & Estate

Recognised for its outstanding architectural merit through its A-listing, Castle Fraser is one of the largest and most elaborate of the Scottish houses built between the fifteenth and early seventeenth centuries and can claim to be of international significance.

Built in several phases over a period of at least 200 years, Castle Fraser, originally known as the House of Muchalls, shares a similar developmental history with many of its counterparts. The plain lower stories, believed to date from the fifteenth and sixteenth centuries, were tied together by the greatly enriched and heraldic skyline, incorporating two-storey studies (turrets), in the late sixteenth and early seventeenth centuries by John Bel.

The scale, quality of design and elaboration of ornament together with connections to the notable Aberdeenshire masons Thomas Leiper and John Bel give the building its national architectural importance. With other comparable houses in the region, such as Craigievar and Crathes, Castle Fraser forms an important group of architectural masterpieces, which represent some of the best Scottish early post-reformation buildings, and it is thus of international significance. Within this group Castle Fraser is distinguished by the survival of the courtyard, which adds a formality and grandeur to the composition.

The house can be viewed as a reflection of Fraser family pride, each development harmonising sensitively with the work of previous generations. The castle contains many Fraser family portraits, including one by Raeburn, and fine nineteenth-century carpets, curtains and bed hangings. It retains the atmosphere of the family home with highlights including the Great Hall dating back to the 1400s, a library filled with family books, and the grand Worked Room featuring eighteenth-century embroideries. There are other interesting features to discover – such as the Laird's Lug, hidden trapdoors revealing secret stairs, a spy hole, a room full of stuffed animals and a wooden leg.

The castle and grounds were given to The National Trust for Scotland by Major and Mrs Michael Smiley in 1976.

Anglo/Dutch School
Four Monks in an Interior
oil on canvas on panel 33.6 x 28.4
2009.1114

Beechey, William (after) 1753–1839
General Francis Humberstone Mackenzie (1782–1815), 1st Lord Seaforth
oil on canvas 89.5 x 69.3
2009.242

Belle, Alexis-Simon (after) 1674–1734
Prince James Edward Stuart (1688–1766)
oil on canvas 73.3 x 61
2009.1145

British (English) School
Portrait of a Man (said to be Prince Henry Frederick, 1592–1612, Prince of Orange) c.1620
oil on canvas 61 x 49.1
2009.315

British (Scottish) School
Portrait of an Officer in Armour with a Sash c.1660
oil on canvas 73 x 59.5
2009.111

British (Scottish) School
Portrait of a Lady in a Red Dress c.1680
oil on canvas 74 x 61.2
2009.313

British (Scottish) School
Portrait of an Officer in Armour with a Stock c.1680
oil on canvas 74.3 x 62
T4468

British (Scottish) School
Portrait of an Officer in Armour c.1690
oil on canvas 73.7 x 61.5
2009.301

British (Scottish) School
Portrait of a Boy in a Brown Coat with a Pink Sash c.1700
oil on canvas 69.2 x 39.8
2009.306

British (Scottish) School
Portrait of a Man in a Black Surplice c.1700
oil on canvas 60.4 x 53.2
2009.308

British (Scottish) School
Portrait of a Man in Classical Costume c.1700
oil on canvas 73 x 54.7
2009.309

British (Scottish) School
Portrait of a Gentleman in a Red Coat c.1730
oil on canvas 67.3 x 49.5
2009.1104

British (Scottish) School
Portrait of a Lady in a Red Dress c.1730
oil on canvas 67.5 x 49.4
2009.1105

British (Scottish) School
James Byres of Tonley (1734–1817) c.1810
oil on canvas 74.5 x 61
2009.967

British (Scottish) School
Portrait of a Lady in a Landscape c.1810
oil on canvas 75 x 62.3
2009.142

British (Scottish) School
A Girl with Two Dogs
oil on canvas 89 x 70
89.52.1

British (Scottish) School
Portrait of a Gentleman in a Slashed Doublet
oil on canvas 61 x 43.2
2009.1233

British (Scottish) School
Portrait of a Lady (said to be the wife of Andrew, 1st Lord Fraser)
oil on canvas 71.6 x 60.6
2009.237

British (Scottish) School
Portrait of a Lady in a Black Dress (possibly Lady Fraser, wife of the 1st Lord Fraser)
oil on canvas 61 x 43.2
2009.1232

British (Scottish) School
Portrait of a Man Holding a Flower
oil on canvas 69.5 x 53.5
2009.302

British (Scottish) School
Portrait of the Wife of Andrew, 1st Lord Fraser
oil on canvas 61 x 42.3
2009.238

British School
Portrait of a Man in a Hat c.1600
oil on panel 28.5 x 21.4
2009.1131

British School
Portrait of a Man with a Ruff c.1600
oil on panel 28.7 x 21.4
2009.1132

British School
Portrait of a Monk c.1600
oil on panel 23 x 17.8
2009.1133

British School
Lady Blanche Drummond (d.1954) c.1920
oil on canvas 44 x 34.2
2009.275

British School
Head of a Lady with a Pearl Necklace
oil on unidentified support 33 x 28
2009.1138

British School
Portrait of a Lady in a White Dress and Black Gown
oil on canvas 23 x 18.5
2009.4

Bronckhorst, Arnold (after) active c.1566–1586
George Buchanan 17th C
oil on canvas 64.8 x 56.6
2009.314

Chinnery, George 1774–1852
Mary Bristow (d.1805)
oil on canvas 74.4 x 61.4
2009.966

Colone, Adam de (after) 1572–1651
James VI and I (1566–1625)
oil on canvas 71 x 61.5
2009.316

Cosway, Richard (attributed to) 1742–1821
Alexander Mackenzie (1758–1809), 9th Lord Fraser of Inverallochy
oil on paper on board 26.4 x 19.7
2009.212

Cosway, Richard (attributed to) 1742–1821
Helen Mackenzie (1764–1802), Wife of Alexander Mackenzie, 9th Lord Fraser of Inverallochy
oil on paper on board 27.4 x 20
2009.211

Dyck, Anthony van (after) 1599–1641
Charles I (1600–1649), in a White Lace Collar and a Blue Sash c.1750
oil on glass 75.6 x 52.7
2009.192

Faulkner, Benjamin Rawlinson 1787–1849
Colonel Charles Mackenzie Fraser of Inverallochy and Castle Fraser (1792–1871)
oil on canvas 74.6 x 62.1
2009.14

Gianni, Giuseppe 1829–1885
Harbour at Malta 1874
oil on canvas 20.5 x 67.4
2009.386.1

Gianni, Giuseppe 1829–1885
Stormy Seas, Malta 1874
oil on canvas 20.5 x 67.4
2009.386.2

Facing page: Crespi, Giovanni Battista, c.1575–1632, *The Flight into Egypt,* The National Trust for Scotland, Leith Hall Garden & Estate (p. 66)

Giles, James 1801–1870
Castle Fraser 1858
oil on canvas 36 x 53.4
2009.19

Gryeff, Peter de
Parrots and a Cockatiel c.1900
oil on panel
88.629

Hay, A.
A Pug: 'Jo'
oil on board 18.1 x 16.5
2009.1072

Isenbrandt, Adriaen (after) 1500–1546
The Mystic Marriage of Saint Catherine with Four Female Saints
oil on canvas 53.2 x 38.7
2009.1135

Jamesone, George (circle of) 1588–1644
Andrew Fraser (1574–1636), 1st Lord Fraser of Castle Fraser
oil on canvas 72.4 x 61.5
2009.235

Jamesone, George (circle of) 1588–1644
Andrew Fraser (1574–1636), 1st Lord Fraser of Castle Fraser
oil on canvas 60.4 x 42.6
2009.235

Jamesone, George (follower of) 1588–1644
Portrait of a Man in a Black Slashed Coat with Lace Collar
oil on canvas 59.5 x 53.3
2009.307

Jamesone, George (follower of) 1588–1644
Portrait of a Man in Armour
oil on canvas 67.1 x 56.6
2009.305

Jouanne, M.
Lieutenant Colonel Frederick Mackenzie Fraser (1831–1887)
oil on canvas 74.4 x 58.6
2009.1004

Largillière, Nicolas de (after) 1656–1746
Prince James Frances Edward Stuart (1688–1766) 18th C
oil on canvas 35.8 x 28.5
2009.1141

Lawrence, Thomas (after) 1769–1830
Arthur Wellesley (1769–1852), 1st Duke of Wellington
oil on canvas 75.4 x 62.3
2009.143

Lawrence, Thomas (after) 1769–1830
Jane Hay (1799–1861), Daughter of Sir John Hay of Haystoun and Inverallochy, and Wife of Colonel Charles Mackenzie of Fraser (...)
oil on canvas 75.2 x 64.4
2009.141

MacIvor, Maurice
Portrait of a Lady with a Cat
oil on canvas 91.5 x 51
2009.385

Mackenzie, Frederick
Mrs Frederick Mackenzie, née Theodora Lovett (d.1947) (Frederick Mackenzie's second wife) 1910
oil on paper on board 40 x 29.3
2009.413

Mytens, Daniel (after) 1590–1647
Charles I (1600–1649), in Robes of State
oil on canvas 66 x 54.5
2009.317

Parrocel, Pierre (after) 1670–1739
George Keith (1693–1778), 10th Earl Marischal
oil on canvas 95.3 x 73
2009.132

Raeburn, Henry 1756–1823
Charles Mackenzie Fraser, MP
oil on canvas 75 x 62
2012.406

Raeburn, Henry 1756–1823
Eliza Fraser of Castle Fraser
oil on canvas 105 x 86
2009.964

Raeburn, Henry (after) 1756–1823
Lieutenant-General Sir Alexander Mackenzie Fraser of Inverallochy (1758–1809)
oil on canvas 124.5 x 99
2009.239

Raeburn, Henry (after) 1756–1823
Martha Fraser of Inverallochy (1727–1803)
oil on canvas 89 x 68
2009.965

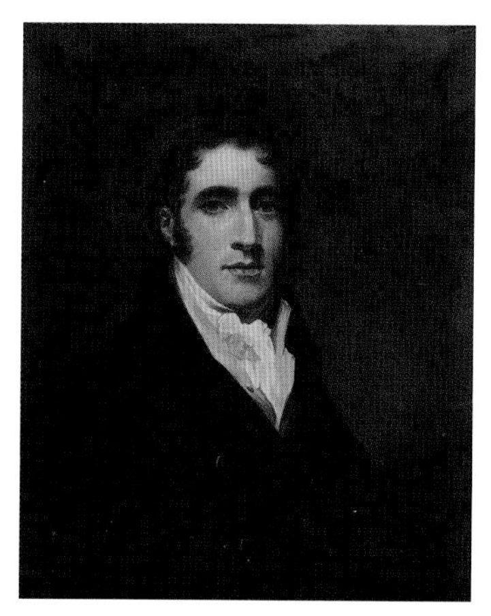

Raeburn, Henry (after) 1756–1823
The Hononourable William Mackenzie (1791–1814), MP
oil on canvas 74 x 61
2009.178

Sanders, George 1774–1846
Lieutenant-General Sir Thomas Bradford (1777–1853)
oil on canvas 75 x 62.5
2009.144

Schunemann, L. (attributed to) active 1651–1681
Portrait of a Gentleman in a Dark Blue Mantle
1661
oil 71.2 x 58
2009.304

unknown artist
'Laddie'
oil on canvas 42 x 57
2009.1077

unknown artist
Leap Castle
oil on board
2009.42

unknown artist
Portrait of a Woman
oil on panel 68 x 55.1
2009.412

unknown artist
Portrait of a Woman in a White Dress with a Red Gown
oil on canvas 75 x 62
2009.396

Webster, A.
An Oriental Harbour 1862
oil on canvas 73.75 x 113
89.52.2

The National Trust for Scotland, Fyvie Castle

Fyvie Castle is situated in north-east Aberdeenshire, about 25 miles from Aberdeen. This Z-plan castle has a complex history dating back to at least the thirteenth century.

Today it appears a fairytale castle of turrets and towers, enfolded in woodlands, and set in a serpentine bend of the River Ythan. Its dominant feature is the symmetrical south front, epitomising the splendour of the Scots seventeenth-century Renaissance style. The history of Fyvie is long and complex, stretching back at least to the thirteenth century and its origins as a royal stronghold. Ghosts, legends and folklore are all woven into the tapestry of Fyvie's 800-year history. Each tower of this magnificent Scottish Baronial fortress is traditionally associated with one of the castle's five successive families – Preston, Meldrum, Seton, Gordon and Forbes-Leith.

The contents of Fyvie largely originate from the Scottish/American steel millionaire Alexander Leith, later Lord Leith of Fyvie, who purchased the castle in 1889. Lord Leith's personal approach to collecting sets Fyvie apart from many other industrialist collections that were often purchased simply as a display of wealth. As a result the contents acquired by the Trust in 1984 are still imbued with a family resonance.

The historic portraits at Fyvie represent the most important element of the collections, purchased mainly through Agnews of London. These pictures were scattered through several of Lord and Lady Leith's homes and were only united at Fyvie by Leith's daughter after his death. Of the portraits, Pompeo Girolamo Batoni's *William Gordon*, John Scougall's *James Gregory*, and Henry Raeburn's *Isabella Macleod (Mrs James Gregory)* and Dr James Gregory rank amongst the best paintings produced by these artists.

The castle also contains significant collections of arms and armour of European and Middle Eastern origin, possibly assembled to decorate the central stair. Leith's furnishings of Fyvie also incorporate many items from their American houses including furniture, tapestries and family portraits.

Amongst these are a number of minor American pieces whose presence in Scotland is exceptional.

Fyvie Castle and its surroundings were purchased by The National Trust for Scotland from the Forbes-Leith family in 1984.

Alexander, John 1686–1766
John Graham (1648–1689), 1st Viscount Dundee 1732
oil on canvas 74.5 x 61.5
84.62

Allan, David 1744–1796
Portrait of a Young Man in a Green Jacket
oil on canvas 46 x 37.5
84.79

Anderson, Douglas Hardinge b.1934
Lady Ruth Forbes-Leith (1897–1973) 1969
oil on panel 79.8 x 64
201.218 (P)

Anderson, Douglas Hardinge b.1934
Sir Ian Forbes-Leith (1902–1973) 1969
oil on panel 79.8 x 63.8
203.219 (P)

Batoni, Pompeo 1708–1787
Colonel William Gordon (1736–1816) 1766
oil on canvas 289.5 x 217
84.16

Beale, Mary (circle of) 1633–1699
Portrait of a Cleric
oil on canvas 74.5 x 61.5
84.63

Beale, Mary (circle of) 1633–1699
Portrait of a Cleric
oil on canvas 73.5 x 59.5
84.7

Beechey, William 1753–1839
William Gordon of Fyvie 1817
oil on canvas 233.6 x 144.7
84.93

Belle, Alexis-Simon 1674–1734
Prince James Stuart (1688–1766), 'The Old Pretender', as a Young Man
oil on canvas 75 x 62.5
84.9

Bertier, Francisque-Edouard active 1888–1906
Lady Forbes-Leith (d.1930), née Mary Louise January 1888
oil on canvas 162.5 x 101.5
2009.779 (P)

Bertier, Francisque-Edouard active 1888–1906
Percy Forbes-Leith (1881–1900) 1890
oil on canvas 162.5 x 103.5
2011.367 (P)

Breun, John Ernest 1862–1921
Arthur Burn 1916
oil on canvas 179.1 x 111.1
84.125 (P)

Breun, John Ernest 1862–1921
Alexander Forbes-Leith (1847–1925), Lord Leith of Fyvie
oil on canvas 116 x 140
2009.78 (P)

Breun, John Ernest (attributed to) 1862–1921
Portrait of a Gentleman (possibly Sir Thomas January)
oil on canvas 73.5 x 58
84.129

British (English) School
Portrait of a Girl, Aged 10 1563
oil on panel 36.2 x 32
84.87

British (English) School
Portrait of a Young Man 1612
oil on panel 51.7 x 43
84.86

British (English) School
Portrait of a Gentleman in Red Robes c.1740
oil on canvas 74 x 61
84.8.2

British (English) School
Portrait of a Lady in a Green Dress and a Red Cloak c.1740
oil on canvas 74 x 61
84.8.1

British (English) School
Mary, Queen of Scots (1542–1587)
oil on canvas 73.5 x 69.5
84.89

British (Scottish) School
Alexander Forbes of Blackford
oil on canvas 75 x 62
2011.363 (P)

British (Scottish) School
John Forbes of Blackford
oil on canvas 76.1 x 61.5
2011.364 (P)

British (Scottish) School
Portrait of a Lady of the Leith Family
oil on canvas 76.2 x 63.5
84.131.1

British (Scottish) School
Portrait of a Gentleman of the Leith Family
oil on canvas 76.2 x 63.5
84.131.2

British (Scottish) School
Portrait of a Highland Officer
oil on panel 29.1 x 23.2
84.11

British (Scottish) School
Portrait of a Lady in a Russet Dress
oil on canvas 70.5 x 57.5
84.37

British (Scottish) School
Portrait of a Gentleman in Red Robes and a White Cravat (possibly John Leith) c.1800
oil on canvas 75 x 62.5
84.66 (P)

Burnet, John 1784–1868
The Trial of Charles I, 1st January 1649
oil on panel 78.5 x 108
84.4

Chalmers, George 1720–1791
Dr John Gregory (1724–1773) 1772
oil on canvas 127 x 101.6
84.122.2

Chalmers, George 1720–1791
Dorothy Montagu Gregory (1755–1830)
oil on canvas 74.5 x 62.5
84.73

Chandler, William (after)
General Alexander Leith-Hay (1758–1838)
oil on canvas 127 x 101.6
84.130.1 (P)

Closterman, John (circle of) 1660–1711
Sarah Jennings (1660–1744), Duchess of Marlborough
oil on canvas 87.5 x 71
84.72

Critz the elder, John de (circle of) 1551–1642
James VI of Scotland and I of England (1566–1625)
oil on panel 57.5 x 42.5
84.52

Dahl I, Michael 1656–1743
Sir Robert Walpole (1676–1745), Later 1st Earl of Orford
oil on canvas 73.7 x 60.5
84.17

James Gregorie
Inventor of the Gregorian Telescope
born 1638. died 1675.

Dance-Holland, Nathaniel (circle of) 1735–1811
Portrait of a Gentleman (said to be Spranger Barry, 1719–1773)
oil on canvas 73.5 x 53.5
84.107

Downman, John 1750–1824
Lord Edward Conway (d.1785) 1777
oil on board 21.5 x 17.5
84.85

Dutch School
Portrait of a Gentleman in a Black Coat c.1730
oil on canvas 30.2 x 22
84.1.2

Dutch School
Portrait of a Lady c.1730
oil on canvas 30.4 x 22.2
84.2.2

Dutch School
Portrait of a Gentleman (said to be George Buchanan, 1506–1682)
oil on panel 30.5 x 24.8
84.24

Dyck, Anthony van 1599–1641
Charles I (1600–1649)
oil on panel 29.8 x 24
84.22

Dyck, Anthony van (circle of) 1599–1641
Algernon Percy (1602–1668), 10th Earl of Northumberland
oil on panel 29.5 x 26.1
84.19

Dyck, Anthony van (style of) 1599–1641
Charles I (1600–1649) 19th C
oil on canvas 99 x 63.5
2011.369.2

Eccardt, John Giles 1720–1779
John Monckton (1695–1751), 1st Viscount Galway
oil on canvas 127 x 101.5
2009.777 (P)

Facing page: Scougal, John, c.1645–1737, *James Gregory (1638–1675), MA, FRS*, The National Trust for Scotland, Fyvie Castle (p. 97)

Eccardt, John Giles (attributed to) 1720–1779
William Monckton (d.1772), 2nd Viscount Galway
oil on canvas 127 x 101.5
2009.778 (P)

Fildes, Luke 1843–1927
The Honourable Ethel Louise Forbes-Leith (1872–1930), Lady Forbes Leith 1906
oil on canvas 139.7 x 106.6
84.84

Flemish School
The Virgin Mary Receiving the Eucharist from Saint John the Apostle c.1650
oil on copper 29 x 22.5
84.49

Franca, Manuel Joachim de 1808–1865
Derrick January 1851
oil on canvas 90 x 71.8
2011.366 (P)

Franca, Manuel Joachim de 1808–1865
Mrs Derrick January and Her Children 1851
oil on canvas 166.5 x 90.5
2011.365 (P)

French School
The Prince of Wales as a Child in Antique Costume c.1700
oil on canvas 72.5 x 59
84.25

French School
Portrait of an Officer
oil on canvas 123 x 100.5
84.3

Gainsborough, Thomas 1727–1788
Major William Tennant (d.1803), of Needwood House, Staffordshire
oil on canvas 124.5 x 99
84.1

German School
Portrait of a Cleric
oil on canvas 25.7 x 18.8
84.77

Giles, James 1801–1870
Anne (1713–1791), Countess of Aberdeen, and Her Son, Lord William Gordon of Fyvie (1736–1816) 1835
oil on canvas 157.5 x 113.2
84.74

Giles, James 1801–1870
Self Portrait in a Maroon Coat and Crimson Beret 1846
oil on canvas 59 x 49.2
84.112

Giles, James 1801–1870
Deer Drinking at a Forest Stream 1851
oil on canvas 90.1 x 69.6
84.116.1

Giles, James 1801–1870
Waterfall 1851
oil on canvas 96 x 69.7
84.116.2

Giles, James 1801–1870
William Elphinstone (1431–1514), Bishop of Aberdeen (after Flemish School)
oil on panel 61 x 45
84.5

Greuze, Jean-Baptiste 1725–1805
The Young Mendicants
oil on canvas 89.5 x 71
84.8

Gruyter, Jacob de (attributed to) 1630–1681
Wreck of a Dutch Fleet after Battle
oil on panel 73.5 x 103.5
84.45

Highmore, Joseph (circle of) 1692–1780
Portrait of a Gentleman
oil on canvas 81.5 x 67.5
84.1.1

Hone I, Nathaniel 1718–1784
James Sinclair-Erskine (1762–1837), Later 2nd Earl of Rosslyn, His Brother John and His Sister Henrietta Maria
oil on canvas 150 x 147.5
84.2

Hoppner, John 1758–1810
Horatio, 1st Viscount Nelson (1758–1805)
oil on canvas 228.6 x 143.5
84.103

Hoppner, John 1758–1810
Mrs Paul Le Mesurier
oil on canvas 75 x 62.5
84.98

Huchtenburgh, Jan van (circle of) 1647–1733
A Cavalry Engagement between Turks and Europeans
oil on canvas 60.5 x 98.5
84.46.1

Huchtenburgh, Jan van (circle of) 1647–1733
A Cavalry Engagement between Turks and Europeans in front of a Town
oil on canvas 60.5 x 98.5
84.46.2

Hudson, Thomas 1701–1779
John Campbell (1696–1782), Lord Glenorchy, Later 3rd Earl of Breadalbane
oil on canvas 115 x 95.2
84.82

Italian School
Portrait of a Cleric
oil on canvas 79 x 54
84.43

Jamesone, George (after) 1588–1644
David Anderson of Finzeach (b.c.1566), Known as 'Davie Do a Thing' 1606
oil on canvas 74.5 x 61.5
84.47

Jamesone, George (after) 1588–1644
Self Portrait of the Artist, His Wife and Child
oil on canvas 77 x 64.7
84.38

Jamesone, George (follower of) 1588–1644
David Gregorie of Kinairdrie
oil 74.5 x 62.5
84.48

Kettle, Tilly 1735–1786
Robert Lovelace (d.1821), of Quiddenham Hall, Norfolk
oil on canvas 75 x 61
84.101

Kneller, Godfrey (circle of) 1646–1723
John Leith of Leith Hall (d.1727)
oil on canvas 126.5 x 100.5
84.65 (P)

Kneller, Godfrey (circle of) 1646–1723
Marjory, Daughter of Arthur Forbes, Wife of John Forbes of Newleslie
oil on canvas 125 x 99.5
84.69

Kneller, Godfrey (circle of) 1646–1723
Portrait of a Gentleman (said to be John Churchill, Duke of Marlborough)
oil on canvas 75 x 62.5
84.61

Kneller, Godfrey (circle of) 1646–1723
The Honourable Janet Ogilvie (1668–1743)
oil on canvas 103 x 99
84.64

Larkin, William (circle of) 1585–1619
Portrait of a Lady (said to be Elizabeth of Bohemia)
oil on panel 52 x 36.5
84.51

László, Philip Alexius de 1869–1937
Sir Charles Burn (1859–1930), Later Forbes-Leith, 1st Bt 1916
oil on canvas 52 x 42
2011.362 (P)

Lawrence, Thomas 1769–1830
Countess of Oxford, Wife of the 4th Earl of Oxford (1728–1804)
oil on canvas 127 x 101.6
84.106

Lawrence, Thomas (after) 1769–1830
Arthur Wellesley (1769–1852), 1st Duke of Wellington
oil on canvas 76 x 63.5
84.108

Leader, Benjamin Williams 1831–1923
The Silent Evening Hour 1900
oil on canvas 120 x 180
84.118

Lely, Peter 1618–1680
James Scott (1648–1685)
oil on canvas 76.5 x 62
84.71

Lely, Peter 1618–1680
James Scott (1648–1685), Duke of Monmouth and Buccleugh
oil on canvas 124.2 x 100.5
84.2.1

Lely, Peter (after) 1618–1680
Louise de Keroualle (1649–1734), Duchess of Portsmouth
oil on canvas 123 x 99
84.4

Lely, Peter (circle of) 1618–1680
Charles II (1630–1685)
oil on canvas 119 x 94
2011.37

Lely, Peter (circle of) 1618–1680
Portrait of a Nobleman (said to be John Maitland, Duke of Lauderdale)
oil on canvas 123.3 x 99.2
84.6

Lely, Peter (style of) 1618–1680
Frances Jennings (1647–1731), Duchess of Tyrconnel
oil on canvas 125 x 100.3
84.7

Maes, Nicolaes 1634–1693
Portrait of a Gentleman (called the Earl of Sheffield)
oil on canvas 112.5 x 88.8
84.9

Maes, Nicolaes 1634–1693
Portrait of a Lady in a Black Dress
oil on canvas 46 x 39.2
84.75

Maes, Nicolaes (circle of) 1634–1693
Portrait of a Nobleman
oil on canvas 89 x 43.5
84.14

Mignard I, Pierre (attributed to) 1612–1695
La duchesse de la Vallière
oil on canvas 106.5 x 82.5
84.76

Mignard I, Pierre (style of) 1612–1695
Henrietta Maria (1609–1669)
oil on canvas 99 x 63.5
2011.369.1

Millais, John Everett 1829–1896
The Sound of Many Waters 1876
oil on canvas 57.5 x 107.8
84.112.1

Minderhout, Hendrik van (attributed to) 1632–1696
Capture of the Royal Prince by Admiral de Ruyter in 1666
oil on panel 110.5 x 145
84.44

More, Jacob (circle of) 1740–1793
Bay of Pozzuoli with the Temple of Serapis
oil on canvas 82.5 x 124.4
84.21

Opie, John 1761–1807
Courtship in the Park
oil on canvas 161.2 x 114
84.15

Opie, John 1761–1807
Lady Kerrison (1738–1825), née Mary Anne Davies, Wife of Sir Roger Kerrison of Brooke, Norfolk
oil on canvas 127.8 x 99.5
84.11

Paton, Waller Hugh 1828–1895
Outlet of Loch Achray, Perthshire
oil on canvas 67.5 x 109
84.114

Pettie, John 1839–1893
The Cavalier
oil on canvas 107 x 92
84.117

Raeburn, Henry 1756–1823
Charles Gordon of Buthlaw, Lonmay and Cairness (1747–1797) 1790
oil on canvas 87 x 66.8
84.32

Raeburn, Henry 1756–1823
Thomas Reid (1710–1796), Professor of Moral Philosophy at Glasgow University 1796
oil on canvas 73 x 61.6
84.3

Raeburn, Henry 1756–1823
Professor James Gregory (1753–1821) 1798
oil on canvas 124.3 x 99.6
84.35

Raeburn, Henry 1756–1823
Alexander Edgar (d.1820), of Auchingrammont, Lanarkshire and Wedderelie, Jamaica
oil on canvas 75 x 62
84.36

Raeburn, Henry 1756–1823
Dr George Bell, Surgeon Extraordinary to George IV and William IV
oil on canvas 30 x 25
84.33

Raeburn, Henry 1756–1823
George Gordon (1770–1836), 5th Duke of Gordon
oil on canvas 75 x 62.5
84.29

Raeburn, Henry 1756–1823
Jane (1748–1812), Duchess of Gordon, Wife of Alexander, 4th Duke of Gordon (after Joshua Reynolds)
oil on canvas 74.5 x 62.5
84.104

Raeburn, Henry 1756–1823
John Stirling of Kippendavie (1742–1816), and His Youngest Daughter, Jean Wilhelmina (1804–1859)
oil on canvas 196.2 x 149.8
84.1

Facing page: Northcote, James, 1746–1831, *Mary Margaret Clarke (d.1859), Wife of Sir Andrew Leith-Hay*, The National Trust for Scotland, Leith Hall Garden & Estate (p. 69)

Raeburn, Henry 1756–1823
Major, Later Lieutenant-Colonel Henry Knight Erskine of Pittodrie, Aberdeenshire
oil on canvas 74.5 x 62.5
84.97

Raeburn, Henry 1756–1823
Mrs Charles Gordon, née Christian Forbes of Ballogie, Wife of Charles Gordon of Buthlaw, Lonmay and Cairness
oil on canvas 88.1 x 67.8
84.31

Raeburn, Henry 1756–1823
Mrs James Gregory, née Isobella Macleod (1770–1847)
oil on canvas 124.5 x 99
84.34

Raeburn, Henry 1756–1823
Sir General William Maxwell (1754–1837), 6th Bt of Calderwood
oil on canvas 249 x 148
84.16.1

Raeburn, Henry 1756–1823
Thomas King, Esq. (c.1772–1802), of Drums and Millbank, Renfrewshire, Aged 18
oil on canvas 125.7 x 100
84.28

Reynolds, Joshua 1723–1792
Elizabeth Kerr (1745–1780), Countess of Ancrum, Later Marchioness of Lothian
oil on canvas 75 x 62.5
84.81

Reynolds, Joshua 1723–1792
Mrs James Fortescue, née Mary Henrietta Hunter
oil on canvas 81.5 x 81.5
84.105

Reynolds, Joshua (after) 1723–1792
Anne, Marchioness Townshend
oil on canvas 73.5 x 61.5
84.6

Reynolds, Joshua (circle of) 1723–1792
Edward Gibbon (1737–1794)
oil on canvas 33 x 27.5
84.78

Romney, George 1734–1802
Captain Arthur Forbes of Culloden (1760–1803)
oil on canvas 72.5 x 61
84.94

Romney, George 1734–1802
John Richard West (1757–1783), 4th Earl de la Warr
oil on canvas 149 x 119
84.18

Romney, George 1734–1802
Mrs Stratford Canning (1777–1831), née Mehetebel Patrick, with Her Daughter Elizabeth
oil on canvas 125 x 99.5
84.99

Romney, George 1734–1802
Mrs William Marwood (1743–1807), née Mary Goulston, Wife of William Marwood of Busby, near Stokesley, Yorkshire
oil on canvas 74.5 x 61.5
84.95

Rubens, Peter Paul (after) 1577–1640
A Tiger Hunt
oil on canvas 94 x 120.6
84.91

Russell, John 1745–1806
Captain Braithwaite
oil on canvas 74.5 x 61.5
84.102

Scougal, John 1645–1737
James Gregory (1638–1675), MA, FRS
oil on canvas 72.5 x 58.5
84.42

Seccombe, Thomas Strong 1835–1890
The Scots Greys at Waterloo 1891
oil on canvas 179 x 303.5
84.111

Serres, John Thomas 1759–1825
Port of Leghorn with a Half Galley of the Grand Duke of Tuscany Putting Out to Sea 1790–1791
oil on canvas 119.8 x 181
84.27

Shackleton, John (studio of) 1697–1767
George II (1683–1760)
oil on canvas 126 x 100.5
84.68

Smith, F. Pierce
Woodland
oil on canvas 50 x 34.4
2009.742

Somer I, Paulus van (school of) 1576–1621
Amalia van Solms (1602–1675) (after Michiel Jansz. van Miereveld)
oil on panel 25 x 19.5
84.23.1

Somer I, Paulus van (school of) 1576–1621
Prince Frederik Hendrik of Orange (1584–1647) (after Michiel Jansz. van Miereveld)
oil on panel 25 x 19.8
84.23.2

Trickett, W. Wadsell active 1901–1937
'Leap Year': A Horse in a Loose Box 1901
oil on canvas 29 x 39
2009.748 (P)

unknown artist
A Man, a Woman and a Donkey
oil on panel
T.3326

unknown artist
Arthur Burn in the Uniform of the Royal Dragoons
oil on canvas 35.5 x 27.7
84.57

unknown artist
Portrait of a Woman in a White Ruff
oil on panel 35.5 x 27.7
84.26

Vigée-LeBrun, Elisabeth Louise (circle of) 1755–1842
Self Portrait
oil on canvas 99.1 x 80
84.83

Wales, James 1747–1795
Charles Leslie of Aberdeen (1677–1782)
oil on metal 15.5 x 12
84.39

Wassdail active from 1745
Prince Charles Edward (1720–1788), 'The Young Pretender'
oil on panel 8 x 6
84.41

Wissing, Willem (circle of) 1656–1687
Mrs James Leith, née Margaret Strachan, Wife of James Leith of Leith Hall
oil on canvas 124 x 99.5
2011.368 (P)

The National Trust for Scotland, Angus Folk Museum

Housed in six eighteenth-century cottages situated within Glamis village in the heart of the Vale of Strathmore, Angus Folk Museum offers a vivid insight into the realities of rural life over the past 200 years. The museum's collection was created by Jean, Lady Maitland, a local Angus resident, principally inspired by the Highland Folk Museum in Kingussie. Lady Maitland recovered items that documented the social and economic life of rural lowland communities in Angus before the agricultural changes of the mid-twentieth century.

Angus Folk Museum provides an opportunity for visitors to re-discover the recent past through interaction with displays that depict the historical development of traditional rural lowland life in Angus. The collection survives to illustrate a story rarely recounted elsewhere with such diversity. It has particular international significance as a regional folk collection and also appeals to specialists and public curiosity, as a distinctive local resource. The collection was amassed by the efforts of Lady Maitland, who recognised the importance of recovering and conserving objects to demonstrate a way of life that no longer exists within the region and to ensure they continue to be accessible to the local community and wider public.

The museum's artefacts reflect a timescale that ranges approximately from 1750 to 1950. Although much of the collection is of everyday objects they have a significant value as a collection that represents the social and economic changes that occurred throughout Angus. A central purpose of the museum is to ensure public access to items that would otherwise have been neglected or lost. This collection represents a lifestyle that has changed dramatically, with a diminishing number of people retaining personal recollections and experience of it.

Angus Folk Museum was handed over into the care of The National Trust for Scotland in 1976.

unknown artist
*Portrait of a Woman in a Shawl**
oil on canvas 68.2 x 55.2
T4451

unknown artist
*Rural Village**
oil on glass 35 x 55 (E)
T4450

The National Trust for Scotland, J. M. Barrie's Birthplace

Barrie's Birthplace comprises three 2-storey terraced cottages in Brechin Road, Kirriemuir. No. 9, the birthplace of J. M. Barrie (1860–1937), with its wash-house and garden is open to the public. J. M. Barrie was born at No. 9 Brechin Road 'The Tenements' on 9 May 1860 and lived there until he left to attend Glasgow Academy aged eight with the family moving in 1870. Although internationally renowned as the author of Peter Pan, Barrie was not purely a children's writer and is known for many other works.

Within the property, a number of items owned by J. M. Barrie are considered to be of national significance in their own right – the sofa and settle from Barrie's London flat, a portrait by Sir John Lavery which is on loan from the National Portrait Gallery shows Barrie reclining in his flat on the settle, his desk, theatrical Peter Pan costumes and an original manuscript of Peter Pan with Barrie's own notations. These are enhanced by a range of other items and memorabilia which include items relating to family history as well as the life of J. M. Barrie himself. Other survivors found within No 9 include fragments of wallpaper from Barrie's time along with original fireplaces and other aspects of interesting decoration.

Apart from their connection with Barrie, the buildings which form Barrie's Birthplace are of some local and regional significance, particularly Nos. 9 and 11, originally weaver's cottages typical of the Angus region in their vernacular design and materials. It is becoming increasingly rare to find such buildings which retain their small windows and interior layout of small rooms (both slightly altered by the Trust) and low ceilings. Additionally their connection with handloom weaving is reflected in some items still contained within the collections on display.

The cottages were gifted to the National Trust for Scotland in 1937 by Mr D. Alves.

Barrie, Sara 1854–1903
*Irises**
oil on glass 59 x 28.6
37.302

Greig, James McGavin 1861–1941
Elizabeth Fyffe
oil on canvas 60.5 x 50.6
37.174.2

Inglis, James 1835–1904
Near the End of the Web 1879
oil on panel 20.2 x 14.2
37.72

unknown artist
J. M. Barrie's St Bernard Glen ('Porthos')
oil on canvas 26.5 x 34
37.201

The National Trust for Scotland, House of Dun

The handsome Georgian house overlooking the Montrose Basin was completed in 1730 by William Adam for David Erskine, the 13th Laird of Dun. The 6th Earl of Mar, a kinsman of Lord Dun, is believed to have inspired the innovative triumphal arch in the entrance. The house is a fine example of William Adam's country house planning, with an intricate interior combining public rooms for formal entertaining alongside family apartments.

Alterations made in the nineteenth century have in some places masked Adam's work. Dun is also significant for its superb plasterwork by Joseph Enzer, a great attraction for visitors. During the years following the Second World War, the house was altered and run as a hotel. When acquired, the Trust was fortunate in the extent of the original collection left with the house. In its entirety, it embraces the history of the Erskine family through the generations. Many elements are of outstanding quality in their own right – the collection of textiles (principally the embroideries), the collection of porcelain, the semicircular parcel gilt tea and card table, and Sir George Hayter's painting of Lady Augusta FitzClarence Kennedy-Erskine (d.1860), Natural Daughter of King William IV and Wife of the Honourable John Erskine, with her Children, Wiliam Henry, Wilhelmina and Millicent Ann Mary.

Other elements, such as the gold Saloon Screen, have an outstanding visual appeal. Some items date to Adam's décor. However much dates to the high quality re-furnishing carried out c.1811 or later. The House of Dun is also home to the Hutchison Collection of twentieth-century paintings including several by the Scottish Colourists, and the Stirling Collection, an eclectic variety of objects – from eighteenth-century Regency furniture to more unusual items from the 1960s.

The property is also important through its associations with royalty, Lady Augusta Fitz-Clarence, wife of John Erskine Kennedy-Erskine, being the natural daughter of William IV; and with the family's close ties to the Kennedys of Culzean. References to each of these connections can be seen within the house in paintings and some of the collections.

The House of Dun, tenanted estate and woodland were bequeathed to the National Trust for Scotland in 1980 by Mrs M. A. A. Lovett.

Facing page: Cadell, Francis Campbell Boileau, 1883–1937, *Pink Roses and Teapot*, The National Trust for Scotland, House of Dun (p. 106)

Aikman, William 1682–1731
Anne Erskine (1709–1735), Daughter of Lord Dun and Wife Successively of James, 9th Earl of Airlie and Sir Alexander Macdonald
oil on canvas 73.6 x 62.2
80.851

Aikman, William 1682–1731
David Erskine (1672–1758), 13th of Dun, in the Robes of the Court of Session
oil on canvas 127 x 124.4
80.936

Aikman, William 1682–1731
John Erskine (1712–1787), 14th of Dun, Son of Lord Dun, Aged 10
oil on canvas 73.6 x 62.2
80.85

Aikman, William (attributed to) 1682–1731
David Erskine (1672–1758), 13th of Dun
oil on canvas 73.6 x 60.9
80.947

Aikman, William (circle of) 1682–1731
Magdalene, Daughter of John Riddell of the Haining, and Wife of David Erskine, Lord Dun
oil on canvas 73.6 x 60.9
80.944

Baillie, William James 1923–2011
Flowers in a Niche
oil on canvas 74.9 x 60.9
99.147

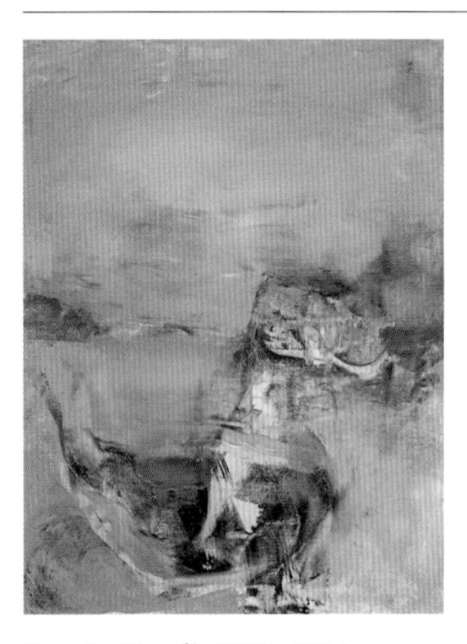

Barrie, Mardi 1930–2004
Storm, Cove
oil on canvas 90.2 x 69.2
99.15

British (English) School
Mr Snell, in the Character of a Lawyer c.1760
oil on canvas 57 x 53.3
80.852

British (Scottish) School
Helen Erskine (thought to be the Daughter of John Erskine, 7th of Dun) 1610
oil on canvas
80.863.2

British (Scottish) School
Ann Beaton, Wife of John Erskine of Dun 1672
oil on canvas
80.864.5

British (Scottish) School
David Erskine (d. before 1710), 11th of Dun c.1680
oil on canvas 101.6 x 76.2
80.86

British (Scottish) School
Ann Ogilvie, Lady Brakie 1694
oil on canvas
80.864.7

British (Scottish) School
James Carnegie of Brakie 1694
oil on canvas
80.864.6

British (Scottish) School
John Carnegie, Junior, of Boysack 1694
oil on canvas
80.863.3

British (Scottish) School
Elen Erskine (b.1634), Daughter of Sir John Erskine c.1700
oil on canvas
80.864.8

British (Scottish) School
General Lumsdaine c.1700
oil on canvas
80.863.1

British (Scottish) School
Margaret Erskine (b.1633), Daughter of Sir John Erskine, Wife of Sir David Ogilvie of Inverquharity, 2nd Bt c.1700
oil on canvas
80.864.9

British (Scottish) School
Margaret Erskine, Daughter of Sir Alexander Erskine, 11th of Dun, and Wife of Sir John Carnegie of Boysack, 1st Bt c.1700
oil on canvas
80.863.4

British (Scottish) School
Portrait of a Carnegie in Armour c.1700
oil on canvas
80.864.6

British (Scottish) School
David, 2nd Lord Cardross
oil on canvas
80.505 (P)

British (Scottish) School
John Erskine (d.1572), 1st Earl of Mar, Regent of Scotland
oil on canvas 120.6 x 113
80.503 (P)

Brown, Edwin (possibly) 1814–1890
A Chestnut Held by a Lancer in a Yard 1872 (?)
oil on canvas 49.5 x 64.7
80.937

Buxton, W.
'Piper' 1895
oil on canvas 74.9 x 63.5
80.912

Buxton, W.
'Piper' 1895
oil on canvas 74.9 x 62.2
80.931

Cadell, Francis Campbell Boileau 1883–1937
Pink Roses and Teapot
oil on canvas 59.7 x 49.5
99.127

Cadell, Francis Campbell Boileau 1883–1937
Venice
oil on panel 43.8 x 34.6
99.128

Casteels, Pieter 1684–1749
A Peacock, a Turkey and Domestic Fowl in a Garden 1721
oil on canvas 113 x 120.6
80.853

Costello, Dudley 1803–1865
William IV
oil on board 13.9 x 10.5
80.895

Cowie, James 1886–1956
Schoolgirl
oil on canvas
99.129

Crosbie, William 1915–1999
Beaune 1982
oil on board 59.7 x 48.3
99.145

Duval, John 1816–1892
'Akbar Khan'
oil on canvas
80.941.4

Duval, John 1816–1892
'Cola'
oil on canvas
80.941.2

Duval, John 1816–1892
'Hungerford Mare'
oil on canvas
80.941.3

Duval, John 1816–1892
'Mona'
oil on canvas
80.941.1

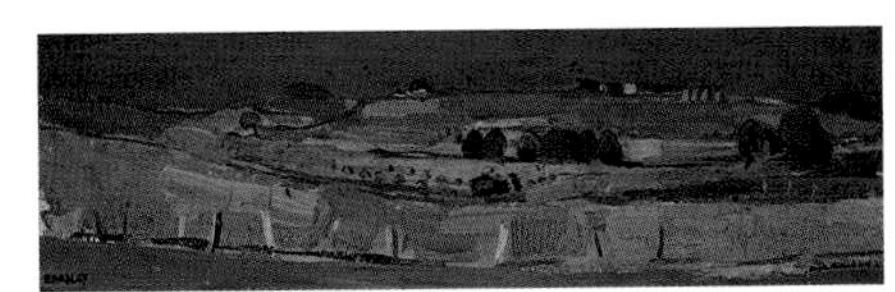

Eardley, Joan Kathleen Harding 1921–1963
Summer Landscape, Catterline
oil on hardboard 13.3 x 40.6
99.133

Eardley, Joan Kathleen Harding 1921–1963
Village, Evening, Catterline
oil on hardboard 10.8 x 45.1
99.132

Erskine, Violet Jacob
A Florentine Spinner 1884
oil on canvas 49 x 42.5
93.29.1

Faugue
Augustus John William Henry Kennedy-Erskine (1866–1908), 19th of Dun, Aged 7
oil on canvas 62.2 x 52
80.903

Flemish School
Flowers on a Ledge
oil on panel 36.8 x 50.8
88.133.1

Gandy, John
Captain James Erskine, Brother of Lord Dun, 1690
oil on canvas 73.6 x 60.9
80.946

Gillies, William George 1898–1973
Midlothian Farm
oil on board 43.2 x 48.3
99.136

Hanneman, Adriaen (after) 1601–1671
Charles II (1630–1685), as Prince of Wales
oil on canvas 72.3 x 57.1
80.913

Hayter, John 1800–1891
A Room at Windsor Castle
oil on canvas 142.2 x 198.1
80.856

Hayter, John 1800–1891
Lady Augusta FitzClarence Kennedy-Erskine (d.1860), Natural Daughter of King William IV and Wife of the Honourable John (...)
oil on canvas 148.5 x 117.4
80.894

Hunter, George Leslie 1879–1931
Fife Pastoral
oil on board 25.4 x 35.6
99.126

Hunter, George Leslie 1879–1931
Still Life with Roses
oil on canvas 59.7 x 49.5
99.125

Italian School
A Moor on a Plumed Charger c.1700
oil on canvas 34.2 x 27.9
88.133.4

Italian School
A Woman Sitting Side-Saddle on a Plumed Horse c.1700
oil on canvas 34.2 x 27.9
88.133.5

Italian School
Amalfi Coast
oil on board
80.900.1

Italian School
Classical Columns in Italy
oil on board
80.900.2

Italian School
Gulf of Naples
oil on board
80.900.4

Italian School
Village near Naples
oil on board
80.900.3

M., H.
William Henry Kennedy-Erskine (1828–1870), 18th of Dun, Captain of the 17th Lancers
oil on canvas 62.2 x 45.7
80.938

Mann, Harrington 1864–1937
Alice Marjorie Cunningham (d.1943), Wife of Augustus Kennedy-Erskine, 18th of Dun, with Their Daughters Marjorie and Millicent 1902
oil on canvas 124.4 x 100.3
80.905

Mann, Harrington 1864–1937
Augustus John William Henry Kennedy-Erskine (1866–1908), 19th of Dun, in Riding Costume
oil on canvas 198 x 101.6
80.904

McClure, David 1926–1998
Toledo in Winter 1955
oil on canvas 43.8 x 61.6
99.148

McClure, David 1926–1998
Salmon Bothy, Dunbeath
oil on board 39 x 48.9
99.149

Milne, John Maclauchlan 1886–1957
Red Roofs, Cassis 1924
oil on canvas 58.4 x 71.1
99.142

Mosman, William 1700–1771
John Erskine (1742–1812), 15th of Dun, as a Boy 1751
oil on canvas 60.3 x 49.5
80.861

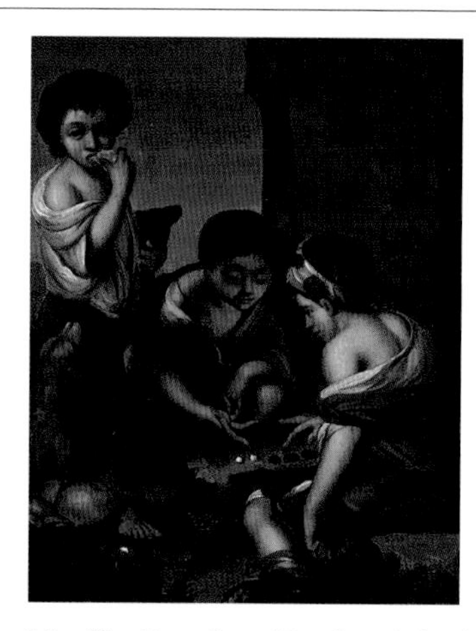

Murillo, Bartolomé Esteban (after) 1617–1682
Children Playing a Game
oil on panel
88.142.3

Murillo, Bartolomé Esteban (after) 1617–1682
Girl, Boy and Fruit
oil on panel
88.142.4

Nasmyth, Alexander 1758–1840
A View of Culzean Castle in the Early Evening
oil on canvas 107.9 x 165.1
80.942

Peploe, Denis Frederic Neal 1914–1993
Grisedale Pike
oil on board
99.153

Peploe, Samuel John 1871–1935
Landscape near Calvine
oil on canvas 39.4 x 48.9
99.124

Peploe, Samuel John 1871–1935
Luxembourg Gardens, Paris
oil on canvas
99.121

Peploe, Samuel John 1871–1935
Still Life with Roses and Mirror
oil on canvas 49.5 x 39.4
99.123

Peploe, Samuel John 1871–1935
Street Scene, Paris
oil on board 26 x 21
99.122

Raeburn, Henry (copy after) 1756–1823
John Erskine of Carnock (1719–1803), DD, Son of J. Erskine 18th C
oil on canvas 95 x 81.3
92.28.1 (P)

Raeburn, Henry (studio of) 1756–1823
The Honourable Christian Erskine, Daughter of George, 3rd Lord Reay, Wife of J. Erskine, DD 18th C
oil on canvas 95 x 81.3
92.28.2 (P)

Ramsay, Allan 1713–1784
Anne Erskine (b.1740), Daughter of John Erskine, 14th of Dun and Wife of John Wauchope of Edmonstone 1747
oil on canvas 60.3 x 49.5
80.854

Ramsay, Allan 1713–1784
John Erskine (1712–1787), 14th of Dun 1747
oil on canvas 73.6 x 62
80.858.1

Ramsay, Allan 1713–1784
Margaret Inglis (1720–1747), Wife of John Erskine, Daughter of Sir John Inglis of Cramond 1747
oil on canvas 73.6 x 62
80.858.2

Ramsay, Allan 1713–1784
Magdaline Erskine (b.1744), Daughter of John Erskine, 14th of Dun, as an Infant 1747
oil on canvas 60.3 x 49.5
80.857

Redfern, June b.1951
The Grassy Beach 1995
oil on linen 43.8 x 59.7
99.151

Redfern, June b.1951
Kitty Eating an Apple
oil on linen 19.7 x 24.4
99.152

Redpath, Anne 1895–1965
Chapelle de la Croix
oil on board 59.7 x 70.5
99.13

Redpath, Anne 1895–1965
Landscape in Skye
oil on board 61.6 x 74
99.131

Scougall, David (attributed to) 1610–1680
Portrait of an Officer (said to be Sir Alexander Erskine, fl.1662, 11th of Dun)
oil on canvas 68.5 x 58.4
80.923

Somer I, Paulus van (after) 1576–1621
John Erskine (d.1634), 2nd Earl of Mar 1626
oil on canvas 73.6 x 62.2
80.504 (P)

Steell, David George 1856–1930
A Labrador, after a Shoot 1887
oil on canvas 57 x 71
80.76

Thomson, Adam Bruce 1885–1976
Harvesting in Galloway
oil on canvas 55.9 x 76.2
99.143

Facing page: Innocenzo Francucci da Imola, 1485–1548, *The Virgin*, The National Trust for Scotland, Haddo House (p. 43)

Thomson, Adam Bruce 1885–1976
St Monance
tempera on paper 40.6 x 50.8
99.144

unknown artist
Portrait of a Girl 1591
oil on panel
88.44.1

unknown artist
Landscape
oil on board
80.900.6

unknown artist
River Scene
oil on board
80.900.7

unknown artist
River Scene with Figure
oil on board
80.900.8

unknown artist
Windmill
oil on board
80.900.5

Wheeler, John Alfred 1821–1903
'The Abbot of St Mark' 1854
oil on canvas 60.9 x 73.6
80.935

Wheeler, John Alfred 1821–1903
'Time Keeper', the Charger of W. H. Kennedy-Erskine, 17th Lancers 1854
oil on canvas 35.5 x 73.6
80.934

The National Trust for Scotland, Alloa Tower

Dating from the fourteenth century, Alloa Tower is the largest, oldest keep in Scotland. The tower was the ancestral home of the Erskine family, the Earls of Mar and Kellie. The Erskines were loyal supporters of several Stuart monarchs who spent part of their early lives in Alloa Tower, including Mary, Queen of Scots and James VI and I. As the family rose to prominence they played a little known but important part in many episodes of Scottish history.

The Erskines were custodians of the young Mary, Queen of Scots; the 1st Earl was Regent of Scotland; and the 6th Earl was involved in the 1715 Jacobite Uprising. The Erskine family of Alloa Tower were, as Earls of Mar, guardians of the Stuart heirs in the sixteenth century and the present Earl of Mar and Kellie is still hereditary keeper of Stirling Castle. This important Scottish family is illustrated by a superb collection of portraits loaned by the present Earl, including paintings by David Allan (1744–1796), Henry Raeburn (1756–1823) and Godfrey Kneller (1646–1723).

The Tower has been altered over the centuries and is now an eighteenth-century mansion contained within a medieval shell. Unusual features include a sweeping Italianate staircase, a rare double groin-vaulted ceiling, a magnificent medieval oak-beamed roof, and a medieval dungeon and first floor well. There is a collection of paintings and silver loaned by the Earl of Mar and Kellie.

Alloa Tower has been managed by The National Trust for Scotland since 1996 in partnership with Clackmannanshire Heritage Trust.

Alison, David 1882–1955
John Francis Ashley (Jock) (1895–1953), Lord Erskine, Governor of Madras, in the Robes of Governor 1946
oil on canvas 122 x 101
97.7.8 (P)

Alison, David 1882–1955
William Augustus Forbes Erskine (1871–1952)
oil on canvas 103.5 x 80
T4446 (P)

Allan, David 1744–1796
Clackmann Pow and Hill with the River Forth Looking East
oil on canvas 51 x 129.5
96.22.10 (P)

Allan, David 1744–1796
John Francis (1741–1825), 7th Earl of Mar, and Family
oil on canvas 150 x 211
97.7.6 (P)

Allan, David 1744–1796
The Forth at Alloa
oil on canvas 51 x 129.5
96.22.11 (P)

Allan, David 1744–1796
Thomas, Lord Erskine (1705–1766)
oil on canvas 71 x 58.5
96.21.9 (P)

Allan, David (attributed to) 1744–1796
Lady Charlotte Erskine
oil on canvas 74.5 x 62
96.22.12 (P)

Allan, David (attributed to) 1744–1796
Sir Hugh Patterson (c.1685–1777), Bt, MP
oil on canvas 73.5 x 61
96.21.12 (P)

Allan, David (attributed to) 1744–1796
View of Linlithgow Palace
oil on canvas 49.5 x 75
97.7.9 (P)

British (English) School
Charles II (1630–1685), as a Boy
oil on canvas 63 x 48
96.21.2 (P)

British (Scottish) School
Alexander Erskine of Gogar (1521–1590) 1588
oil on panel 57.5 x 48
97.7.2 (P)

British (Scottish) School
John Erskine (1675–1732), 6th Earl of Mar, as a Boy c.1690
oil on canvas 145 x 91.5
96.22.2 (P)

British (Scottish) School
James Erskine, Lord Grange (1672–1754), Lord Justice Clerk c.1730
oil on canvas 72.5 x 60
97.7.1 (P)

British (Scottish) School
Anne of Denmark (1574–1619)
oil on panel 73.5 x 56
96.21.4 (P)

British (Scottish) School
James Erskine (1679–1754), 2nd Lord Grange, Second Son of Charles, 5th Earl of Mar, as a Boy
oil on canvas 142 x 87
96.21.25 (P)

British (Scottish) School
John Erskine (1562–1634), 2nd Earl of Mar, KG, Lord High Treasurer of Scotland (1616–1630)
oil on canvas 72.5 x 58.5
96.21.2 (P)

British (Scottish) School
John Erskine of Mar (d.1572), 1st Earl Regent
oil on canvas 70 x 58
97.7.3 (P)

British (Scottish) School
John Francis Ashley (1895–1953), Lord Erskine
oil on canvas 50 x 39.5
T4447 (P)

British School
The Honourable Alistair Erskine, MC, Brother of John, 13th Earl of Mar and 15th Earl of Kellie after 1945
oil on canvas 40 x 30
96.21.20 (P)

Dahl I, Michael (follower of) 1656–1743
John Erskine (d.1732), 6th Earl of Mar
oil on canvas 61 x 61
96.21.5 (P)

Davidson, Duncan 1876–1946
Kildrummie Castle 1899
oil on canvas 35.5 x 45.5
96.21.19 (P)

Davidson, Duncan 1876–1946
Mar Castle, Earldom of Mar 1899
oil on canvas 35 x 45
96.21.18 (P)

Edwards, John b.1940
The Earl of Mar and Kellie
oil on canvas 75 x 65
T4448 (P)

Hudson, Thomas (circle of) 1701–1779
Lady Caroline Brand
oil on canvas 76 x 63.5
96.21.22 (P)

Jervas, Charles (attributed to) 1675–1739
Thomas (c.1705–1766), Lord Erskine, Son of John, 6th Earl of Mar
oil on canvas 160 x 137
96.21.26 (P)

Kneller, Godfrey 1646–1723
Frances (1690–1761), Daughter of Evelyn Pierpont, 1st Duke of Kingston
oil on canvas 233 x 142
97.7.5 (P)

Kneller, Godfrey 1646–1723
John Erskine, 6th Earl of Mar (1672–1732), with His Son Thomas, Lord Erskine (1705–1766)
oil on canvas 233 x 139
97.7.4 (P)

Kneller, Godfrey (circle of) 1646–1723
The Honourable Henry Erskine (1682–1707)
oil on canvas 122 x 99
97.7.7 (P)

Laidlaw, Nicol 1886–1929
Prince Charles Edward (1720–1789), as a Boy
oil on canvas 34.5 x 26
96.21.16 (P)

Laidlaw, Nicol 1886–1929
Prince Henry Stuart (1725–1807), Cardinal of York
oil on canvas 34 x 26
96.21.17 (P)

Lorimer, John Henry 1856–1936
Walter John Francis Erskine (1865–1955)
oil on canvas 140 x 101 (E)
96.22.7 (P)

Medina, John 1720–1796
Colonel John Erskine
oil on canvas 72.5 x 58.5
96.21.24 (P)

Medina, John 1720–1796
Lady Jane Erskine (d.1763), Daughter of Charles, 5th Earl of Mar, Wife of Sir Hugh Patterson
oil on canvas 71 x 60
96.21.13 (P)

Medina, John (circle of) 1720–1796
James Erskine (1672–1754), Lord Grange
oil on canvas 71 x 60
96.21.1 (P)

Morrocco, Alberto 1917–1998
John Francis Hervey Erskine (1921–1993), 13th Earl of Mar and 15th of Kellie 1970
oil on canvas 75.5 x 101.5
96.21.14 (P)

Nasmyth, Charlotte 1804–1884
View of Alloa and Stirling Castle from Clackmann Hill 1850
oil on canvas 45 x 60
96.22.17 (P)

Raeburn, Henry 1756–1823
John Francis Erskine (1741–1825), 7th Earl of Mar
oil on canvas 125 x 99.5
96.22.14 (P)

Raeburn, Henry 1756–1823
The Honourable Henry Erskine (1746–1817)
oil on canvas 76 x 63.5
96.22.16 (P)

Ramsay, Allan (attributed to) 1713–1784
John Francis (1741–1825), 7th Earl of Mar, Aged 17
oil on canvas 70 x 50 (E)
T4449 (P)

Rigaud, Hyacinthe (follower of) 1659–1743
John Erskine (1675–1732), 6th Earl of Mar, KT
oil on canvas 70.5 x 57
96.21.6 (P)

Scougal, John 1645–1737
Charles (1650–1689), 5th Earl of Mar
oil on canvas 73.5 x 61
96.21.23 (P)

Scougal, John (circle of) 1645–1737
Mary (b.c.1631), Daughter of Walter Scott, 1st Earl of Buccleuch
oil on canvas 71 x 58.5
96.21.10 (P)

Slaughter, Stephen 1697–1765
Gertrude (1715–1794), Daughter of John Leveson Gower, 1st Lord Gower 1742
oil on canvas 73.5 x 61
96.21.15 (P)

Trevisani, Francesco 1656–1746
Frances (1690–1761), Wife of John, 6th Earl of Mar, Daughter of Evelyn, 1st Duke of Kingston
oil on canvas 150 x 98 (E)
2012.513 (P)

unknown artist
John Francis Miller Erskine (1795–1868), 9th Earl of Mar and 11th of Kellie c.1840
oil on panel 54.5 x 42
96.21.11 (P)

unknown artist
Philadelphia (d.1853), Wife of the 9th Earl of Mar c.1840
oil on panel 53.5 x 40.5
96.21.8 (P)

The National Trust for Scotland, Threave Estate

This Scottish Baronial house, located only a mile from Castle Douglas, commands superb views over the magnificent gardens and surrounding estate, owned in the fourteenth century by the Black Douglas family and now a renowned wildlife habitat. William Gordon, a successful Liverpool businessman, bought the estate in 1867, and built the impressive sandstone house that dominates the garden. The wider estate provides an example of a typical lowland Galloway landscape, characterised by the River Dee meandering through its floodplain and associated wetlands, overlooked by drumlins (locally drums).

Threave House, with the stables, lodge and walled garden form a B-listed group and are important to the property as the most tangible relics of the Victorian estate of the Gordon family. Designed in 1871 by Peddie and Kinnear, the chief aesthetic/architectural interest of the house lies in its carefully chosen site, baronial exterior and logical interior plan, especially the handling of the stair. Some interior features were altered during the 1920s, and the contents date mainly from this time, although a few individual pieces have been identified which are believed to date from the 1870s.

The principal rooms have been meticulously restored to the decorative scheme of the 1930s, following a 1938 inventory by Jenners of Edinburgh. The Threave Collection includes a small number of items of outstanding importance original to the house. In 2001, the Maxwelton Collection was gifted to the Trust by Mrs Stenhouse Stewart. It is now displayed in the laundry area of Threave House, adding an additional element of social history to the house.

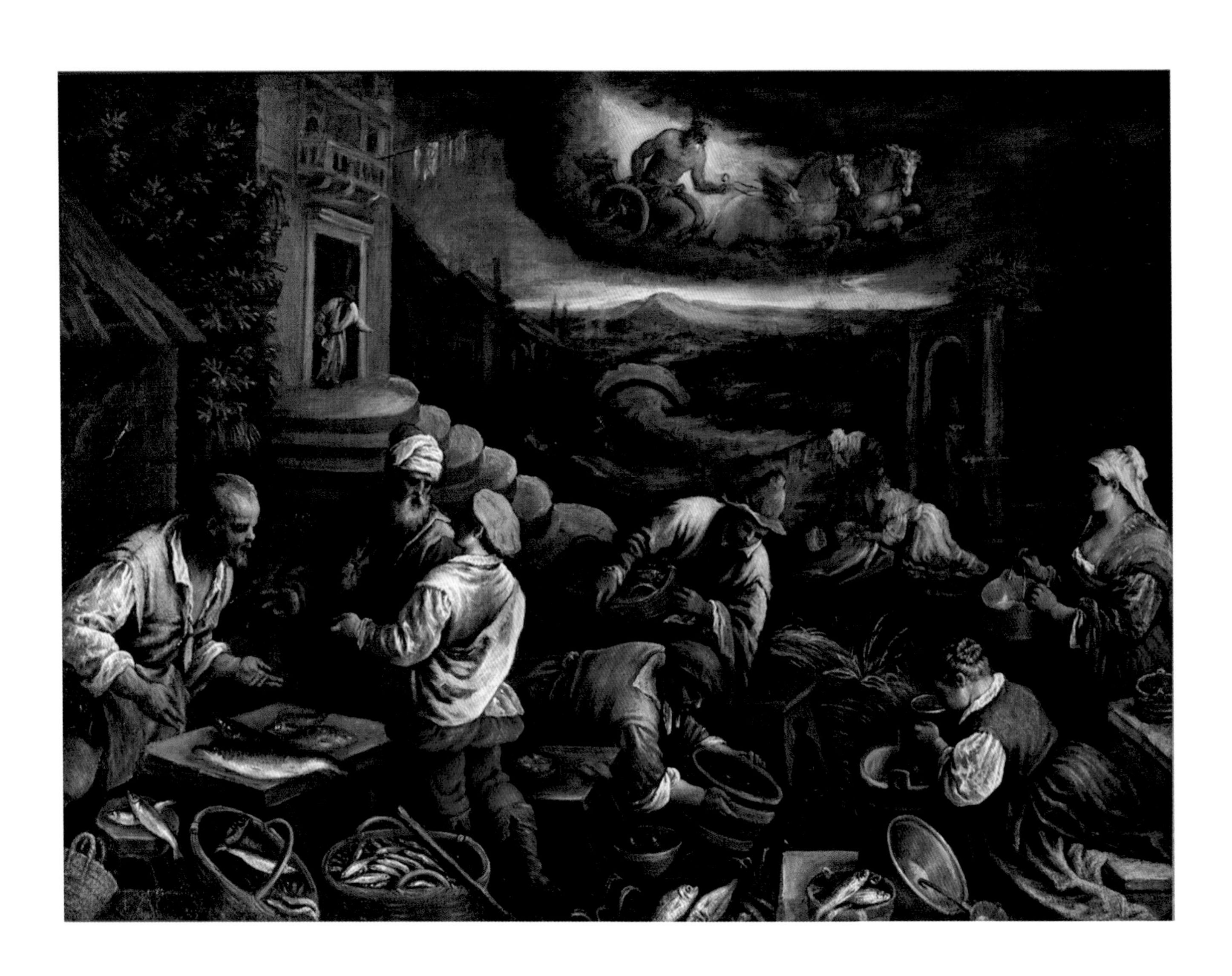

Earl, J.
Kitten and Rabbits by a Hutch 1901
oil on canvas 48 x 59
25.4

Faed, John 1819–1902
The Wappenschaw c.1863
oil on canvas 150.6 x 238.9
50.1518

Gilbert, C. Hersley
Preston Mill, North Berwick 1947
oil on board 29.6 x 50
T4455

Harper, M. M.
*Threave Castle** 1881
oil on canvas 50 x 75.2
T4456

unknown artist
*Mountain Lake**
oil on canvas 37.1 x 49.3
T4457

unknown artist
*Rocky Pool**
oil on canvas 20 x 29.5
T4458

Facing page: Bassano II, Francesco, 1549–1592, *The Element of Water,* The National Trust for Scotland, Leith Hall Garden & Estate (p. 62)

The National Trust for Scotland, Thomas Carlyle's Birthplace

Looking upon this humble house today, it is inspiring to reflect that this was the birthplace of one of Britain's most influential thinkers. Thomas Carlyle was born here in 1795, and went on to become a great writer and historian, as well as one of the leading voices on nineteenth-century morals and social equality. The Arched House in which Carlyle was born was built in 1791 by his father and uncle, both of whom were master masons.

The museum has been open to the public since 1883 and during that time has changed little. The three rooms retain much of their original Victorian character and provide a fascinating insight into Scottish town life during the nineteenth century. The interior of the house is furnished to reflect domestic life at Carlyle's time and contains a collection of portraits and Carlyle's personal belongings.

Herdman, Robert 1829–1888
Thomas Carlyle 1876
oil on canvas 64.1 x 53.3
36.8

The National Trust for Scotland, Broughton House & Garden

Broughton House and Garden represents the home, workplace and collections of E. A. Hornel (1864–1933), one of the Glasgow Boys and one of Scotland's most successful and distinctive artists. Broughton House is a unique cultural resource, housing a nationally significant collection, library and archive. Broughton House and Garden is situated in the town of Kirkcudbright in Dumfries & Galloway. Both the private and commercial aspects of Hornel's life as an artist and a respected member of the community are presented within Broughton House.

The townhouse, as it stands now, is thought to originally date from the 1730s with cellars remaining from a previous structure. It is an amalgamation of 10 and 12 High Street, with quality nineteenth-century and early twentieth-century modifications. Both front and rear elevations have high aesthetic significance and the house is recognised as a key building within the Kirkcudbright townscape.

The art collections at Broughton House are significant for their associational value with Hornel, their links to the place, their intrinsic artistic merit and their ability to inform us about the art scene in Scotland at the turn of the twentieth century. The value of the whole collection is increased by it being held in its original setting, which is where a number of the works of art were made.

The library is significant as it reflects Hornel's comprehensive approach to collecting and use of local expertise. From 1919, Hornel consciously set out to gather a collection of books on local and related topics based around Dumfries & Galloway, intending always to open Broughton House as a 'public art gallery and library for the benefit of the inhabitants of the Stewartry and visitors thereto'. This comprehensive approach began before the creation of the National Library of Scotland and showed remarkable foresight.

The collections as a whole create an exceptionally authentic experience for the visitor, providing an insight into Hornel's life and eclectic tastes, his interests in both local and wider cultures and most importantly his commitment in documenting local literature with the aim of providing access to this resource for the local community. The collection also demonstrates Hornel's creative artistic process within its original setting from his photographic compositions and sketches to his completed canvases.

A., W. active 19th C
An Estuary Landscape
oil on canvas 25.5 x 30.5
5.48

Blacklock, Thomas Bromley 1863–1903
A Red-Headed Girl in a Grey Dress in a Wood
1886
oil on panel 30.5 x 36.2
5.214

British (English) School
Preparing the Scarecrow
oil on canvas 53.5 x 43
5.54

Faed, John 1819–1902
The Artist's Mother
oil on canvas 75.5 x 62.3
5.14

Faed, John (attributed to) 1819–1902
The Standard Bearer and Helmeted Warrior
mid-19th C
oil on canvas on board 63.5 x 53.5
5.99

Faed, Thomas 1826–1900
A Highland Tryst
oil on canvas 46 x 61
5.23

Hewat, H.
Edward Atkinson Hornel (1864–1933)
oil on canvas board 60.9 x 50.8
5.102

Hornel, Edward Atkinson 1864–1933
Portrait of a Man in a Red Tunic (An Antwerp or Flemish veteran) 1885
oil on canvas 71 x 58.5
5.22.1

Hornel, Edward Atkinson 1864–1933
An Elderly Gentleman 1886
oil on canvas on board 26.5 x 22.5
5.215

Hornel, Edward Atkinson 1864–1933
Two Geishas 1894
oil on canvas on panel 75.6 x 32.5
2010.214

Hornel, Edward Atkinson 1864–1933
A Winter Wonderland 1897–1933
oil on canvas 63.5 x 76
5.41

Hornel, Edward Atkinson 1864–1933
Apple Blossom 1897–1933
oil on canvas 51 x 40.7
5.63

Hornel, Edward Atkinson 1864–1933
Apple Blossom, Buckland Burn 1897–1933
oil on canvas 51.3 x 61.3
5.61

Hornel, Edward Atkinson 1864–1933
Balloons and Blossom, Brighouse Bay
1897–1933
oil on canvas 122 x 152.5
5.71

Hornel, Edward Atkinson 1864–1933
Blue Flax, Brighouse Bay 1897–1933
oil on canvas 63.5 x 76
5.42

Hornel, Edward Atkinson 1864–1933
Girl with Nesting Swans 1897–1933
oil on canvas 101.5 x 127
5.27

Hornel, Edward Atkinson 1864–1933
Girl with Wild Flowers 1897–1933
oil on canvas 51 x 40.5
5.33

Hornel, Edward Atkinson 1864–1933
The Bluebell Wood, Gathering Primroses
1897–1933
oil on canvas 127.5 x 102.5
5.69

Hornel, Edward Atkinson 1864–1933
The Flower Princess 1897–1933
oil on canvas 152.5 x 122
5.73

Hornel, Edward Atkinson 1864–1933
The Scent of Primrose 1897–1933
oil on canvas 18 x 44.5
5.55

Hornel, Edward Atkinson 1864–1933
Three Girls 1897–1933
oil on canvas 183 x 152.5
5.36

Hornel, Edward Atkinson 1864–1933
Woody Briar, Buckland Bay 1897–1933
oil on canvas 51 x 40.7
5.62

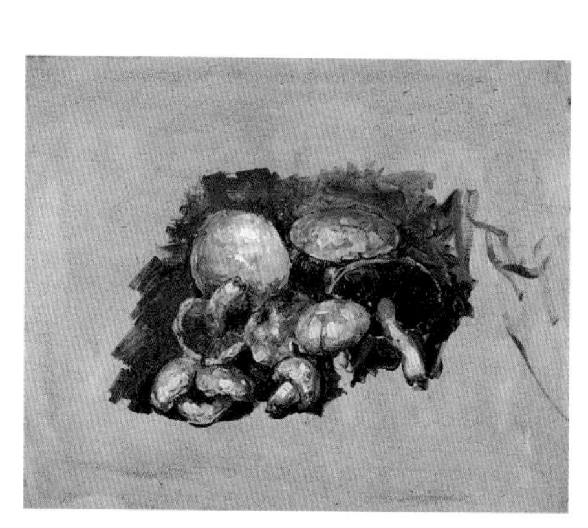

Hornel, Edward Atkinson 1864–1933
Still Life – Mushrooms 1899–1912
oil on canvas 40.6 x 50.8
5.79

Hornel, Edward Atkinson 1864–1933
Studies of a Red Waterlily 1899–1912
oil on canvas 60.9 x 59.7
5.82

Hornel, Edward Atkinson 1864–1933
Study of Datura 1899–1912
oil on canvas 61 x 51
5.81

Hornel, Edward Atkinson 1864–1933
Waterlilies 1899–1912
oil on canvas on panel 60.5 x 50.8
5.53

Hornel, Edward Atkinson 1864–1933
Sheep Grazing in an Autumn Landscape 19th C
oil on canvas 29.2 x 40
5.217

Hornel, Edward Atkinson (attributed to) 1864–1933
Still Life – Time Running Out late 19th C
oil on canvas 49.5 x 61
5.77

Hornel, Edward Atkinson 1864–1933
Young Girl with Primroses 1906
oil on canvas 51 x 40.5
205.15 (P)

Hornel, Edward Atkinson 1864–1933
Studies of Autumn Leaves c.1906
oil on canvas (?) 76.2 x 91.4
5.132

Hornel, Edward Atkinson 1864–1933
Woodland (possibly Buckland Wood) c.1906
oil on canvas 91.4 x 76.2
5.135.1

Hornel, Edward Atkinson 1864–1933
Ceylon Water Pots 1907–1909
oil on canvas 76 x 63.5
5.26

Hornel, Edward Atkinson 1864–1933
Ceylonese Water Carriers by a River Bank
1907–1909
oil on canvas on panel 51 x 61
5.6

Hornel, Edward Atkinson 1864–1933
Lace Makers, Ceylon 1908
oil on canvas 61 x 51.5
202.22

Hornel, Edward Atkinson 1864–1933
A Bamboo Forest, Ceylon c.1908
oil on canvas 124.5 x 152.4
5.131

Hornel, Edward Atkinson 1864–1933
Girls Picking Blue Flax (Gathering Bluebells, Brighouse Bay) 1917
oil on canvas 63.5 x 76
5.2

Hornel, Edward Atkinson 1864–1933
Playing in the Woods 1917
oil on canvas on panel 56 x 23
5.21

Hornel, Edward Atkinson 1864–1933
A Geisha Girl 1921–1925
oil on canvas on panel 55.6 x 23
5.56

Hornel, Edward Atkinson 1864–1933
A Geisha Girl Holding a Fan 1921–1925
oil on canvas 76 x 35.5
5.51

Hornel, Edward Atkinson 1864–1933
Geisha Girls 1921–1925
oil on canvas 125.5 x 102.3
5.7

Hornel, Edward Atkinson 1864–1933
Japanese Dancers 1921–925
oil on canvas 63.5 x 76
5.4

Hornel, Edward Atkinson 1864–1933
Japanese Dancers 1921–1925
oil on canvas 101.5 x 76
5.76

Hornel, Edward Atkinson 1864–1933
Japanese Dancers 1921–1925
oil on canvas 60.3 x 48.3
5.86

Hornel, Edward Atkinson 1864–1933
Japanese Girls on a Verandah 1921–1925
oil on canvas 62.9 x 62.9
5.8

Hornel, Edward Atkinson 1864–1933
Japanese Musician 1921–1925
oil on canvas on panel 45.5 x 35.5
5.38

Facing page: Raeburn, Henry, 1756–1823, *Alexander Leith of Freeland*, The National Trust for Scotland, Leith Hall Garden & Estate (p. 69)

Hornel, Edward Atkinson 1864–1933
Japanese Woman by a Flowering Tree (A Geisha Girl by a Bonsai Tree) 1921–1925
oil on canvas 40.5 x 51
5.18

Hornel, Edward Atkinson 1864–1933
Tea Ceremony with Japanese Girls 1921–1925
oil on canvas 59.7 x 50.8
5.83

Hornel, Edward Atkinson 1864–1933
The Pink Kimono 1921–1925
oil on canvas 76 x 35.5
5.49

Hornel, Edward Atkinson 1864–1933
Three Japanese Peasants (Japanese Dancers) 1921–1925
oil on canvas 63.5 x 76
5.25

Hornel, Edward Atkinson 1864–1933
Two Geisha Girls 1921–1925
oil on canvas 51 x 40.5
5.57

Hornel, Edward Atkinson 1864–1933
Two Geisha Girls in a Japanese Garden 1921–1925
oil on canvas 61 x 50.4
5.84

Hornel, Edward Atkinson 1864–1933
Two Japanese Girls 1921–1925
oil on canvas 91.5 x 76
5.3

Hornel, Edward Atkinson 1864–1933
Burmese Maidens on a Terrace 1922
oil on canvas on panel 56 x 23
5.17

Hornel, Edward Atkinson 1864–1933
Maiden in a Pink Kimono 1922
oil on canvas on panel 56 x 23
5.9

Hornel, Edward Atkinson 1864–1933
The Green Parasol 1922
oil on canvas 102.5 x 77
5.68

Hornel, Edward Atkinson 1864–1933
A Balustrade, Mandalay 1922–1923
oil on canvas 91.4 x 47.6
5.134

Hornel, Edward Atkinson 1864–1933
Burmese Maidens outside a Temple 1922–1923
oil on canvas (?) 90.2 x 47.6
5.133

Hornel, Edward Atkinson 1864–1933
A Burmese Market 1922–1927
oil on canvas 152.5 x 122
5.72

Hornel, Edward Atkinson 1864–1933
Burmese Dancers 1922–1927
oil on canvas 76 x 91.5
5.66

Hornel, Edward Atkinson 1864–1933
Burmese Figures by a Gateway 1922–1927
oil on canvas 92.3 x 77.4
5.67

Hornel, Edward Atkinson 1864–1933
Burmese Girls and Market Stalls 1922–1927
oil on canvas 76.5 x 64
5.65

Hornel, Edward Atkinson 1864–1933
Burmese Maidens 1922–1927
oil on canvas on panel 56 x 23
5.16

Hornel, Edward Atkinson 1864–1933
Burmese Musicians and Dancers 1922–1927
oil on canvas 151 x 120.5
5.95

Hornel, Edward Atkinson 1864–1933
Burmese Water Carriers 1922–1927
oil on canvas 61 x 50.5
5.85

Hornel, Edward Atkinson 1864–1933
Burmese Water Carriers on the Banks of the Irrawaddy 1922–1927
oil on canvas 62 x 50.5
5.78

Hornel, Edward Atkinson 1864–1933
Girls Resting by the Irrawaddy 1922–1927
oil on canvas 61 x 51
5.89

Hornel, Edward Atkinson 1864–1933
Sketch of a Native Girl, Burma 1922–1927
oil on canvas 51 x 40.5
5.88

Hornel, Edward Atkinson 1864–1933
Memories of Mandalay 1923
oil on canvas 152.5 x 203
5.28

Hornel, Edward Atkinson 1864–1933
Water Carriers on the Banks of the Irrawaddy 1923
oil on canvas 56 x 23
5.91

Hornel, Edward Atkinson 1864–1933
The Toy Boat, Brighouse Bay 1925
oil on canvas 101.5 x 127
5.75

Hornel, Edward Atkinson 1864–1933
Balloons at Brighouse Bay 1929
oil on canvas 76 x 92
5.32

Hornel, Edward Atkinson 1864–1933
Brighouse Bay, Wild and Burnet Roses 1929
oil on canvas 122 x 152.5
5.29

Hornel, Edward Atkinson 1864–1933
Gathering Mushrooms 1930
oil on canvas 61.5 x 51.1
5.58

Hornel, Edward Atkinson 1864–1933
Wild Flax and Burnet Roses 1932
oil on canvas 89 x 76
5.34

Hornel, Edward Atkinson 1864–1933
Wild Flax at Brighouse 1932
oil on canvas 51 x 61
5.31

Hornel, Edward Atkinson 1864–1933
Burmese Dancers
oil on board 35.4 x 45.7
5.97.1

Hornel, Edward Atkinson 1864–1933
Burmese Dancers
oil on board 35.5 x 45.5
5.97.2

Hornel, Edward Atkinson 1864–1933
Ceylonese Tea Pickers
oil on canvas 122 x 152.5
5.96

Hornel, Edward Atkinson 1864–1933
Daffodils
oil on canvas 30.5 x 22.8
5.107

Hornel, Edward Atkinson 1864–1933
Figures (sketch)
oil on board 35.5 x 23.7
5.106

Hornel, Edward Atkinson 1864–1933
Geisha Girl in an Oriental Garden
oil on canvas on panel 35.5 x 25.5
5.92

Hornel, Edward Atkinson 1864–1933
Geisha Girls with Screen
oil on canvas 101.5 x 76
5.87

Hornel, Edward Atkinson 1864–1933
Sketch of a Bamboo Trunk
oil on canvas 88.5 x 57
5.136.2

Hornel, Edward Atkinson (circle of) 1864–1933
Washing Day
oil on canvas on board 21.5 x 18
5.125

MacGeorge, William Stewart 1861–1931
Captain Malcolm McLachlan Harper c.1880
oil on canvas 54 x 36.3
5.101

MacGeorge, William Stewart 1861–1931
Edward Atkinson Hornel (1864–1933), Aged 17 1881
oil on canvas 41.3 x 31.1
5.44

MacGregor, Harry 1864–1934
A Tree-Lined Country Lane 1903
oil on canvas 25.5 x 30.5
5.47

MacNicol, Bessie 1869–1904
Edward Atkinson Hornel
oil on canvas 74 x 63.5
5.35

McCubbin, Frederick 1855–1917
Glasgow 'Barras' 1906
oil on board 25.4 x 35.2
5.108

Oppenheimer, Charles 1875–1961
The Harbour, Kirkcudbright 1958
oil on board 118 x 228.5 (E)
5.37 (P)

Oppenheimer, Charles 1875–1961
My Garden at Twilight (14 High Street from the Garden)
oil on canvas 91.5 x 122
5.19

Rembrandt van Rijn (after) 1606–1669
Self Portrait
oil on board 13.2 x 11
5.216

Rink, Paulus 1861–1903
Dutch Head, 'The Artist Painted by Himself'
1885
oil on canvas on panel 47 x 37
5.59

unknown artist
A Victorian Gentleman 1906
oil on board 25.5 x 20.3
5.138

unknown artist
Birds among Trees with Peony and Apple Blossoms
oil on panel & leather 67.3 x 51.5
5.3166

unknown artist
Portrait of a Man
oil on board 10.3 x 9.5
5.15

unknown artist
Study of a Man in a Hat
oil on canvas 40.5 x 30.5
5.1

Velde II, Willem van de (style of) 1633–1707
Dutch Schooner and Fishing Boats in Full Sail
oil on panel 39.5 x 53.5
5.98

The National Trust for Scotland, Newhailes

Newhailes in Mussleburgh, just outside Edinburgh, is an amazing survival of early eighteenth-century decorative art and collections, set within a late seventeenth-century 'villa' and surrounded by an eighteenth-century designed landscape. The house is remarkable for the superbly intact interiors, together with much of their collections of furniture and paintings, created by the Dalrymple family from 1709 onwards through much of the eighteenth century.

James Smith (c.1645–1731) was a leading architect of his day in Scotland and was at the forefront of the development of British Palladianism, an architectural style that became dominant in the eighteenth century. The plan, fabric and architectural detail of Smith's classical Palladian villa, which he designed for himself, is exceptional in that the essential structure survives to an unusual degree, almost untouched within the later additions of library and state apartment wings. The addition of the library is important as the largest private library of its time in Scotland and, if further research proves that it was designed by James Gibbs, it would be significant on a national level. Following the addition of the balancing reception suite, other architectural periods followed, including Miss Christian's creation of the decorative neo-classical stables and the extensive modernisation of the house in the Aesthetic taste, working with earlier eighteenth-century interiors, by Lord Shand in the nineteenth century. In terms of the landscape, the key buildings carefully placed within it reflect the quality and style of the villa and it is obvious that they were built to enhance the villa. This can be seen in the Palladian Tea House and the Rococo Shell House, both of which are considered to be the finest surviving examples of their kind within Scotland.

The interiors and collections at Newhailes combine to create the important aesthetic calm or mellow quality, a feeling of entering a place that has been lived-in, with a deep patina and layers of continuity of occupation up to the present day. This is considered to be one of the key experiences of Newhailes. The house contains the most important Rococo interior scheme complemented by the finest collection of decorative art from the early to mid-eighteenth century in Scotland, which together as one scheme survives remarkably intact, giving it exceptional national significance. The interiors include stucco-work by Thomas Clayton and painted decoration executed directly onto the panelling by James Norrie, together with features unique to Scotland at the time such as; chimneypieces by Henry Cheere of Westminster; the Dining Room service-screen; the Green Bedroom buffet recess; and the first panoramic Chinese wallpaper in the country.

The paintings, including works by John Medina (1721–1796) and Allan Ramsay (1713–1784), are also exceptional examples, through their individual outstanding quality and through their architectural treatment. Their incorporation into the panelling of the building has preserved them as a collection within the overall decorative scheme for which they were commissioned. A high degree of the furniture and collections also survive together from this period, including impressive Chinese lacquer cabinets, exceptional examples of French furniture, London furniture by Nix and Sam Smith and porcelain of the finest quality. In addition to this there are period fixings extant on the White Dressing Room tapestry and early lining papers beneath the Chinese wallpaper that are extremely rare. The discovery of the Chinese silks for the Best Bed, which are of a very high quality, is also of national significance.

Aikman, William (attributed to) 1682–1731
Portrait of a Man
oil on canvas 74.9 x 63.5
21.63

Aikman, William (attributed to) 1682–1731
Sir James Dalrymple, Bt, MP
oil on canvas 74.3 x 60.9
21.9

Beale, Mary (circle of) 1633–1699
Janet Rochead, Wife of the Honourable Sir David Dalrymple, 1st Bt of Hailes
oil on canvas 74.9 x 60.9
21.57

Beale, Mary (style of) 1633–1699
Janet Rochead, Wife of the Honourable Sir David Dalrymple, 1st Bt of Hailes
oil on canvas 74 x 62
21.49

Blackburn, Samuel active 1838–1857
Helen Boyle, Daughter of the Honourable Patrick Boyle, Wife of Thomas Mure of Warriston (after Henry Raeburn) 1838
oil on canvas 89 x 69
21.36

Blackburn, Samuel active 1838–1857
Thomas Mure of Warriston (after Henry Raeburn) 1838
oil on canvas 73.5 x 61
21.37

British (English) School
Landscape with Trees and Figures
oil on canvas 35.6 x 27.9
21.48

Flemish School
Coastal Scene with Sailing Ships and Rowing Boats
oil on canvas 39.5 x 56.8
21.15

Glauber, Johannes (circle of) 1646–1727
An Italianate Landscape with a Ruined Temple, Figures and Cattle
oil on canvas 55.2 x 64.8
21.41

Glauber, Johannes (circle of) 1646–1727
Italian Landscape with Figures and a Distant View of a Castle and Town
oil on copper 21.5 x 31.8
21.45

Grant, Francis (follower of) 1803–1878
Sir Charles Dalrymple Fergusson, Bt
oil on canvas 71.1 x 58.4
21.17

Hoppner, John (circle of) 1758–1810
Sir James Dalrymple, Bt
oil on canvas 71.3 x 61.5
21.16

Hulst, Frans de 1610–1661
Coastal Scene with Sailing Boats, a Rowing Boat and Figures Hauling Nets
oil on panel 39.4 x 60.3
21.6

Jervas, Charles (circle of) 1675–1739
Anne Young Pringle, Wife of John Dalrymple
oil on canvas 126 x 101.1
21.38

Jervas, Charles (circle of) 1675–1739
Lady Christian, Wife of Sir James Dalrymple, Mother of Lord Hailes
oil on canvas 73.5 x 61
21.42

Facing page: Gascars, Henri, 1634–1701, *Portrait of a Woman,* The National Trust for Scotland, Haddo House (p. 36)

Kneller, Godfrey 1646–1723
The Honourable Sir David Dalrymple, Bt, Youngest Son of the 1st Viscount Stair
oil on canvas 74.9 x 62.9
21.7

Martin, David 1736–1798
John Dalrymple, Son of Sir James Dalrymple, Bt, Lord Provost of Edinburgh
oil on canvas 124.3 x 99
21.4

Maskell, Christopher Mark 1846–1933
A Waterside Inn and Ferryman
oil on board 30.2 x 35.6
21.117

Medina, John Baptist de 1659–1710
The Honourable Sir David Dalrymple, Bt, Younger Son of 1st Viscount Stair, and His Son Sir James Dalrymple, Bt
oil on canvas 121.9 x 99.1
21.2

Medina, John Baptist de (circle of) 1659–1710
John, 2nd Viscount and 1st Earl of Stair
oil on canvas 124.4 x 100.3
21.24

Medina, John Baptist de (circle of) 1659–1710
Portrait of a Gentleman in Armour
oil on canvas 31.5 x 26.8
21.47

Medina, John Baptist de (circle of) 1659–1710
Sir James Dalrymple of Stair, President of the Court of Session, Created 1st Viscount Stair
oil on canvas 71 x 58.5
21.25

Medina, John Baptist de (circle of) 1659–1710
The Honourable Sir Hew Dalrymple, Bt, MP, President of the Court of Session (1698), (...)
oil on canvas 73.7 x 60.9
21.11

Mitchell, E.
A Black Highland Bull in a Highland Landscape 1880
oil on canvas 63.5 x 76.8
21.241

Nattier, Jean-Marc 1685–1766
The Honourable General James Sinclair of Dysart (after Allan Ramsay) 1749
oil on canvas 80 x 64.1
21.67.2

Norie, James 1684–1757
Landscape with Castle, River and Figures
oil on panel 40.6 x 81.3
21.58.1

Norie, James 1684–1757
Landscape with Castle, River and Figures
oil on panel 40.6 x 83.8
21.58.2

Norie, James 1684–1757
Landscapes with Ruined Buildings and Figures
oil on panel 72.4 x 54.6
21.10.1

Norie, James 1684–1757
Landscapes with Ruined Buildings and Figures
oil on panel 72.4 x 54.6
21.10.2

Norie, James 1684–1757
River Landscape with Buildings and Figures
oil on panel 62.8 x 97.8
21.59

Norie, James (attributed to) 1684–1757
A Procession of the Gods above a Riverscape
oil on panel 27.3 x 53.3
21.3184

Ramsay, Allan 1713–1784
Agnes Murray Kynynmond, Daughter of Hugh Dalrymple Murray Kynynmond, Wife of the Right Honourable Sir Gilbert Elliot (...) 1739
oil on canvas 139.8 x 99.8
21.39

Ramsay, Allan 1713–1784
Sir James Dalrymple, Bt, MP, Auditor of the Exchequer 1740
oil on canvas 124.7 x 100.8
21.18

Ramsay, Allan 1713–1784
Lady Christian Dalrymple 1744
oil on canvas 74.9 x 62.2
21.66

Ramsay, Allan 1713–1784
Janet, Daughter of the Honourable Sir David Dalrymple, Bt 1749
oil on canvas 78.7 x 64.1
21.67.1

Ramsay, Allan 1713–1784
Hew Dalrymple, Lord Drummore 1754
oil on canvas 73.7 x 60.9
21.6

Ramsay, Allan 1713–1784
Field Marshal John, 2nd Earl of Stair, KT
oil on canvas 124.5 x 100.5
21.26

Ramsay, Allan 1713–1784
Sir David Dalrymple, Bt, Lord Hailes
oil on canvas 73.7 x 60.9
21.8

Ruysdael, Salomon van (attributed to) 1602–1670
Wooded River Landscape with Cottages, a Ferry Boat, Cattle and Figures
oil on canvas 48.2 x 68
21.2

Seton, John Thomas 1730–1806
Helen Ferguson, Wife of Sir David Dalrymple, Later Lord Hailes
oil on canvas 73.5 x 61
21.28

Smibert, John (attributed to) 1688–1751
Lady Christian Dalrymple, Wife of Sir James Dalrymple, Bt, Daughter of Thomas, 6th Earl of Haddington
oil on canvas 125 x 100.8
21.23

Stewart, F. E. S.
A Brown Pony
oil on canvas 43.2 x 53.5
21.232

Stewart, F. E. S. (attributed to)
A Bay Pony
oil on canvas 29.5 x 40.3
21.231

Symonds, William Robert 1851–1934
The Right Honourable Sir Charles Dalrymple, Bt 1906
oil on canvas 124.5 x 99
21.32

Thomson, John 1778–1840
Landscape with Hailes Castle and Traprain Law
oil on canvas 128.9 x 116.8
21.3

unknown artist
A Jack Russell Terrier
oil on canvas 45.1 x 33
21.233

unknown artist
A West Lothian Beach (possibly Longniddry)
oil on panel 13.9 x 23.8
21.276

unknown artist
Capriccio Coastal Inlet with Classical Ruins, Figures, Cattle and Sheep
oil on canvas 139.8 x 114.4
21.7

unknown artist
Sailing Boats off a Rocky Shore
oil on board 21.6 x 29.8
21.72

unknown artist
A Covered Urn c.1720
oil on panel 226.1 x 124.5
21.3126

Vogelsang, Isaac (attributed to) 1688–1753
Views around Newhailes
oil on panel 53.2 x 90
21.19.1

Vogelsang, Isaac (attributed to) 1688–1753
Views around Newhailes
oil on panel 53.2 x 90
21.19.2

Vogelsang, Isaac (attributed to) 1688–1753
Views around Newhailes
oil on panel 53.2 x 90
21.19.3

Vogelsang, Isaac (attributed to) 1688–1753
Views around Newhailes
oil on panel 53.2 x 90
21.19.4

Walker, F. Hanson
Margaret, Lady Blake, Previously Lady Dalrymple, Wife of Sir Charles Dalrymple
1909
oil on canvas 64 x 54.5
21.31

Walker, F. Hanson
Alice Mary Hunter Blair, Wife of Charles Dalrymple of Newhailes
oil on canvas 64.8 x 55.2
21.3

Watson, George 1767–1837
Sir John Pringle Dalrymple, Bt
oil on canvas 74.9 x 62.2
21.46

The National Trust for Scotland, Gladstone's Land

Gladstone's Land is a seven-storey (including the cellar and attic) tenement on the Lawnmarket end of the Royal Mile in Edinburgh. It dates largely from the seventeenth century, though parts of the rear of the building date back to the sixteenth century. Like many properties in the Old Town, by the early twentieth century, Gladstone's Land was in poor condition and severely overcrowded, with several families living in each subdivided room. In 1934 it was condemned for demolition, but was saved when acquired by The National Trust for Scotland.

Gladstone's Land is an exceptionally early and well-preserved survival of a characteristically Scottish domestic architectural type – the tall tenement. While other tenements along the Royal Mile mostly contain some early fabric and preserve some of the flavour of a post-medieval streetscape, most have been altered, re-fronted and internal layouts reworked. What makes Gladstone's Land so special is the degree to which both in internal layout and decoration, and in the main street elevation, it remains an authentic survival in comparison to the much-changed buildings all around it. It is thus one of the few surviving examples anywhere in Scotland which is able to give physical shape to the changes that were brought about by the urban development trends of the late sixteenth century. Internally, the surviving room layouts and painted decoration is of high national importance. Today Gladstone's Land provides an opportunity for visitors to explore and understand the development of the Old Town experienced through a single building and the property is a key player in the city's tourism market.

The interiors are of national significance, because of the large amount of surviving original features. These include original sixteenth-century chimneypieces and a surviving panelled room in the later (eighteenth-century) south jamb of the building. But the most significant interior features are the painted walls and ceilings of the first, second and third floor front rooms, which are of a standard and quality which bear comparison with the best of other urban properties in Scotland. Though not now on the scale of some of the grandest examples in the country, sufficient traces of painted decoration survive to show that there was a complete suite of such work in every important room throughout the building and to give a valuable insight into the fashionable interior decoration of the day (the second floor ceiling being dated 1620) – representative of a large body of work that has been lost. On the first floor, the combination of ceiling and mural decoration is probably unique among Scottish town houses.

Aikman, William 1682–1731
Elizabeth Graham of Airth
oil on canvas 76 x 63.2
203.38

Aikman, William 1682–1731
John Lumsden of Blanearn
oil on canvas 75.5 x 63
203.36

Aikman, William 1682–1731
Rachel Graham, Wife of John Lumsden of Blanearn
oil on canvas 76 x 63.5
203.37

Aikman, William (attributed to) 1682–1731
Katherine Erskine, Daughter of Sir Charles Erskine of Alva, Wife of Patrick Campbell of Monzie
oil on canvas 75.5 x 63
203.26

Belle, Alexis-Simon (circle of) 1674–1734
James, 5th Earl of Linlithgow and 4th Earl of Callendar (d.1723)
oil on canvas 76 x 65
203.32

British (Scottish) School
Admiral Thomas Gordon (1658–1741)
oil on canvas 76.5 x 63.5
203.67

Claesz. the younger, Anthony (attributed to) 1616–1652
Spring Flowers in a Delft Vase: Iris, Rose and Lily of the Valley
oil on board 29.2 x 18.4
34.250.2

Claesz. the younger, Anthony (attributed to) 1616–1652
Spring Flowers in a Delft Vase: Iris, Roses and a Tulip
oil on board 29.2 x 18.4
34.250.1

Kneller, Godfrey (circle of) 1646–1723
Lady Henrietta Livingstone
oil on canvas 76 x 64
203.40.2

Facing page: Mosman, William, c.1700–1771, *Elizabeth Graham of Airth, Wife of William MacDowall of Castle Semple and Garthland,* Gladstone's Land (p. 150)

Kneller, Godfrey (circle of) 1646–1723
Lady Mary Graham, née Livingstone
oil on canvas 75.5 x 63
203.40.1

Larkin, William (attributed to) 1585–1619
Countess of Shirley
oil on board 57.2 x 44.5
34.245

Mosman, William 1700–1771
Elizabeth Graham of Airth, Wife of William MacDowall of Castle Semple and Garthland
oil on canvas 76.5 x 65
203.27

Ramsay, Allan (studio of) 1713–1784
Judge James Graham of Airth, Dean of the Faculty and Judge of the Court of Admiralty
oil on canvas 77.5 x 65
203.35

unknown artist
Dame Margaret Lauder
oil on canvas 75 x 62
34.407

unknown artist
Sir Alexander Seton
oil on canvas 75 x 62.4
34.406

The National Trust for Scotland, Hermiston Quay

Annand, Louise Gibson 1915–2012
Circe's Island 1966
oil on canvas 49 x 59.5
204.3

Bannatyne, John James 1836–1911
Clyde Estuary
oil on canvas 50 x 76
96.164

Breun, John Ernest 1862–1921
Foreign Dispatches 1891
oil on canvas 110.5 x 141.5
2011.1334

British (English) School
Chillingham Cattle by an Ancient Oak Tree
oil on canvas 28.1 x 39
200.137

British (Scottish) School
James, The 'Admirable' Crichton 1581
oil on canvas 74 x 61.1
203.21

British School
Two Children Paddling
oil on board 49.5 x 39.7
24.21

Brodie, Alexander Kenneth active 1894–c.1898
A Breton Interior
oil on canvas 117 x 144
200.9 (P)

C., T. A.
Wooded Landscape
oil on canvas 26.5 x 36.9
26.2

Cadell, Francis Campbell Boileau 1883–1937
The Steading, Strachur
oil on canvas 44.6 x 37
203.4

Cameron, David Young 1865–1945
Loch Awe
oil on board 22 x 30.3
203.8

Cameron, David Young 1865–1945
Loch Ness
oil on canvas 39.5 x 74
203.12

Cameron, David Young 1865–1945
Rannoch Moor
oil on canvas 35.4 x 60.8
203.5

Claesz., Pieter 1597–1660
A Silver Beaker, a Roehmer and a Peeled Lemon 1636
oil on board 58.1 x 38.5
34.134

Clairval, F.
Vase of Roses
oil on board 44.3 x 36.3
203.14

Clarkson, Albert
Fraisthorpe Maid 1896
oil on canvas 41.8 x 52.1
2011.1325

Corbett, Lucy b.1980
Professor Roger Wheater, OBE, FRSE 2007
oil on canvas 109.5 x 89.4
T4467

Craven, Helen
Roses 1898
oil on canvas 25 x 76.2
205.39

Crowe, Victoria b.1945
The Earl of Wemyss and March, KT, President of The National Trust for Scotland 1989
oil on canvas 96.5 x 111
2012.407

Donald, John Milne 1819–1866
Rural Idyll
oil on canvas 34.5 x 52.8
24.2

Dujardin, Karel (attributed to) 1626–1678
Figures outside a Building
oil on canvas 40 x 50.3
34.13

Ellis, Edwin 1842–1895
North Wales
oil on canvas 45 x 83
24.23

Faed, Thomas 1826–1900
The Old Road round Knock Veoch 1898
oil on board 18 x 23.7
2011.1025

Faed the younger, James 1857–1920
A Heather Burn in Galloway
oil on board 19.4 x 15.2
2011.1026

Giordani
Bay from a Terrace Garden
oil on board 39 x 48
96.60.2a

Godward, John William 1861–1922
On the Terrace 1904
oil on canvas 37.2 x 75.5
203.1

Greig, James McGavin 1861–1941
James Fyffe, Friend of Sir James Barrie
oil on canvas 60.3 x 50.2
37.174.1

Gysaerts, Gualetrus Wouter 1649–1679
Tulips, Roses and Other Flowers
oil on board 49 x 36.2
34.132.1

Gysaerts, Gualetrus Wouter 1649–1679
Tulips, Roses and Other Flowers
oil on board (?) 49 x 36.6
34.132.2

Hall, Dora M.
Rhododendrons
oil on canvas 33.2 x 26.2
205.38

Harley, Daisy
A Steep Highland Glen c.1890
oil on canvas 59.6 x 49.5
2011.133

His, René Charles Edmond 1877–1960
Le Sentier du Moulin
oil on canvas 32 x 44.8
24.10.1

Hoog, Bernard de 1867–1943
Interior with a Mother and Child (A Happy Family)
oil on canvas 39.5 x 49.7
203.17

Hornel, Edward Atkinson 1864–1933
Japanese Girl
oil on canvas 49.4 x 39.8
BTN.PCF.01

Hornel, Edward Atkinson 1864–1933
Unknown Fragment of a Larger Painting
oil on canvas 72.5 x 184.5
5.136.1

Houghton-Smith, Ann
'Found', a Bloodhound Seated beside a Cross 1922
oil on canvas 29.5 x 24.5
207.9

Hunter, George Leslie 1879–1931
Anemones and Fruit
oil on board 45 x 39.7
203.15

Hunter, George Leslie 1879–1931
The Old Mill
oil on canvas 55 x 68
203.16

Hutchison, W.
Figures in an Interior
oil on canvas 35.5 x 44
2011.1331

Kay, James 1858–1942
View on the Clyde 1870
oil on canvas 29 x 44.4
203.3

Kay, James 1858–1942
Square in Paris, 2 Clichy
oil on board 46.5 x 61
203.9

Lawrence, Thomas 1769–1830
The Countess of Aberdeen
oil on canvas 58.5 x 48.3
2011.1328

Lawrence, Thomas (after) 1769–1830
Prince Metternich 1843
oil on canvas 140.5 x 108.7
79.122

Lee-Hankey, William 1869–1952
In My Garden
oil on canvas 44.6 x 60.2
203.13

Lely, Peter (circle of) 1618–1680
John Graham, 1st Viscount Dundee
oil on canvas 73.5 x 61.2
203.22

MacWhirter, John 1839–1911
Ben Blaven
oil on canvas 30.5 x 48
26.3.2

MacWhirter, John 1839–1911
Broadford Bay
oil on canvas 31 x 48.1
26.3.1

MacWhirter, John 1839–1911
Broadford Bay
oil on canvas 44.5 x 71.2
26.5

MacWhirter, John 1839–1911
Broadford from the Mainland
oil on canvas 42 x 68.7
26.4

MacWhirter, John 1839–1911
Skye from Lochalsh
oil on canvas 44.5 x 71.1
26.6

Medina, John (attributed to) 1720–1796
Major John Forbes of Pittencrieff
oil on canvas 74 x 61.3
203.39

Medina, John Baptist de (follower of) 1659–1710
Ann, Countess of Callander c.1700
oil on canvas 71.5 x 57.9
203.29

Medina, John Baptist de (follower of) 1659–1710
Alexander Livingston, Earl of Callandar
oil on canvas 64 x 55
203.28

Miller, William Ongley 1883–1960
Trees 1944
oil on canvas 48.1 x 52.1
204.131

Molenaer, Klaes 1630–1676
Ice-Skating Scene
oil on board 30.5 x 36.8
34.133

Molenaer, Klaes 1630–1676
Winter Scene
oil on board 20.5 x 26
34.128

Neeffs the elder, Peeter 1578–1656
Interior of Antwerp Cathedral
oil on board 13 x 16.5
34.135

Neer, Aert van der 1603–1677
Moonlit Landscape
oil on board 33 x 48.5
34.127

Nicholson, John P. active late 19th C
Landscape with Farm
oil on canvas 29.3 x 49.7
2011.1327

Noble, James Campbell 1846–1913
Dutch Canal Scene
oil on canvas 50 x 59.7
96.162

Noble, James Campbell 1846–1913
Waves
oil on canvas 58.8 x 90.5
96.108

Peploe, Samuel John 1871–1935
Roses
oil on canvas 49.7 x 39.5
203.7

Pettie, John 1839–1893
The First Step 1876
oil on canvas 78.9 x 121
203.6

Ramsay, Allan 1713–1784
John, 3rd Earl of Bute 1758
oil on canvas 239.4 x 147
65.468

Ruisdael, Jacob van (attributed to) 1628–1682
A Country Scene
oil on board 35.2 x 29
34.404

Scott, J. B.
A Fishing Boat Beached in a Sandy Bay 1836
oil on canvas 17 x 24.5
26.1

Sheagreen, Lena
Bridge with Trees 1900
oil on canvas 33.7 x 49.3
205.36

Sheagreen, Lena
Old Cottage, Criccieth, in Wales
oil on canvas 21.2 x 32
205.37

Smith, George A. active 1959–1961
Morning Mist, Aberdeen Harbour
oil on canvas 65 x 75
2011.1329

Tol, Dominicus van 1635–1676
An Old Woman Fleecing a Boy
oil on board 42 x 33.3
34.129

unknown artist
Mrs J. Drinkwater 1810
oil on canvas 23.5 x 18.3
99.1626.3

unknown artist
Colonel Drinkwater c.1810
oil on board 21.5 x 16.5
99.1626.1

Facing page: Bellangé, Hippolyte, 1800–1866, *Comrades*, 1861, The National Trust for Scotland, Brodick Castle, Garden & Country Park (p. 236)

unknown artist
Mrs Drinkwater c.1810
oil on board 21.5 x 16.6
99.1626.2

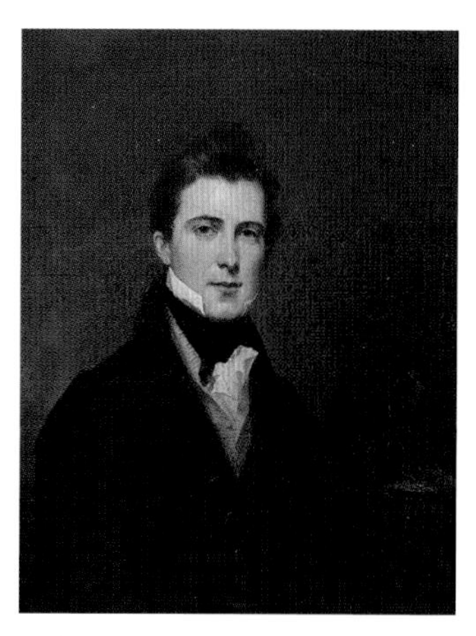

unknown artist
Charles Drinkwater 1820
oil on canvas 23.4 x 18.2
99.1626.4

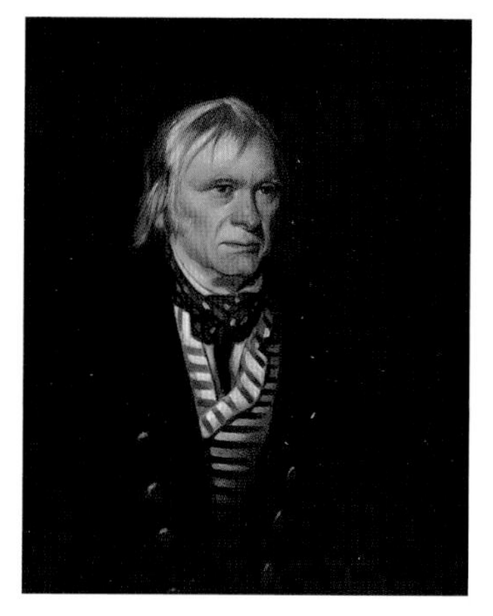

unknown artist
Duncan Turner c.1820
oil on canvas 41 x 33
50.1520.1

unknown artist
Miss Drinkwater 1821
oil on canvas 23.5 x 18.3
99.1626.7

unknown artist
Edward Drinkwater 1823
oil on canvas 23 x 18
99.1626.6

unknown artist
William Bethune 1823
oil on canvas 23 x 18
99.1626.5

unknown artist
Janet Anderson (Learmonth) (d.1838) c.1830
oil on canvas 36.5 x 31.2
204.4

unknown artist
A Horseman Talking to Two Villagers
oil on board 29 x 38.6
24.24.2

unknown artist
James, 1st Marquess of Montrose
oil on canvas 72.5 x 59.9
203.24

unknown artist
Landscape with Castle Ruins
oil on canvas 75.5 x 65.2
2011.1323

unknown artist
Man with a Pipe in an Interior
oil on canvas 25.5 x 20.5
2011.1337

unknown artist
Marshy Landscape
oil on board 19.5 x 29.5
2011.1326

unknown artist
Mrs Elizabeth Turner
oil on canvas 41 x 33
50.1520.2

unknown artist
Portrait of a Gentleman (said to be Peter the Great)
oil on canvas 122 x 87.5
2011.1335

unknown artist
Portrait of a Man (A Cavalier)
oil on canvas 40 x 30
2011.1324

unknown artist
Roman Soldiers about to Arrest a Woman
oil on canvas 113.5 x 151
5.137

unknown artist
Sir Hugh Innes (1754–1831), Bt, of Lochalsh and Coxtown
oil on canvas
26.7

unknown artist
Steps and a Balustrade
oil on canvas 16.3 x 23.4
2011.1322

unknown artist
Travellers with a Covered Wagon
oil on board 28.5 x 39
24.24.1

Wells, William Page Atkinson 1872–1923
Teignmouth from Torquay Road
oil on canvas 31.6 x 39.3
203.19

Y., M. B.
Mountainous Landscape
oil on canvas 37 x 55
T685

Yeoman, M. B.
The Grampians 1913
oil on board 29.6 x 45.8
T670

The National Trust for Scotland, Malleny Garden

Malleny House was probably built towards the end of the sixteenth century, although the majority of the current house, together with walled garden and doocot date from the seventeenth century. The estate was acquired in 1634 by Sir James Murray of Kilbaberton, architect to King Charles I.

In 1647, the estate passed to the William Scott, an Edinburgh lawyer, then through the hands of a variety of families until Commander and Mrs Gore-Browne-Henderson gave the house and gardens to The National Trust for Scotland in 1968. There is a small display of portraits in two rooms of the house and entrance.

Much appreciated for its atmosphere of peace and tranquillity, Malleny is the garden to visit for a few hours of quiet contemplation among beautiful surroundings. Malleny is a walled garden with a delightful collection of old-fashioned roses and fine herbaceous borders. A particular feature of the garden is the four 400-year-old clipped yew trees. The large Victorian greenhouse offers a summer display of scented-leaf pelargoniums, fuchsias and heliotropes.

Nasmyth, Alexander 1758–1840
John Scott (1705–1793), 3rd of Malleny
oil on canvas 74.5 x 62
T4462

unknown artist
Cartaret George Scott (d.1875)
oil on canvas 70 x 59.5 (E)
T4463

unknown artist
Charlotte Elizabeth Cunningham, Wife of Francis Cartaret Scott
oil on board 29.5 x 23
2010.104

unknown artist
Francis Cartaret Scott (1754–1835), Sixth Son of John Scott, 3rd of Malleny
oil on board 70 x 60
2010.93

unknown artist
*Genre Interior (Men in a Tavern Playing Cards)**
oil on canvas 34.5 x 44
T4464

unknown artist
John Scott (1640–1709), 1st of Malleny
oil on canvas 73 x 61
2010.33

unknown artist
Landscape
oil on canvas 34 x 44.4
2010.42

unknown artist
Landscape
oil on canvas 28 x 41.8
2010.81

unknown artist
*Landscape with a Ruined Castle in the Background**
oil on board 76.5 x 181
T4465

unknown artist
Landscape with Cows and Horses
oil on canvas 72 x 99
2010.34

unknown artist
Thomas Scott (d.1729), 2nd Scott of Malleny
oil on canvas 73.5 x 63.5
2010.35

The National Trust for Scotland, The Georgian House

The north side of Charlotte Square in Edinburgh is Robert Adam's masterpiece of urban architecture.

The Georgian House, with its elegant furnished interior, is located at No.7 Charlotte Square. The Square was conceived by Robert Adam as a paradigm of the Georgian ideal in the centre of Edinburgh. A heady vision of sweeping crescents, broad boulevards and elegant squares, the New Town of Edinburgh offered wealthy citizens in the late eighteenth century a means of escape from the overcrowded tenements of the Old Town. It provides a unique opportunity for visitors to see inside a New Town building, decorated to demonstrate late eighteenth-century and early nineteenth-century upper middle class life, and is an important site for conveying the story of New Town life to the public.

Within the Edinburgh New Town, Charlotte Square stands as an architectural high point. It is of international importance because of the quality of the Adam design, which set the pattern for much of the later development of the New Town. The strength and commonality of purpose required to achieve their vision for the New Town was held to by the town council throughout the eighteenth and nineteenth century, and is without parallel in the UK.

The Georgian House was built in 1796 for John Lamont, 18th Chief of the Clan Lamont, and he lived here with his family until 1815. The house has been magnificently restored to show a typical Edinburgh New Town House of the late eighteenth to early nineteenth-century. The fine collection of period furniture, porcelain, paintings, silver and glass reflects the lifestyle and social and economic conditions of the time. This is complemented by the Trust's properties in the Old Town and Edinburgh suburbs to offer the visitor a real understanding of the range of lifestyles in Edinburgh at different times in the city's history.

Anglo/Flemish School
James Graham, Marquis of Montrose
oil on canvas 125 x 99
75.11

Balen I, Hendrik van (circle of) 1575–1632
The Virgin and Child with a Female Martyr
oil on copper 22 x 16.5
75.172 (P)

Barber
William Henry Wayne, Esq.
oil on canvas 76 x 63.5
75.55 (P)

Barclay, John MacLaren 1811–1886
Thomas Graham-Stirling of Strowan 1860
oil on canvas 52.5 x 39.5
203.41

Barker II, Benjamin (attributed to) 1776–1838
A View of a Wooded Mountainous Landscape
oil on canvas 91.5 x 119.5
75.14 (P)

Beechey, William 1753–1839
Portrait of a Gentleman in a Black Coat
oil on canvas 76.5 x 63.5
75.94.1

Bentley, Joseph Clayton 1809–1851
A Wooded Landscape with a Mill and Peasants 1851
oil on canvas 79 x 117
74.16 (P)

Bonington, Richard Parkes 1802–1828
River Scene with Gondolas, Rouen (after Joseph Mallord William Turner)
oil 67 x 89
2010.221 (P)

British (English) School
Anne Salmon
oil on canvas
74.11 (P)

British (English) School
Lord Curzon
oil on canvas 122 x 99
75.12 (P)

British (Scottish) School
Captain Thomas Graham of Airth, in Old Age
oil on canvas 76.5 x 63.5
203.34

British (Scottish) School
Helen Colt of Auldhame, Later Lady Rae
oil on canvas 76.5 x 64
203.5

Facing page: Hornel, Edward Atkinson, 1864–1933, *Two Geishas*, 1894, The National Trust for Scotland, Broughton House & Garden (p. 127)

Burton, Mungo 1799–1882
John Hamilton Colt II of Gartsherrie
oil on canvas 138 x 102.5
203.70.1

Burton, Mungo 1799–1882
Jane Colt
oil on canvas 138 x 102.5
203.70.2

Carse, Alexander 1770–1843
A Seated Man Holding a Chanter and Family in an Interior
oil on panel 38 x 31
99.1508

Chalmers, George 1720–1791
Oliver Colt of Auldhame and Inveresk (1708–1782) 1763
oil on canvas 76 x 63.5
203.53

Clovio, Giulio 1498–1578
Marriage of the Virgin
oil or tempera on vellum 15 x 20
75.27 (P)

Duncombe, Thomas
Mrs Morris
oil on canvas 30 x 20 (E)
75.444

Dutch School
Portrait of a Bearded Man in a Hat
oil on board
74.15 (P)

Dutch School
Shipping Offshore, a Dutch Seascape
oil on canvas 35.5 x 44
75.2 (P)

Gordon, John Watson 1788–1864
An Extensive View of Elliock, Dumfriesshire
oil on canvas 98.5 x 127.4
203.31

Goyen, Jan van 1596–1656
A Town Wall by a River with Figures
oil on panel 46 x 40.5
75.201 (P)

Hondecoeter, Melchior de (circle of) 1636–1695
A White Cockatoo and Other Birds in a Wooded Landscape
oil on canvas 79 x 60
75.206 (P)

Italian School
Landscape with a Classical Building, Town, Lake and Mountains
oil on canvas 75 x 50 (E)
75.169

Kneller, Godfrey 1646–1723
Portrait of a Gentleman in a Grey Robe
oil on canvas 74 x 61
75.115 (P)

Knox, John 1778–1845
View of Glasgow Green and a Passing Storm
oil on canvas 64.5 x 87.5
75.199

Labruzzi, Carlo (circle of) 1747–1817
View of Lake Albano with the Alban Hills and Peasants
oil on canvas 71 x 99
75.209 (P)

Luny, Thomas 1759–1837
An Estuary with Shipping
oil on panel 20 x 30 (E)
75.202.2 (P)

Luny, Thomas 1759–1837
Mouth of the River Teign
oil on panel 20 x 30 (E)
75.202.1 (P)

Martin, David 1736–1798
Elizabeth Holt (d.1803) 1789
oil on canvas 129.5 x 102
203.52

Martin, David 1736–1798
Helen Stewart (1729/1730–1828), Later Mrs Colt of Auldhame, and Her Son, Adam
oil on canvas 127 x 101
203.51

Martin, David 1736–1798
The Honourable Helen Colt of Auldhame (1729/1730–1828), and Her Granddaughter, Grace (1781–1802)
oil on canvas 129 x 102.7
203.48

McInnes, Robert 1801–1886
Carolus Graham of Airth
oil on canvas 76 x 63.5
203.33

Moir, John (attributed to) 1776–1857
Captain Thomas Graham of Airth, Later Graham-Stirling of Airth and Strowan
oil on canvas 78 x 66.8
203.23

Morland, George (attributed to) 1763–1804
'Jack Ashore', an Inn Scene with Sailors
oil on panel 39.5 x 32.5
75.275 (P)

Morland, George (circle of) 1763–1804
A Barn with Three Men and a Calf
oil on canvas 48 x 75
75.204 (P)

Morland, George (circle of) 1763–1804
Gypsies in a Wood
oil on canvas 43 x 52
75.205 (P)

Müller, William James 1812–1845
Landscape with a Woman in a Quarry
oil on board 21 x 42.5
74.8 (P)

Müller, William James (style of) 1812–1845
Street Scenes in Cairo
oil on board 21 x 26
74.1 (P)

Muziano, Girolamo 1528–1592
The Flight into Egypt
oil on panel 61 x 48
74.17

Nasmyth, Alexander 1758–1840
Jane Ross of Shandwick
oil on canvas 70 x 40
75.266

Nasmyth, Alexander 1758–1840
Landscape with a Bridge and Ruined Castle
oil on canvas 44.5 x 57 (E)
75.21

Nasmyth, Alexander 1758–1840
St Bernard's Well and the Water of Leith
oil on canvas 69 x 87.5
75.196

Niccolò dell'Abate (circle of) 1509–1571
Head of a Woman
oil on canvas 30.5 x 20.3
74.12 (P)

Northcote, James 1746–1831
Miss Lydia Hobson, Lady Grant
oil on canvas 76 x 64.5
75.35 (P)

Patel, Pierre I 1605–1676
Italianate Landscape with a Ruined Temple
oil on canvas 71 x 99
75.208 (P)

Raeburn, Henry 1756–1823
Alexander Keith c.1810
oil on canvas 240 x 148
204.163 (P)

Raeburn, Henry 1756–1823
Mrs Walter Buchanan
oil on canvas 76 x 63.5
75.32

Ramsay, Allan 1713–1784
Portrait of a Lady
oil on canvas
75.198 (P)

Ramsay, Allan (circle of) 1713–1784
Elizabeth Fullerton of Carberry, née Colt
oil on canvas 107 x 72
203.49

Reni, Guido (follower of) 1575–1642
Madonna and Child
oil on canvas 101.5 x 80
74.13 (P)

Riley, John 1646–1691
Sir Christopher Wren
oil on canvas 76 x 63.5
75.94.2

Teniers II, David (after) 1610–1690
Tavern Interior
oil on board 40.5 x 46
75.197 (P)

Teniers II, David (style of) 1610–1690
Four Monkeys Smoking and Drinking
oil on board 15 x 22.5
75.207 (P)

unknown artist
Dugald Gilchrist
oil on canvas 77 x 56 (E)
2010.2031

unknown artist
Elanor Middleton
oil on canvas 77 x 56 (E)
2010.2032

unknown artist
Family Group
oil on canvas 45 x 63 (E)
2010.2033

unknown artist
'Man of Feeling', Henry Mackenzie
oil on panel 20.4 x 16.8
91.29

unknown artist
St Bernard's Well and the Water of Leith
oil on board 18.5 x 28
98.1501

Watson, William Smellie 1796–1874
Thomas Philip Graham of Airth
oil on canvas 79 x 65.7
203.3

Wright of Derby, Joseph 1734–1797
Captain Edward Salmon 1770s
oil on canvas
75.112 (P)

The National Trust for Scotland, Royal Burgh of Culross

Situated on the north shore of the Firth of Forth, approximately seven miles west of Dunfermline, the Royal Burgh of Culross is one of the best-conserved examples of a seventeenth and eighteenth-century Scottish burgh. Culross has a long and distinguished history with its earliest importance being as a religious centre. It later became a powerful and prosperous trading centre, and in 1592 James VI elevated Culross to Royal Burgh status. Culross suffered a decline in its fortunes from the mid-seventeenth century until a concerted effort, led by The National Trust for Scotland, was made in the twentieth century to conserve and restore the burgh.

The role of the Trust in the conservation and restoration of much of the burgh is an important part of the organisation's history and highly significant in a national context, as a precursor to the Building Preservation Trust Movement. The conservation of not only the grander buildings such as Culross Palace, but also the conservation and restoration of the little houses in the burgh was an important initiative, which ensured that much of the townscape remains intact. As a result the Royal Burgh of Culross is a fascinating survival of a sixteenth and seventeenth-century Scottish burgh and one of the best preserved examples of a sixteenth-century industrial town.

Culross Palace consists of two blocks situated on the north and west sides of an enclosed courtyard. It was constructed for Sir George Bruce in the late sixteenth and early seventeenth centuries and stands as a testament to the fortune he made in the burgh. A small selection of paintings related to the family are on display in the palace. The palace interiors are decorated with Scottish Renaissance wall paintings, one of the most extensive examples of such decoration in the care of the Trust.

British (Scottish) School
Lilias Stirling, Daughter of Stirling of Keir and Wife of Colonel John Erskine
oil on canvas 74.5 x 61.8
80.501 (P)

De Wett
The Honourable C. John Erskine, Son of David, 2nd Lord Cardross
oil on canvas 51.5 x 42.5
34.242 (P)

Jamesone, George 1588–1644
Sir George Bruce of Carnock
oil on canvas 98 x 74.5
33.4

unknown artist
'Black' Sir John of Erskine of Cardross c.1680
oil on canvas 70 x 59.5
80.502 (P)

unknown artist
Ships at Sea
oil on panel 104.5 x 153
T4466

The National Trust for Scotland, Falkland Palace & Garden

Falkland Palace and the Royal Burgh are situated in rural Fife, approximately one hour away from Edinburgh. Once a favoured place of retreat and leisure for the Kings and Queens of Scotland, particularly the royal Stewarts, it is these historical associations that make Falkland Palace so significant to the National Trust for Scotland and to the history of Scotland as a whole. This is expressed most tangibly in the palace, a seminal building in the development of Renaissance architecture in Britain, and the Stewart foundation of the Royal Burgh of Falkland. Also of particular significance is the palace's place as a demonstration of the desire to conserve Scotland's cultural heritage – first undertaken here by the 3rd Marquis of Bute in the nineteenth century and continued by subsequent members of his family and latterly by the Trust. In particular, the Marquis' restoration work was pioneering for its time – strongly artistic, but informed by archaeological and documentary evidence, yet allowing his reconstruction work to be easily differentiated from the surviving original remains.

Thanks in large part to the work of these conservationists much of the original built structure of the palace still remains, showing clearly the varying architectural styles that were employed. The fact that since the nineteenth century, until 1947, the Keeper's primary residence was the House of Falkland and not the palace, therefore not necessitating any major alterations for domestic arrangements, has also contributed to the completeness of the building today.

Of the original interiors, very little remains. The Chapel is the most significant survival – with its high quality screen and ceiling, it is of national importance, both as historic fabric and work of art. Elsewhere, what is seen today is the work of two of Scotland's most gifted nineteenth and twentieth-century architects, John Kinross and Schomberg Scott, working 'in the spirit' of the original building. Today these interiors are of considerable significance as nationally important works of art and for the quality of their design and craftsmanship.

Many of the furnishings are owned by the Crichton Stuart family and came from the House of Falkland having been made in the Bute workshops as part of its designed interiors. These create atmospheric interiors which add to the quality of the visitor experience and have the potential to tell an engaging story of the post-war occupation of the palace.

The palace is the property of the Crown, though management of the site is delegated through the office of Keeper. The National Trust for Scotland (the Trust) was appointed Deputy Keeper of Falkland Palace, the palace gardens and policies in 1952.

Belle, Alexis-Simon (circle of) 1674–1734
Prince James Edward Stuart (1720–1788), 'The Old Pretender', as a Boy
oil on canvas 66 x 53.4
88.138.1

British (English) School
Anne of Denmark (1574–1619)
oil on panel 49.5 x 42
52.709

British (English) School
Mary, Queen of Scots (1542–1587)
oil on panel 72 x 58.5
52.715

British (English) School
Prince Henry, Duke of Gloucester
oil on canvas 70 x 56.5
52.71

British School
Lord Ninian Crichton-Stuart (1883–1915), and His Mother, the Marchioness of Bute (1854–1932) 1904
oil on canvas 174 x 123.3
52.568 (P)

British School
Lord Ninian Crichton-Stuart (1883–1915)
c.1920
oil on canvas 48.3 x 34
52.569 (P)

Facing page: Clovio, Giulio, 1498–1578, *Marriage of the Virgin*, The National Trust for Scotland, The Georgian House (p. 168)

British School
James V (1512–1542), and Queen Mary of Guise (1515–1560)
oil on canvas 108 x 142
52.702

Dujardin, Karel 1626–1678
The Halt
oil on canvas 81.3 x 96.5
52.572

Dutch School
Portrait of an Old Woman 1616
oil on panel 58 x 49
90.66

Hanneman, Adriaen (circle of) 1601–1671
Charles II (1630–1685)
oil on canvas 75 x 61.5
52.714

Huysmans, Jacob (studio of) 1628–1696
Queen Catherine (1638–1705)
oil on canvas 125.8 x 105.8
52.712

Kneller, Godfrey (after) 1646–1723
Lady Mary Pierrepont (1689–1762), Later Wortley Montagu 1710
oil on panel 29.5 x 23
52.698

Kneller, Godfrey (after) 1646–1723
The 4th Earl of Moray (c.1611–1653)
oil on canvas 100 x 120 (E)
95.16 (P)

Larkin, William (circle of) 1585–1619
Henry, Prince of Wales (1594–1612)
oil on panel 49.5 x 42
52.708

Lauder, John Ettrick
The Ten Virgins
oil on canvas 46 x 80 (E)
52.214

Lely, Peter (circle of) 1618–1680
Charles II (1630–1685)
oil on canvas 73 x 61
52.713

Lorimer, John Henry 1856–1936
Ninian Patrick (1907–1910), Son of Lady and Lord Crichton-Stuart
oil on canvas 132 x 90
T4468 (P)

Sánchez Coello, Alonso (circle of) 1531–1588
James VI (1566–1625) c.1600
oil on panel 35 x 25.5
52.707

Somer I, Paulus van (after) 1576–1621
James VI and I (1566–1625), with the Collar of the Order of the Garter
oil on canvas 104 x 74.5
2011.1027

Somer I, Paulus van (attributed to) 1576–1621
James I (1566–1625)
oil on panel 61 x 51
52.706

Spanish School
Queen Margaret of Scotland (c.1045–1093)
oil on gilt gesso panel 162.2 x 68.5
52.716

Thomson, John 1778–1840
Conway Castle
oil on canvas 80 x 105
52.213

Troy, François de (after) 1645–1730
Prince of Wales with His Sister, Louise Marie
(after Nicolas de Largillière) after 1695
oil on canvas 37 x 29
52.511

unknown artist
Charlotte Jane Windsor, Viscountess Mountstuart, Baroness Cardiff of Cardiff Castle 1785
oil on canvas 240 x 144
97.6 (P)

unknown artist
Adoration of the Magi
oil on glass 19.4 x 17.3
T4469

unknown artist
Christ
tempera & metal on panel 27 x 23
T4473

unknown artist
Landscape
oil on canvas 43 x 73
T3404

unknown artist
Madonna and Child
oil on panel 30.2 x 24.1
88.138.26.15

unknown artist
Madonna and Child
tempera & metal on panel 17.5 x 14.5
T4472

unknown artist
Madonna and Child
oil & gold on panel 30.5 x 26
T4475

unknown artist
Mary, Queen of Scots (1542–1587)
oil on canvas 74.5 x 61.5
96.66 (P)

unknown artist
Our Lady of Ostrobrama
oil, leather & metal on panel 120 x 71.5
T4474

unknown artist
Saint Michael and the Dragon (?)
tempera on plaster 56.7 x 41.4
T4470

unknown artist
Scenes from the Life of Christ
tempera on panel 38 x 31.7
T4471

The National Trust for Scotland, Hill of Tarvit Mansionhouse & Garden

Hill of Tarvit Mansionhouse is one of the most modern properties in the care of The National Trust for Scotland. It is an outstanding example of the work of Scotland's leading architect of the day, Robert Lorimer, who was knighted for his work on the Thistle Chapel in St Giles Cathedral and went on to design the Scottish National War Memorial in Edinburgh Castle.

The property (created in 1906 partly out of and on the site of Wemyss Hall which had occupied the site since 1696) is also highly significant as a collector's house – the family home of Frederick Sharp whose collection provided the inspiration for the design of the building. This charming home exuded an air of reserved elegance, comfort and practicality – an atmosphere which is still very evident today.

The high quality collection of English, Scottish and European furniture, Chinese porcelain and bronzes, Flemish tapestries and paintings by European artists (including Henry Raeburn, Allan Ramsay and Barent Avercamp) contains some very important individual pieces but is also unusual in its entirety and survival.

Sharp and Lorimer's seamless approach to building the collection to suit the evolving design of the house is significant because of its completeness and rare survival, given the very common tendency to re-arrange objects and alter interiors as styles and fashions change. Hill of Tarvit thus has a modern significance in that it is now practically the only Lorimer house where the totality of a collection remains in situ within its surrounding complementary architecture.

The Hill of Tarvit estate in north-east Fife was bequeathed to the National Trust for Scotland in 1949, by Elizabeth Sharp.

Abbott, Lemuel Francis (after) 1760–1803
The Golf Players
oil on panel 40.6 x 29.2
49.236

Anglo/Dutch School
Hawking Party on Horseback by a Ruin c.1720
oil on canvas 74 x 68
49.49

Avercamp, Barent Petersz. 1612–1679
Winter Landscape with Skaters on a River c.1620–1630
oil on canvas 25 x 33.4
49.456

Avercamp, Barent Petersz. (follower of) 1612–1679
Winter Landscape with Skaters on a River near a Town c.1620–1630
oil on panel 32.3 x 48
49.486

Avercamp, Hendrick (follower of) 1585–1634
A Winter Landscape with Figures around a Bridge c.1630–1670
oil on panel 34.1 x 53
49.452

Beecq, Jan Karel Donatus van 1638–1722
A Naval Engagement
oil 58.4 x 91.4
49.57

Beerstraten, Anthonie active c.1635–c.1665
Winter Landscape with Figures by a Bridge to a Church
oil on canvas on panel 63.5 x 82.6
49.564

Berckheyde, Gerrit Adriaensz. (circle of) 1638–1698
Winter Landscape with Men Playing Kolf
oil on canvas 42 x 55.5
49.451

Beyeren, Abraham van 1620–1690
Still Life with a Lobster
oil on canvas 64.1 x 57.2
49.469

Bogdany, Jakob 1660–1724
Peacocks and Other Exotic Birds
oil on canvas 198 x 169
49.48

Bogdany, Jakob (style of) 1660–1724
Still Life of Fruit and Birds
oil on canvas 54 x 69
49.464.1

Bogdany, Jakob (style of) 1660–1724
Still Life of Fruit and Birds
oil on canvas 54 x 69.5
49.464.2

British (Scottish) School
Frederick Sharp c.1920
oil on canvas 128 x 102.5
49.241

Brueghel the younger, Pieter 1564–1638
The Bird Trap (Winter Landscape)
oil on panel 30.8 x 57.6
49.453

Claesz., Pieter (follower of) 1597–1660
Still Life
oil on panel 54 x 73
49.485

Constable, John (follower of) 1776–1837
Hampstead Heath
oil on panel 25 x 40
49.7049

Cuyp, Aelbert (style of) 1620–1691
A Ferry Boat
oil on panel 58.4 x 71.1
49.246

Cuyp, Jacob Gerritsz. 1594–1651
Portrait of a Girl in Red and White
oil on panel 94.6 x 67.3
49.46

Dubbels, Hendrik Jacobsz. (follower of) 1621–1707
Winter Landscape with a Frozen River
1660–1700
oil on canvas 25.4 x 29.8
49.565

Dutch School
A Pronk Still Life c.1660
oil on canvas 119 x 219.5
49.248

Dutch School
Portrait of a Gentleman
oil on metal 48.9 x 41.9
49.247

Dutch School
Still Life with Flowers in a Vase
oil on canvas 41.9 x 55.9
49.484

Fantin-Latour, Henri 1836–1904
Flowerpiece 1869
oil on canvas 64.1 x 53.9
49.467

Fantin-Latour, Henri 1836–1904
Les violettes et les giroflées
oil on board 28.6 x 28.6
49.457

German School
Portrait of a Lady in Black and Red 1659
oil on canvas 91.4 x 66
49.476

Gordon, John Watson 1788–1864
Mrs Brown of Newhall, Penicuik, and Her Daughter
oil on canvas 76.2 x 63.5
49.473

Heda, Willem Claesz. (circle of) 1594–1680
Still Life
oil on panel 97.8 x 121.9
49.478

Facing page: Hunter, George Leslie, 1879–1931, *Fife Pastoral*, The National Trust for Scotland, House of Dun (p. 108)

Heem, Jan Davidsz. de (follower of) 1606–1684
Still Life
oil on panel 49.5 x 35.6
49.483

Heeremans, Thomas 1640–1697
Winter Landscape with Skaters on a Canal
1660–1697
oil on canvas on panel 33.7 x 41.9
49.569

Heeremans, Thomas (follower of) 1640–1697
Winter Landscape with Figures on a River
c.1660–1680
oil on panel 51.5 x 71.5
49.45

Herring I, John Frederick 1795–1865
The Fresh Team 1841
oil on canvas 69 x 90
49.493

Herring I, John Frederick 1795–1865
The Forge 1850
oil on canvas 59.5 x 84.5
49.492

Highmore, Joseph 1692–1780
Peg Woffington
oil on canvas 157.5 x 128.5
49.479

Hondecoeter, Melchior de (follower of) 1636–1695
Fighting Cocks
oil on canvas 152.2 x 213.4
49.489

Ibbetson, Julius Caesar 1759–1817
Waiting for the Coach 1806
oil on canvas 36.8 x 50.2
49.243

Ibbetson, Julius Caesar (circle of) 1759–1817
A Wooded Landscape with Cattle Watering
oil on panel 20.3 x 25.4
49.245

Italo/Dutch School
Landscape with a Villa c.1700
oil on canvas 44 x 152.5
49.463

Italo/Dutch School
River Landscape with a Tower c.1700
oil on canvas 44 x 152.5
49.463

Maddersteeg, Michiel 1659–1714
Dutch Shipping in a Breeze
oil on panel 12.7 x 17.2
49.25

Martin, David (attributed to) 1736–1798
Jean, Daughter of John Bernie of Broomhall and Wife of Alexander Chancellor of Shieldhall
oil on canvas 124.5 x 99.1
49.47

Monamy, Peter 1681–1749
The Evening Gun
oil on canvas 58.5 x 81
49.244

Moreelse, Paulus 1571–1638
Portrait of a Lady 1635
oil on panel 80 x 63.5
49.477

Morland, George 1763–1804
Winter Landscape with Peasants and Donkeys
oil on canvas 69.8 x 90.2
49.468

Muir, Anne Davidson 1875–1951
Carnations in a Vase
oil & mixed media on canvas 45.7 x 34.3
49.551

Neer, Aert van der (attributed to) 1603–1677
Winter Landscape with a River, Cottage and Village Beyond
oil on panel 36.8 x 48.9
49.566

Noble, John Sargeant 1848–1896
Still Life with a Dead Swan
oil on canvas 83.8 x 144.8
49.238

Peeters I, Bonaventura 1614–1652
A Vessel Wrecked beneath a Fort in a Storm
oil on panel 25.4 x 34.3
49.568

Pickenoy, Nicolaes Eliasz. 1588–1655
Vrouw Elizabeth Coreboult 1631
oil on canvas 113.4 x 87.5
49.461

Raeburn, Henry 1756–1823
John Tait of Harvieston
oil on canvas 72.4 x 62.2
49.475

Raeburn, Henry 1756–1823
Mrs Tyndall Bruce
oil on canvas 73.7 x 62.2
49.474

Ramsay, Allan 1713–1784
Captain Thomas Wallace 1750
oil on canvas 74.9 x 62.2
49.471

Ramsay, Allan 1713–1784
Mrs William Mure of Caldwell
oil on canvas 73.7 x 60.9
49.472

Ramsay, Allan (circle of) 1713–1784
The Honourable Mrs Young, Daughter of the 1st Lord Holland
oil on canvas 63.5 x 60.9
49.239

Ravesteyn, Jan Anthonisz. van (attributed to) 1570–1657
Portrait of a Gentleman with a White Ruff
oil on panel 68 x 57
49.459

Rolzhoven, Julius 1858–1930
Hugh Sharp (1897–1937), as a Boy in Highland Dress 1904
mixed media on canvas 139.7 x 88.9
49.481

Rolzhoven, Julius 1858–1930
Mrs Frederick Sharp c.1904
mixed media on canvas 73.7 x 53.3
49.237

Ruysdael, Salomon van 1602–1670
Wooded River Landscape
oil on panel 43.2 x 69.8
49.571

Schotanus, Petrus active c.1663–1687
Vanitas Still Life
oil on panel 50.8 x 38.1
49.466

Shields, Robert Gordon
Frederick Sharp c.1920
oil on canvas 100 x 75
49.24

Shields, Robert Gordon
Still Life with a Vase of Flowers
oil & mixed media on canvas 59.7 x 49.5
49.242

Storck, Abraham Jansz. 1644–1708
Seaport
oil on canvas 64.8 x 82.6
49.455

Stralen, Antoni van (attributed to) 1594–1641
Winter Landscape 1620–1650
oil on panel 34 x 47.8
49.563

Teniers I, David 1582–1649
River Landscape with Peasants and Cattle
oil on canvas 121.9 x 201.9
49.462

Towne, Charles 1763–1840
A Gentleman Shooting with a Spaniel
oil on canvas 43.8 x 51.1
49.249

Turner, Daniel active 1782–c.1828
Southwark Bridge c.1800
oil 36.8 x 54
49.454

Turner, Daniel (circle of) active 1782–c.1828
Westminster Bridge c.1800
oil 36.8 x 54
49.454

Weenix, Jan Baptist (attributed to) 1621–1661
Hounds and an Owl with Dead Birds and Sculptures in a Landscape
oil on canvas 152 x 193
49.488

Weenix, Jan Baptist (attributed to) 1621–1661
Still Life with Dead Birds
oil on canvas 154.9 x 193
49.487

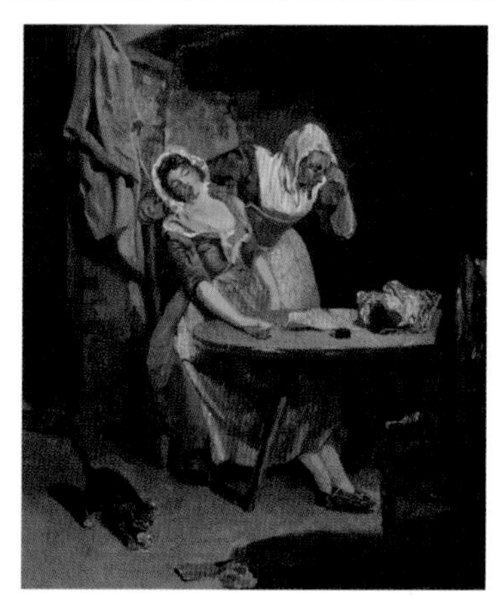

Wheatley, Francis (style of) 1747–1801
The Love Letter
oil on canvas 53.3 x 44.4
49.491

Wilkie, David 1785–1841
The Reading of the Will
oil on panel 16.5 x 24.7
49.7048

Wyck, Jan 1645–1700
A Pointer in a Landscape
oil on canvas 87 x 107
49.465

Zuylen, Hendrick van active 1613–1646
Still Life
oil on canvas 29 x 39
49.482

The National Trust for Scotland, Kellie Castle & Garden

Hidden in a quiet corner of Fife, Kellie Castle and Garden offers a surprisingly diverse experience to those who visit. Alongside the tangible elements that give the property significance, Kellie also possesses a real sense of history and an aura that can be felt throughout the property. The castle, an A-listed structure of national significance, stands at the heart of the property. Saved from ruin by the Lorimer family, the castle is renowned as the most influential tower house restoration in Scotland, boasting interiors which continue to reflect the 1950s tastes originally introduced by Mary and Hew Lorimer.

Kellie Castle dates from the fourteenth or early fifteenth century; with the castle thought to have originally developed from two separate towers. Kellie Castle is a highly significant example of Scottish lowland architecture with the absence of corridors being a notable feature which reflects the lack of prior influence of English and continental architecture. The T-form layout of the castle is also unusual and unlike the only other similar design at Elcho in Perthshire, Kellie seems to have evolved into such a design over the centuries. The castle and its interiors reflect the development of architecture in Scotland over several hundred years, which is again unusual.

In the period 1890–1916, Kellie emerged as one of Scotland's most important Arts and Crafts houses and was highly influential on Scottish taste. The interiors then developed further between 1942 and 1970 under the influence of Hew and Mary Lorimer when they displayed a taste and style heavily influenced by Christian Dior. The pictures and furnishings found at Kellie are important due to their totality and serve to complement the interiors.

A great deal of the significance of Kellie also lies in the connection with the Lorimer family, famous for their outstanding artistic talents. The architecture, gardens and picturesque quality of Kellie influenced members of the Lorimer family – an influence that can be seen in the work of Robert Lorimer (the architect) and John Henry Lorimer (the painter) in particular - and the property was in turn influenced by the family through the years.

The property was acquired by The National Trust for Scotland through three main phases of acquisition: the castle and policies were bought from the renowned sculptor Hew Lorimer in 1970; further land was acquired from a neighbouring farm in 1973; and finally the farmhouse was acquired in 1984.

Boyter, Ian Hugh b.1943
Crail 1974
oil on board 75 x 75 (E)
T3374

British (Scottish) School
Kellie Castle, Fife
oil on canvas 36 x 54
70.1507

Chalmers, A. J.
St Andrews Harbour
oil on canvas 30.5 x 45.7
94.76.3

de Wet, Jacob Jacobsz. 1640–1697
Classical Scene of Gods
oil on canvas 163.2 x 163.2
70.224

Droochsloot, Joost Cornelisz. 1586–1666
The Market Place at Amersfoort
oil on canvas 96.5 x 154.9
70.146

L'Espinasse (Comtesse), Marie
A Peasant in a Field
oil on canvas 34.3 x 22.2
70.331

Lorimer, Hannah active late 19th C
Portrait of a Man (copy after Henry Raeburn)
oil on canvas 75 x 61.6
2010.2038

Lorimer, Hannah active late 19th C
The Madonna of the Magnificat (after Sandro Botticelli)
oil 71.1 x 71.1
70.7

Lorimer, John Henry 1856–1936
San Giovanni Crisogono Altarpiece (after Giovanni Bellini) 1880
oil on canvas 81 x 56.5
70.198

Lorimer, John Henry 1856–1936
A Beech Tree at Kellie 1881
oil on canvas 43.1 x 59.6
70.326

Lorimer, John Henry 1856–1936
Hannah Lorimer Embroidering a Bedcover 1885
oil on canvas 122 x 240
70.33

Lorimer, John Henry 1856–1936
T. W. Lorimer 1890
oil on canvas 44.5 x 34.3
89.114.4

Lorimer, John Henry 1856–1936
Sunlight in the South Room, Kellie c.1913
oil on canvas 102 x 63.5
203.2 (P)

Lorimer, John Henry 1856–1936
The Long Shadows c.1918
oil on canvas 102 x 127
203.1 (P)

Lorimer, John Henry 1856–1936
A Gentleman Holding a Glove (after Titian)
oil on canvas 63.5 x 52
70.1556

Lorimer, John Henry 1856–1936
A Still Life with a Vase of Flowers
oil on canvas 29.5 x 20.9
90.7

Lorimer, John Henry 1856–1936
Any Port in a Storm
oil on canvas 142.5 x 101.6
70.13

Lorimer, John Henry 1856–1936
December Roses
oil on canvas 25.4 x 20.3
70.261.2

Lorimer, John Henry 1856–1936
Le peintre des fleurs
oil on canvas 94.5 x 56.5
70.1682

Lorimer, John Henry 1856–1936
Sir David Chalmers
oil on canvas 128.7 x 108.5
202.2

Lorimer, John Henry 1856–1936
Striped Roses in a Ship Mug
oil on canvas 20.3 x 30.5
70.261.1

Lorimer, John Henry 1856–1936
The Finding of Moses (after Giovanni Battista Tiepolo)
oil on canvas 49.3 x 39.4
90.117.1

Lorimer, John Henry 1856–1936
The Madonna and Child with Two Musical Angels
oil on canvas 77.5 x 81
70.1668

Lorimer, John Henry 1856–1936
View through a Window
oil on board 30 x 18
2011.993

Lorimer, Mary
Monica, Aged 7
oil on canvas 45.7 x 32.4
94.18.3 (P)

Lorimer, Robert Stodart 1864–1929
Church Spire 1880
oil on canvas 23.7 x 23.3
91.36.6

Lorimer, Robert Stodart 1864–1929
A Cock and Hens early 20th C
oil on board 13.9 x 26.7
70.1648

Os, Jan van (circle of) 1744–1808
Still Life with Fruit and Flowers
oil on panel 67.4 x 50.8
70.71

Raeburn, Henry (after) 1756–1823
Robert Stodart
oil on canvas 76.2 x 61.6
70.1557

Sellon, William active 1882–1887
A Bedroom in Holyrood Palace 1887
oil on board 12.1 x 15.9
70.793.2

Sellon, William active 1882–1887
A Drawing Room in Holyrood Palace 1887
oil on board 12.1 x 15.9
70.793.1

Traquair, Phoebe Anna 1852–1936
Cupid's Darts 1897
oil on canvas on board 195.6 x 171.45
70.76

unknown artist
Landscape
oil on panel 73.4 x 23.2
2010.2037.1

unknown artist
Landscape
oil on panel 81 x 24
2010.2037.2

unknown artist
Landscape
oil on panel 126.5 x 25
2010.2037.3

unknown artist
Landscape
oil on panel 80 x 31
2010.2037.4

unknown artist
Landscape
oil on panel
2010.2037.5

unknown artist
Landscape
oil on panel 45.5 x 74
2010.2037.7

unknown artist
Landscape
oil on panel 70 x 57
2010.2037.8

unknown artist
Landscape
oil on panel 75 x 57.5
2010.2037.9

unknown artist
Landscape
oil on panel 156 x 80
2010.2037.10

unknown artist
Landscape
oil on panel 43.5 x 77
2010.2037.11

unknown artist
Landscape
oil on panel 43.5 x 60.5
2010.2037.12

unknown artist
Landscape
oil on panel 44 x 60.7
2010.2037.13

unknown artist
Landscape
oil on panel 85.4 x 61.4
2010.2037.14

unknown artist
Landscape
oil on panel 85.3 x 61.2
2010.2037.15

unknown artist
Landscape
oil on panel 105.5 x 39.5
2010.2037.16

unknown artist
Landscape
oil on panel 105 x 39
2010.2037.17

unknown artist
Landscape
oil on panel 105 x 39.2
2010.2037.18

unknown artist
Landscape
oil on panel 40 x 40
2010.2037.19

unknown artist
Landscape
oil on panel 72 x 78.5
2010.2037.20

unknown artist
Landscape
oil on panel 117.8 x 78.5
2010.2037.21

unknown artist
Landscape
oil on panel 154 x 79.8
2010.2037.22

unknown artist
Landscape
oil on panel 45.4 x 100
2010.2037.23

unknown artist
Landscape
oil on panel 47 x 58.5
2010.2037.24

unknown artist
Landscape
oil on panel 45.5 x 90.5
2010.2037.25

unknown artist
Landscape
oil on panel 72.5 x 45
2010.2037.26

unknown artist
Landscape
oil on panel 45 x 52.5
2010.2037.27

unknown artist
Landscape
oil on panel 71 x 78.5
2010.2037.28

unknown artist
Landscape
oil on panel 120.2 x 80
2010.2037.29

unknown artist
Landscape
oil on panel 155 x 75
2010.2037.30

unknown artist
Landscape
oil on panel 72.5 x 67.5
2010.2037.31

unknown artist
Landscape
oil on panel 119 x 67.5
2010.2037.32

Facing page: Hambling, Maggi, b.1945, *Archibald, 5th Marquess of Aberdeen and Temair,* The National Trust for Scotland, Haddo House, (p. 42)

unknown artist
Landscape
oil on panel
2010.2037.33

unknown artist
Landscape
oil on panel 69 x 43.5
2010.2037.34

unknown artist
Landscape
oil on panel 119.5 x 44
2010.2037.35

unknown artist
Landscape
oil on panel 92 x 44.5
2010.2037.36

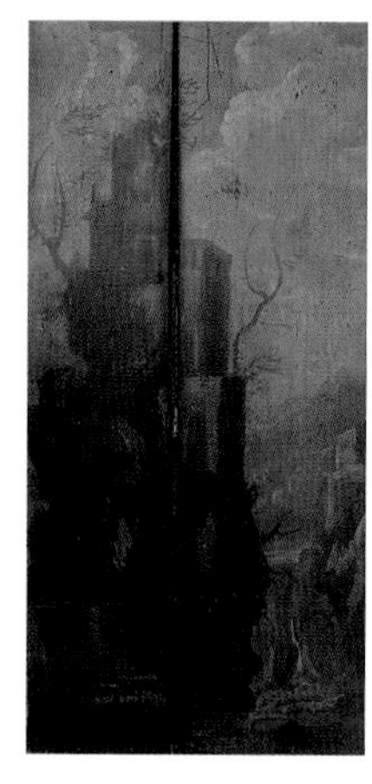

unknown artist
Landscape
oil on panel 73 x 44
2010.2037.38

unknown artist
Landscape
oil on panel 129 x 43.5
2010.2037.39

unknown artist
Landscape
oil on panel 80.5 x 43.5
2010.2037.40

unknown artist
Landscape
oil on panel 30 x 80
2010.2037.41

unknown artist
Landscape
oil on panel 77 x 63
2010.2037.42

unknown artist
Landscape
oil on panel 153 x 63
2010.2037.43

unknown artist
Landscape
oil on panel
2010.2037.44

unknown artist
Landscape
oil on panel
2010.2037.45

unknown artist
Landscape
oil on panel
2010.2037.46

unknown artist
Landscape
oil on panel
2010.2037.47

unknown artist
Landscape
oil on panel
2010.2037.48

unknown artist
Landscape
oil on panel
2010.2037.49

unknown artist
Landscape
oil on panel
2010.2037.50

unknown artist
Landscape
oil on panel
2010.2037.51

unknown artist
Landscape
oil on panel
2010.2037.52

unknown artist
Landscape
oil on panel
2010.2037.53

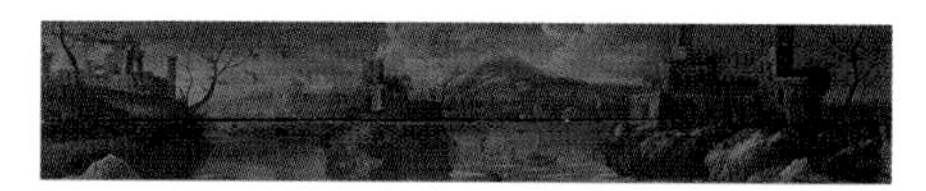

unknown artist
Landscape
oil on panel
2010.2037.54

unknown artist
Landscape
oil on panel
2010.2037.55

unknown artist
Landscape
oil on panel
2010.2037.56

unknown artist
Landscape
oil on panel
2010.2037.57

unknown artist
Landscape
oil on panel
2010.2037.58

unknown artist
Landscape
oil on panel
2010.2037.59

unknown artist
Landscape
oil on panel
2010.2037.60

unknown artist
Landscape
oil on panel
2010.2037.62

unknown artist
Landscape
oil on panel
2010.2037.63.1

unknown artist
Landscape
oil on panel
2010.2037.63.2

unknown artist
Landscape
oil on panel
2010.2037.64.1

unknown artist
Landscape
oil on panel
2010.2037.64.2

unknown artist
Landscape
oil on panel
2010.2037.65

unknown artist
Study of a Corner of a Room
oil on canvas 76.2 x 50.8
70.996

unknown artist
Thomas, 6th Earl of Kellie
oil on canvas 99 x 73.7
70.73 (P)

unknown artist
Vanitas
oil on panel 56.4 x 70
2011.991

Wylie, Mary
Monica with a Blenheim Cavalier King Charles Spaniel
oil on canvas 60.9 x 55.9
70.997

The National Trust for Scotland, Greenbank Garden

Greenbank House was built in 1763 by a Glasgow merchant by the name of Robert Allason. Allason was a local man who had begun life as a baker, before setting up with his brothers in Port Glasgow as a trader. He made his fortune trading with Britain's American colonies, eventually becoming a land-holder in the Caribbean. The profits from trade in both tobacco and slaves, allowed him to purchase Flenders Farm (land his family had worked for centuries) and establish the house.

However, Allason's trading interests later suffered during the American War of Independence. Over the next two centuries, the house was owned by a number of families. In 1962 it was bought by W. P. Blyth who, with his wife, transformed the grounds from fruit and vegetable growing to the ornamental gardens that are seen today. Then, in 1976, Mr and Mrs Blyth gifted the house, walled garden, and the 16-acre (65,000 square metre) estate to The National Trust for Scotland.

A small collection of portraits is on display in the house, along with a still life by the Scottish Colourist Samuel Peploe.

Peploe, Samuel John 1871–1935
Anemones in a Brown Jar
oil on canvas 44.5 x 39.5
94.908

Turner, Joseph Mallord William (after) 1775–1851
Venice
oil & oil pastel on paper 19.3 x 23.7
94.909

unknown artist
Helen Wilson, née Primrose, Wife of James Wilson c.1860
oil on canvas 73.4 x 60.6
94.12.3

unknown artist
James Wilson (1794–1863), Soap Maker and Candlemaker, Glasgow c.1860
oil on canvas 73.8 x 61
94.12.4

unknown artist
Margaret Wilson, née Blackburn, Wife of James Wilson
oil on canvas 73 x 62.8
94.12.1

unknown artist
James Wilson, Cooper of Pollockshaws, Glasgow
oil on canvas 74.5 x 62
94.12.2

Hugh Miller Museum & Birthplace Cottage

Hugh Miller Museum and Birthplace Cottage are situated in the small town of Cromarty in the Black Isle, about 20 miles from Inverness. Hugh Miller, a stonemason to trade, was a dominant force in Scottish society in his time, and played a very important part not only in the progress made in the understanding of geology in the nineteenth century, but also the development of the Presbyterian Church in Scotland. Miller became a major figure in the nineteenth century and this is underlined by the fact that thousands congregated in Edinburgh to pay their last respects after his death and a monument was erected in his honour in Cromarty three years later, in 1859.

A substantial collection is held at the property, much of which is on loan to the Trust from National Museums Scotland. It is an important resource, enabling the interpretation of the story of Hugh Miller, particularly his geological work and religious background. Of particular note is the national collection of geological items, largely made up of items that Miller himself collected. A small selection of portraits is also on display, mainly of the Miller family.

The Miller family gifted the cottage to the Trust and presented the keys formally on 28 September 1938 at a ceremony in Cromarty. Miller House was purchased by the Trust at the time of the acquisition of the cottage.

Bonner
Hugh Miller and Harriet
oil on board 60.5 x 45.4
11.225

Kay, William
Lydia, Hugh Miller's Wife
oil on canvas 43 x 33.5
11.1566

Taylor, Mike
Sundial Carved by Hugh Miller 1997
oil on canvas board 60.5 x 75.7
97.3

Facing page: Ferrari, Luca, 1605–1654, *Herod and Mariamne,* The National Trust for Scotland, Brodie Castle, (p. 217)

unknown artist
Hugh Miller
oil on canvas 40.6 x 30.4
11.111

The National Trust for Scotland, Culloden Battlefield & Visitor Centre

Culloden Battlefield lies on Culloden Muir near the village of Culloden and about four miles east of Inverness, just off the A9 trunk road. The Battlefield is the site of the last major battle to take place on the British mainland, where government forces defeated the Jacobite uprising under Prince Charles Edward Stuart on 16 April 1746.

The name and story of Culloden is to many Scots an icon, representing their identity and sense of nationhood (whether historically justified or not), and Culloden Battlefield is to them a place of the greatest spiritual significance. To the descendants of the Scottish and Highland diasporas it is a significant site in terms of their identity and the rediscovery of their ancestors' culture. The site's iconic status, its continuing conservation as a memorial to the fallen (of both sides), and its importance as a watershed in the history of Gaelic culture, mark it out as one of the most important sites in the guardianship of the Trust.

As the site of the last pitched battle fought on the UK mainland, Culloden Muir is a historically important site in local, national and international terms. The primary significance of Culloden, however, is the tremendous emotion that its name and the event of the battle arouses and the battlefield provides a tangible focus and setting for imaginative connection with these events. Because of its outstanding historic and cultural significance, Culloden is of prime importance to the Trust's education remit in promoting the understanding of Scotland's heritage.

Alexander, Cosmo (attributed to) 1724–1772
Portrait of a Jacobite Lady c.1745
oil on canvas 45 x 35 (E)
207.132 (P)

Hamilton, Hugh Douglas 1739–1808
Prince Charles Edward Stuart (1720–1788) c.1785
oil on canvas 20 x 15 (E)
207.293

unknown artist
Prince Charles Edward Stuart (1720–1788)
oil on canvas 17.8 x 12.7 (E)
207.156 (P)

The National Trust for Scotland, Brodie Castle

Brodie Castle has outstanding historical value due to its associations with the Brodie Family, who are one of the oldest established families in the north east of Scotland, being first endowed with the lands by Malcolm IV in 1160.

The development of the castle and estate indicates the rise and fall of the Brodie family fortunes with successive generations all leaving their mark. The architectural evolution of the castle takes place in three stages: the sixteenth and seventeenth centuries with later additions in the nineteenth century. Each stage marks a transition within the family quite often coupled with developments in politics and fashion. Therefore the castle is an example of a long-standing family home that has evolved through family change and social climate.

The architects William Burn and James Wyslon designed some of the most notable architectural additions to the castle. These changes were of great importance, not only in terms of marking the castle's transition from tower house to Victorian Mansion but also in the development of Scottish architecture and the treatment of old Scots houses in the 1840s. Alongside the castle there are various estate buildings which are still in existence such as the lodges, stables, ice house and laundry. Collectively these features are of interest as indicators of the practical workings of the estate.

A unique feature of the property is the daffodil collection, which is considered to be of great horticultural importance. Ian Brodie, 24th Laird of Brodie, established the collection in the late nineteenth century and the early twentieth century. Ian Brodie was an eminent breeder of daffodils and has gained international recognition for his work.

Brodie Castle is further enhanced by the impressive interiors and collections it contains. The castle has several very fine plaster ceilings and a collection of paintings, which are notable in their range and quality. Including many works from the Golden Age of Dutch painting, the eighteenth-century English School, late nineteenth and early twentieth-century School of Scottish Colourists and some very beautiful English

Abbott, Lemuel Francis (attributed to) 1760–1803
Alexander Brodie of Armhall and the Burn
oil on canvas 75.5 x 62
73.503

Alexander, Robert L. 1840–1923
'Mr Wu' – A Pekingese
oil on canvas 44.5 x 36.8
73.223

Anderson, Douglas Hardinge b.1934
Ninian Brodie of Brodie (1912–2003), 25th Brodie of Brodie 1985
oil on canvas 98.4 x 78.4
73.6

Barclay, John MacLaren 1811–1886
Hugh Brodie (1840–1889), 23rd Laird
oil on canvas 90.2 x 59.7
73.29

Barker II, Benjamin 1776–1838
A Wooded River Landscape with a Bridge
oil on canvas 19.1 x 24.8
73.33

Barraud, Henry 1811–1874
Black Horse in a Loose Box 1836
oil on canvas 63.5 x 76.2
73.75

Barret the elder, George (circle of) 1728–1784
Wooded Landscape
oil on panel 17.8 x 29.2
73.328

Berchem, Nicolaes Pietersz (style of) 1620–1683
A Ford
oil on panel 31.1 x 36.8
73.83

Blanche, Jacques-Emile 1861–1942
Racing Yachts on the Seine
oil on canvas 37.5 x 55
73.551

Bloemaert, Abraham 1566–1651
Boy with a Flute
oil on canvas 67.3 x 57.2
73.11

Bol, Ferdinand 1616–1680
Portrait of a Man 1669
oil on canvas 106.7 x 86.4
73.102

Brangwyn, Frank 1867–1956
Two Bridges, Perugia (The Viaduct)
oil on board 50 x 58.8
73.535

British (English) School
Maidservant c.1750
oil on canvas 127 x 101.6
73.36

British (Norwich) School
Farm among Trees c.1800
oil on canvas 36.8 x 30.5
73.9

British (Scottish) School
Portrait of a Lady in a Red Wrap (said to be Mary Sleigh) c.1740
oil on canvas 76.2 x 63.5
73.46

British (Scottish) School
Elizabeth Baillie (1819–1914), Wife of William Brodie, 22nd Laird c.1840
oil on canvas 72.4 x 60.3
73.51

British School
Portrait of a Nobleman (said to be King James VI and I) c.1600
oil on panel 114.3 x 86.4
73.42

British School
Anne, Wife of James Brodie c.1810
oil on canvas 72.4 x 60.3
73.48

British School
William Douglas Brodie (1799–1873), Son of James Brodie, 21st Laird c.1810
oil on canvas 74.9 x 61
73.47

British School
Oliver Cromwell (1599–1658)
oil on panel 18.4 x 15.2
73.78

Brodie, H.
A Woodland Path with Children (possibly at Osterley) 1867
oil on canvas 59.7 x 48.3
73.91

Brodie, Joseph
James Brodie of Spynie (d.1756) 1736
oil on canvas 125.7 x 99.1
73.54

Brown, John Alfred Arnesby 1866–1955
A Norfolk Landscape with Potato Pickers
oil on canvas 40.5 x 51
73.524

Brown, William Beattie 1831–1909
Trees in Perthshire at Dusk
oil on canvas 35.5 x 27.5
73.38

Brueghel, Abraham (1631–1690) & Courtois, Guillaume (1628–1679)
Putti with Fruit and an Urn of Flowers
oil on canvas 129.5 x 94, 129.5 x 94
73.99

Brundrit, Reginald Grange 1883–1960
Stainforth, a Welsh Valley Farm
oil on canvas 50.8 x 61
73.681

Cadell, Francis Campbell Boileau 1883–1937
Still Life with a Blue Jug, a Fan and an Apple
oil on panel 35.5 x 44
73.547

Cameron, Hugh 1835–1918
Among the Olives 20th C
oil on canvas 37.5 x 86
73.576

Camphuysen, Govert Dircksz. (attributed to) 1623–1672
A Herdsman with Cattle, Sheep and Goats 1657
oil on panel 31.7 x 40
73.93

Carracci, Annibale (after) 1560–1609
The Lamentation (Pietà)
oil on canvas 88.9 x 114.3
73.37

Chalon, Alfred Edward (attributed to) 1780–1860
Elizabeth Brodie (1794–1864), Wife of the 5th Duke of Gordon
oil on canvas 67.3 x 54.6
73.92.2

Chalon, Alfred Edward (attributed to) 1780–1860
George (1770–1836), 5th Duke of Gordon
oil on canvas 67.3 x 54.6
73.92.1

Ciardi, Emma 1879–1933
Venice from the Lagoon
oil on panel 34.9 x 48.3
73.325

Clérisseau, Charles Louis (circle of) 1722–1820
A Classical Capriccio
oil on canvas 27.9 x 21.6
73.65

Coello, Claudio (after) 1642–1693
Portrait of a Prince of the House of Spain, in Armour
oil on canvas 182.9 x 119.4
73.43

Cossiers, Jan (attributed to) 1600–1671
The Concert
oil on canvas
73.86

Coypel, Antoine 1661–1722
Leda and the Swan 18th C
oil on canvas 98 x 136
73.57

Craddock, Luke
Birds in a Landscape
oil on canvas 87.6 x 81.3
73.157.1

Craddock, Luke
Birds in a Landscape
oil on canvas 81.3 x 87.6
73.157.2

Crosbie, William 1915–1999
Inlet
oil on board 64.8 x 96.5
73.537

Currie, James active from 1846
Caithness (b.1842), and William Brodie (1845–1865), as Children in a Nursery 1846
oil on canvas 60.9 x 71.1
73.201.1

Currie, James active from 1846
Elizabeth Baillie (1819–1914), Wife of William Brodie 1846
oil on canvas 71.1 x 60.9
73.87.2

Currie, James active from 1846
George (1839–1868), and Hugh Brodie (1840–1889), as Children in Highland Dress on a Moor 1846
oil on canvas 42.5 x 50.8
73.201.2

Currie, James active from 1846
Family of William Brodie, 22nd Laird
oil on canvas 50.8 x 42.5
73.27

Currie, James active from 1846
William Brodie (1799–1873), 22nd Laird
oil on canvas 88.9 x 66
73.87.1

Cuyp, Jacob Gerritsz. (after) 1594–1651
Portrait of a Lady 1647
oil on panel 72.4 x 57.8
73.107.1

Cuyp, Jacob Gerritsz. (after) 1594–1651
Portrait of a Man 1647
oil on panel 72.4 x 57.8
73.107.2

Delorme, Anthonie de 1610–1673
Interior of the Church of St Bavo, Haarlem
1654
oil on canvas 80 x 63.5
73.28

Dickson, Thomas Francis
The Penitent Magdalen
oil on canvas 73.7 x 61
73.105

Douglas, Andrew 1871–1935
Highland Cattle in a Landscape
oil on board 27.7 x 44.4
73.507

Douglas, Phoebe Sholto b.1906
Ian Brodie (1868–1943), 24th Brodie of Brodie
20th C
oil on canvas 76.2 x 55.9
73.295

Downman, John 1750–1824
Lady Margaret Duff (1745–1786), Daughter of the 1st Earl of Fife and Wife of James Brodie, 21st Laird 1770
oil on canvas 74.9 x 60.9
73.5

Duck, Jacob 1600–1667
Soldiers and Women Revelling in an Interior
oil on panel
73.77

Dupré, Jules 1811–1889
Cattle at a Woodland Pond
oil on canvas 26 x 31.8
73.1

Dutch School
A Footbridge across a River c.1800
oil on panel 49.5 x 35.6
73.97

Dutch School
Riverscape with a Castle
oil on panel 27.9 x 38.7
73.15

Dyck, Anthony van (after) 1599–1641
Charles I (1600–1649)
oil on canvas 73.7 x 61
73.89

Dyck, Anthony van (follower of) 1599–1641
The Penitent Magdalen
oil on canvas 124.5 x 99
73.76

Ewbank, John Wilson 1799–1847
Edinburgh
oil on panel 29.8 x 21.6
73.286

Ewbank, John Wilson (circle of) 1799–1847
Shipping off Dover
oil on canvas 67.3 x 104.1
73.81

Faed, Thomas 1826–1900
Old Woman Reading 1861
oil on canvas 73.7 x 54.6
73.512

Ferguson, William Gouw 1632–1695
Still Life with Game Birds
oil on canvas 86.4 x 67.3
73.13

Ferrari, Luca 1605–1654
Herod and Mariamne
oil on canvas 127 x 165.1
73.41

Facing page: Nicholson, William, 1872–1949, *The Paper Poppies*, 1919, The National Trust for Scotland, Brodie Castle (p. 224)

Franco/German School
Landscape with a Herdsman and Women
oil on panel 29.2 x 39.4
73.156

Frazer, William Miller 1864–1961
Kings Lynn, Norfolk
oil on board 23 x 35.5
73.539

G., D. C.
Fruit on a Salver on a Marble Ledge
oil on paper 27.9 x 33
73.151

Gaultier, A. M.
Flowers and Fruit on a Marble Ledge 1830
oil on canvas 39.4 x 45.1
73.33.2

Gaultier, A. M.
Fruit and a Wedgwood Vase
oil on canvas 45.1 x 40
73.33.1

Gibbon, Benjamin b.1914
Spring Flowers in a Silver Mug 1951
oil on board 35.5 x 27.3
73.513

Goltzius, Hendrick (circle of) 1558–1617
Saint John the Evangelist
oil on panel 21 x 21
73.158.1

Goltzius, Hendrick (circle of) 1558–1617
Saint Luke
oil on panel 21 x 21
73.158.2

Gordon, John Watson 1788–1864
William Brodie (1845–1865), 23rd Laird
oil on canvas 73.7 x 62.2
73.52

Gordon, John Watson (circle of) 1788–1864
Elizabeth (1794–1864), Duchess of Gordon c.1850
oil on canvas 77 x 62.5
73.226

Gordon, John Watson (circle of) 1788–1864
Earl of Caithness in Highland Dress
oil on canvas 78.7 x 66
73.39

Guardi, Francesco (circle of) 1712–1793
Venetian Fondamenta
oil on canvas 44.5 x 76.2
73.15

Guillaumin, Armand 1841–1927
The Jetty c.1895
oil on canvas 52.5 x 63.5
73.555

H., J. A.
Military Scene in a Landscape
oil on panel
73.85.1

H., J. A.
Military Scene in a Landscape
oil on panel
73.85.2b

Hardie, Charles Martin 1858–1916
Old Church, Whittinghame 1889
oil on board 26.5 x 35.8
73.51

Haupt, Zygmunt 1907–1975
The Street of Lapalud
oil on canvas 69 x 81.5
73.3

Hayter, George 1792–1871
The Honourable Mrs William Ashley
oil on canvas 88.9 x 68.6
73.168

Hendriks, Gerardus 1804–1859
A Dutch River Scene
oil on canvas 50.8 x 60.7
73.109

Hickey, Thomas 1741–1824
James Brodie (1769–1802)
oil on canvas 24.1 x 19
73.68

Holland, James 1799–1870
Entrance to the Grand Canal, Venice 1843
oil on panel 22.9 x 17.1
73.31

Hondecoeter, Melchior de (circle of) 1636–1695
Birds in a Landscape
oil on canvas 101.6 x 121.9
73.25

Hope, Robert 1869–1936
The Vanity Glass
oil on canvas on board 66 x 91.4
73.559

Huet I, Jean-Baptiste (style of) 1745–1811
Pastoral Scene
oil on panel 12.7 x 17.8
73.70.1

Huet I, Jean-Baptiste (style of) 1745–1811
Pastoral Scene
oil on panel 12.7 x 17.8
73.70.2

Hughes-Stanton, Herbert Edwin Pelham 1870–1937
The Path to the Village 1911
oil on canvas 45.7 x 61
73.291

Hunter, George Leslie 1879–1931
Still Life with a Wine Bottle, a Glass, Fruit and Flowers
oil on canvas 43 x 53.5
73.558

Hutchison, Robert Gemmell 1855–1936
Interior with an Old Woman at a Hearth
oil on canvas 61 x 50.8
73.534

Hutchison, Robert Gemmell 1855–1936
On the Bents, Carnoustie
oil on board 42.6 x 58.4
73.506

Hutchison, Robert Gemmell 1855–1936
The Goldfish Bowl
oil on canvas 61 x 50.8
73.605

Italian (Florentine) School
Angel of the Annunciation
oil on canvas 63 x 59.7
73.504

Italian (Venetian) School
Grand Canal, Venice
oil on canvas 34.3 x 50.8
73.17

Jurnet, F. active 1850–1857
A Donkey and Cattle at a Pool 1857
oil on canvas 68.6 x 101.6
73.103

Jurnet, F. (attributed to) active 1850–1857
Cattle and Sheep
oil on canvas 81.3 x 127
73.101

Keyser, Thomas de (attributed to) 1596–1667
Portrait of a Man
oil on canvas 90.8 x 69.9
73.19

Knoop, M.
An Old Woman Reading
oil on panel 26.7 x 20.8
73.508

Lambinet, Emile Charles 1815–1877
French River Landscape with Cattle Grazing
oil on canvas 29 x 46.2
73.29

Lamorinière, Jean Pierre François 1828–1911
The Pools, near Antwerp
oil on panel 21 x 36.2
73.516

Lampi, Giuseppe
Czarina Catherine the Great (1729–1796)
18th C
oil on canvas 110.5 x 88.9
73.16

Landseer, Edwin Henry 1802–1873
Head of 'Driver', a Deerhound Owned by the 5th Duke of Gordon
oil on canvas 39.4 x 29.2
73.26

Loiseau, Gustave 1865–1935
Snow at Saint-Ouen-l'Aumône 1908
oil on canvas 49 x 60.5
73.264

Loiseau, Gustave 1865–1935
Printemps à Vaudreuil 1909
oil on canvas 58.5 x 71.5
73.265

Luce, Maximilien 1858–1941
Spring, Trees in a Landscape 1905
oil on board 20 x 26.3
73.556

MacTaggart, William 1903–1981
Evening, Oslofjord
oil on board 40.6 x 50.8
73.55

Marquet, Albert 1875–1947
Toits à Venise
oil on panel 34.3 x 40.6
73.552

Martin, David 1736–1798
James Brodie (1744–1824), 21st Laird
1785/1795
oil on canvas 74.9 x 62.2
73.49

Martin, David (circle of) 1736–1798
Portrait of a Woman and Her Child
oil on canvas 73.7 x 61
73.1

McCulloch, Horatio 1805–1867
Coastal Landscape with a Castle at Sunset
1850
oil on panel 27.3 x 41.3
73.293

McKay, William Darling 1844–1924
Landscape, Harrowing
oil on canvas 26.2 x 36
73.509

Medina, John (circle of) 1720–1796
David Petty
oil on canvas 124.5 x 99.1
73.7

Michel, Georges 1763–1843
The Gathering Storm (Landscape with Quarry and Figures)
oil on canvas 46.5 x 56
73.296

Mieris the elder, Frans van (after) 1635–1681
Violinist 1660
oil on panel 28.6 x 21.6
73.21

Munro, Mary
A Highland Estuary 1977
oil on board 21.5 x 26.5
73.753

Musscher, Michiel van (circle of) 1645–1705
Portrait of a Lady
oil on canvas 51.4 x 40.6
73.106.2

Musscher, Michiel van (circle of) 1645–1705
Portrait of a Man
oil on canvas 51.4 x 40.6
73.106.1

Nash, John Northcote 1893–1977
The Farm
oil on canvas 115.6 x 154.9
73.533

Neeffs the elder, Peeter 1578–1656
A Cathedral Interior 1657 (?)
oil on panel 15.5 x 21.6
73.309

Nevinson, Christopher 1889–1946
Fishermen on the Seine 1939
oil on panel 38 x 28
73.557

Nicholls, Bertram 1883–1974
Pitigliano 1926
oil on board 26 x 25.4
73.3

Nicholls, Bertram 1883–1974
A Mountain Village 1937
oil on canvas 29.8 x 34.3
73.331

Nicholls, Bertram 1883–1974
Philippe le Bel's Tower
oil on canvas 39.4 x 31.8
73.32

Nicholson, William 1872–1949
The Paper Poppies 1919
oil on board 40.8 x 32.8
73.518

Northcote, James (attributed to) 1746–1831
Ann, Wife of James Brodie, and Her Son, presumably William (1799–1873), Later 22nd Laird
oil on canvas 75.6 x 64.1
73.56

Facing page: Coypel, Antoine, 1661–1722, *Leda and the Swan*, The National Trust for Scotland, Brodie Castle (p. 214)

O'Connor, James Arthur (attributed to) 1792–1841
A Classical Landscape
oil on panel 48.3 x 41.9
73.95

Olsson, Albert Julius 1864–1942
Moonlight on the Coast
oil on board 36 x 45
73.519

Opie, John 1761–1807
James Brodie (1769–1802), Son of the 21st Laird
oil on canvas 71.8 x 58.4
73.54

Opie, John 1761–1807
William Brodie (1799–1873), Later 22nd Laird, with His Brothers, Sisters and a Dog
oil on canvas 208.3 x 180.3
73.94

Ostade, Adriaen van (circle of) 1610–1685
A Toper
oil on panel 15.9 x 14
73.24

Padwick, Philip Hugh 1876–1958
Distant Hills
oil on board 44.5 x 59.8
73.301

Pavy, Philippe 1860–1930
A Street Scene in Malaga with a Child and Donkeys 1891
oil on canvas 17 x 23
73.505

Peploe, Samuel John 1871–1935
Douglas Hall 1918
oil on panel 31.5 x 39.5
73.548

Phillips, Charles (attributed to) 1708–1748
Alexander (Sandy) Brodie (1741–1759), Later 20th Laird, as a Child with a Dog
oil on canvas 35.6 x 29.2
73.67

Pickenoy, Nicolaes Eliasz. 1588–1655
Portrait of a Lady 1631/1632
oil on panel 50.8 x 42.5
73.88.1

Pickenoy, Nicolaes Eliasz. 1588–1655
Portrait of a Man 1631/1632
oil on panel 50.8 x 42.5
73.88.2b

Poelenburgh, Cornelis van 1594–1667
Tobias with the Angel
oil on panel 21.6 x 29.2
73.82.2

Poelenburgh, Cornelis van (circle of) 1594–1667
Nymphs Bathing in a Classical Landscape
oil on panel 17.8 x 27.9
73.82.1

Poelenburgh, Cornelis van (circle of) 1594–1667
The Crucifixion, with Castel Sant'Angelo
oil on panel 26.7 x 19.7
73.64

Pritchett, Edward active c.1828–1879
The Dogana and Santa Maria della Salute, Venice
oil on canvas 23.5 x 34.3
73.332

Quinn, James Peter 1869–1951
Fish Market at Étaples, France
oil on canvas 56 x 40.5
73.501

Ramsay, Allan (after) 1713–1784
Alexander Brodie (1697–1754), 19th Laird, Lord Lyon early 20th C
oil on canvas 76.2 x 63.5
73.55

Reid, George 1841–1913
Loch Spynie with a Figure Wildfowling
oil on canvas 43.5 x 84.3
73.297

Richardson the elder, Jonathan (attributed to) 1664–1745
Portrait of a Lady
oil on canvas 127 x 99.1
73.108

Roberts, David (follower of) 1796–1864
The Cathedral, Mainz 1848
oil on panel 48.9 x 73.7
73.31

Romney, George (after) 1734–1802
Jane (1749–1812), Duchess of Gordon, and Her Son, George (1770–1836)
oil on canvas 127 x 101.6
73.104

Rosa, Salvator (circle of) 1615–1673
Figures in an Upland Classical Landscape
oil on canvas 20.3 x 44.5
73.14

S., R.
Daffodils
oil on canvas
T4454

Saedeleer, Valerius de 1867–1941
Printemps 1938
oil on canvas 25.5 x 35
73.531

Schoevaerdts, Mathys 1665–1723
An Extensive River Landscape with a Travelling Theatrical Troupe
oil on copper 49.5 x 67.3
73.9

Schutz, J. A. H.
Banditti Attacking a Coach
oil on panel 26.7 x 33
73.84.1

Schutz, J. A. H.
Banditti Dividing Their Spoil
oil on panel 26.7 x 33
73.84.2

Serres, John Thomas 1759–1825
Fishing Boat at Fulham 1780
oil on panel 31.8 x 38.1
73.18

Shields, Harry Gordon 1859–1935
Still Life, Pompom Dahlias
oil on board 46 x 50
73.515

Smart, John 1838–1899
Highland Cattle in a Cornfield 1878
oil on panel 15.5 x 23
73.502

Smith, Colvin (circle of) 1795–1875
George (1770–1836), 5th Duke of Gordon
c.1800
oil on panel 44 x 36.8
73.622

Spanish School
Saint Lawrence c.1650
oil on canvas 101.6 x 81.3
73.98

Steelink II, Willem 1856–1928
Changing Pastures
oil on canvas 30.4 x 48
73.149

Stevens, Alfred Emile Léopold Joseph Victor 1823–1906
Fishing Boats at Dusk
oil on panel 31 x 22
73.511

Sustermans, Justus (circle of) 1597–1681
Portrait of a Woman
oil on copper 11.4 x 8.9
73.66

Teniers II, David (after) 1610–1690
The Alchemist
oil on copper 27.9 x 22.2
73.80.2

Teniers II, David (after) 1610–1690
The Dentist
oil on copper 27.9 x 22.2
73.80.2a

Thaulow, Fritz (attributed to) 1847–1906
Watermill
oil on panel 29.5 x 39.5
73.5

Thomson, John 1778–1840
Gorge with a Bridge (Bridge over a Ravine)
oil on panel 45.2 x 35
73.292

Thornton, Robert John 1763–1837
Project for a Ceiling
oil, chalk, pen & brown ink on paper 40.6 x 50.8
73.35

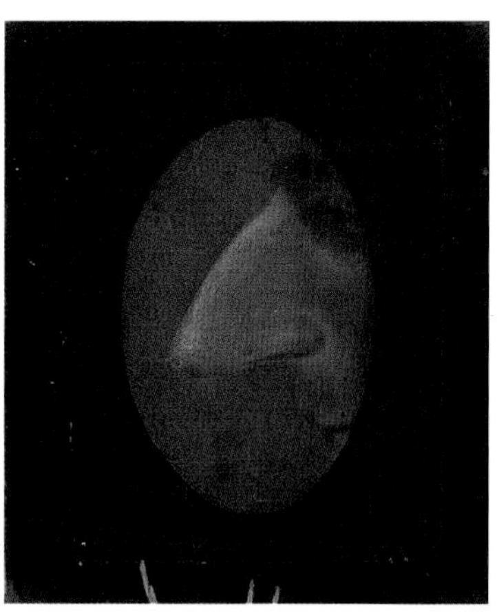

unknown artist
Caricature c.1850
oil on canvas 22.6 x 17
73.755

unknown artist
Portrait of a Lady in a Feigned Oval
oil on canvas
T4453

unknown artist
Portrait of a Woman in White
oil on panel
T4452

Vaillant, Wallerand 1623–1677
Young Artist 1656
oil on panel 35.6 x 43.2
73.2

Vincent, George 1796–1831
Woodland Road with a Horseman and Sheep
oil on panel 45.7 x 33
73.63

Vliet, Willem van der 1583–1642
Philosopher and His Pupils 1626
oil on panel 83.8 x 113
73.22

Vollon, Antoine 1833–1900
A Bowl of Fruit and Silver on a Table
oil on panel 22.9 x 17.8
73.23

Walker, Robert (style of) 1599–1658
Portrait of a Gentleman in Armour
oil on copper 18.4 x 14.6
73.79

Walls, William 1860–1942
A Leopard 1906
oil on canvas 45.9 x 61.3
73.574

Walls, William 1860–1942
Lion Cubs c.1906
oil on canvas 41 x 61.5
73.575

Ward, James 1769–1859
A Grey in a Stable 1812
oil on panel 45.7 x 58.4
73.74

Watteau, Jean-Antoine (follower of) 1684–1721
Fête champêtre: Music Party under an Awning
oil on panel 38.1 x 50.8
73.155

Watts, Frederick W. (circle of) 1800–1870
In the Meadows
oil on panel 15.9 x 23.5
73.298

Weiss, José 1859–1919
In Hampshire, a Landscape with Cottages
oil on panel 15.5 x 26
73.302.1

Weiss, José (attributed to) 1859–1919
A Wooded River Landscape in Winter
oil on panel 15.6 x 25.5
73.302.2

Wilkie, David 1785–1841
The Village School
oil on panel 50.8 x 64.8
73.603

Wintour, John Crawford 1825–1882
Wooded Riverscape at Sunset
oil on panel 33.7 x 28.6
73.8

Wood, Christopher 1901–1930
Gates in Paris
oil on board 68.6 x 88.9
73.523

Wouwerman, Philips (circle of) 1619–1668
Figures under a Tree
oil on panel 36.8 x 30.5
73.12

The National Trust for Scotland, Brodick Castle, Garden & Country Park

Brodick Castle, with its magnificent gardens and designed landscape, rises majestically above Brodick Bay on the Isle of Arran. Once owned and created by the Dukes of Hamilton, one of Scotland's grandest aristocratic families, the property derives much of its significance from this association. Brodick is the Trust's only Ducal property and this is reflected in the opulence of its decoration and the richness of its art collection (which includes the Beckford Collection). The collection as a whole is one of the finest to have come into Trust ownership.

Brodick Castle is of national importance for its architectural and archaeological interest. A seemingly large modern castle, this belies the castle's medieval origins and its complex developmental history. From its origins as a simple enclosure castle built for defensive purposes, the castle has been progressively transformed, through centuries of destruction, repair and enlargement and through the changing circumstances and aspirations of its owners into a large Victorian country house, fit for a princess.

Transformation of the exterior of Brodick Castle in the mid-nineteenth century, was matched by the transformation within. No Scottish architect of this period had a greater feeling for the design of dramatic interiors than Gillespie Graham and he reworked and created the interiors in a pioneering Scots Baronial style of the greatest quality, reflecting the princely status of the Dukes of Hamilton. The surviving original aspects, such as the outstanding plasterwork and the stairs, remain an exceptionally fine example of Scottish Baronial woodwork.

Gillespie Graham's grand interiors were furnished with both modern and antiquarian furnishings and works of art of the highest quality. From the Inventory of 1856 it is known that much of the furnishing remains in the same rooms today, increasing its importance and creating a very grand and unusually well preserved early Victorian ensemble. At the end of the nineteenth century and early twentieth century the collection continued to grow with the break-up of the Hamilton estates elsewhere and with Brodick becoming the beneficiary of a spectacular series of retrenchments and inheritance.

The collection created is one of extravagant richness, again a reflection of the Dukes of Hamilton's princely status and in terms of its quality and value it is the Trust's most exceptional collection. However, much of the charm of Brodick today lies in the low key and often homely way in which the Duke and Duchess of Montrose incorporated these family treasures and works of art that became available as a result of the retrenchments, into the castle. One notable aspect of the collection is that part of it from the Beckford collection, a collection of exceptional small scale objets de vertu, silver and porcelain, created by the extremely wealthy connoisseur, William Beckford of Fonthill, father-in-law to the 10th Duke of Hamilton.

Alken, Henry Thomas 1785–1851
The Dead Heat for the Doncaster St Leger, with 'Voltigeur' and 'Russborough' 1850
oil on panel 19 x 26.3
58.1.2

Alken, Henry Thomas 1785–1851
A Chestnut Racing with a Jockey Up, with Red Colours
oil on board 21.3 x 38.7
58.7.1

Alken, Henry Thomas 1785–1851
A Chestnut with the Jockey Up, with Green Colours
oil on board 21.3 x 29.2
58.7.2

Alken, Henry Thomas 1785–1851
Cockfighting
oil on panel 24.4 x 29.3
58.115.1

Alken, Henry Thomas 1785–1851
Cockfighting
oil on panel 24.6 x 29.4
58.115.2

Alken, Henry Thomas 1785–1851
Fighting Cock in a Landscape
oil on paper on canvas 49 x 35.6
58.118

Alken, Henry Thomas 1785–1851
The Doncaster Cup, 1858, with 'Voltigeur' and 'The Flying Dutchman'
oil on panel 19.2 x 26.6
58.1.1

Alken, Henry Thomas 1785–1851
The Meet
oil on canvas 29.2 x 38.7
2012.514

Alken, Samuel Henry 1810–1894
'Ossian', Winner of the Doncaster St Leger 1883
oil on board 27 x 19.5
2010.1883

Facing page: Master of the Female Half-Lengths, active c.1525–1550, *The Magdalene Reading*, The National Trust for Scotland, Brodick Castle, Garden & Country Park (p. 245)

Balmer, George 1805–1846
On the Coast of Fife
oil on panel 20.4 x 45.7
2009.535

Bardwell, Thomas 1704–1767
Portrait of a Lady (possibly of the Nassau de Zuylestein family) 1735
oil on canvas 73 x 60.4
2009.568

Bardwell, Thomas 1704–1767
William Henry Nassau de Zuylestein (1717–1781), 4th Earl of Rochford 1741
oil on canvas 161.2 x 212
58.19

Bell, Edward
On the Road to Port Patrick, near Maybole
oil on panel 9.1 x 23
2009.534

Bellangé, Hippolyte 1800–1866
Comrades 1861
oil on canvas 123.5 x 172.1
58.13

Berchem, Nicolaes Pietersz. (follower of) 1620–1683
A Woman with Cattle and Sheep
oil on panel 16.5 x 22.4
2009.541

Beul, Henri de 1845–1900
Chickens in a Farmyard 1896
oil on panel 26.7 x 41.9
2010.1877

Bravell, Rospar
Michael McCarfrae (1820–1876), Piper to the 11th Duke of Hamilton 1852
oil on canvas 140.9 x 111.7
58.3 (P)

Breenbergh, Bartholomeus (circle of) 1598–1657
Classical Ruins with Figures
oil on copper 15.3 x 21.6
2009.572

British (English) School
The Fight between Jackson and Mendoza at Hornchurch, 1795 1795
oil on canvas 79 x 91.2
58.103

British (English) School
'Nimrod' in at the Death c.1820
oil on canvas 39.4 x 53.3
2010.1896

British (English) School
The Old Front Door, Brodick Castle 1851
oil on canvas 102.8 x 126.5
58.91

Buckner, Richard 1812–1883
William (1845–1893), 12th Duke of Hamilton, as a Boy
oil on canvas 182.8 x 119.3
58.6

Buckner, Richard 1812–1883
William Alexander (1811–1863), 11th Duke of Hamilton
oil on canvas 75 x 62.1
58.9

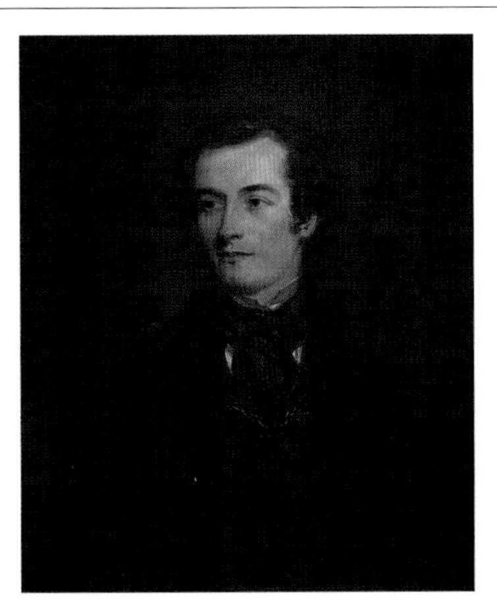

Buckner, Richard (attributed to) 1812–1883
William Alexander (1811–1863), 11th Duke of Hamilton
oil on canvas 73 x 61
2009.562

Chalon, Henry Bernard 1771–1849
Boy with Three Bullmastiffs 1834
oil on panel 17.1 x 22.3
2010.1886.1

Chalon, Henry Bernard 1771–1849
Three Terriers with Two Dead Rats
oil on panel 17 x 20.2
2010.1886.2

Clouet, François 1515–1572
Charles IX of France (1550–1574) 1569
oil on panel 35.5 x 25.4
2009.567

Cordrey, John 1765–1825
'Darnock' Beating 'Ledongheds' for the King's Plate at Newmarket
oil on canvas 16 x 25.2
2010.1879.2

Cordrey, John 1765–1825
'Gimcrack' Beating Two Other Horses at Epsom
oil on canvas 16 x 24.8
2010.1879.1

Dandridge, Bartholomew 1691–1754
William Henry Nassau de Zuylestein (1717–1781), 4th Earl of Rochford 1735
oil on canvas 123.2 x 100.3
58.112

Dou, Gerrit 1613–1675
Portrait of an Old Lady (The Painter's Aunt)
oil on panel 11.5 x 7.5
2009.53

Duval, John 1816–1892
'Friday' with Jockey on a Racecourse 1883
oil on canvas 49 x 69.2
2009.606

Duval, John 1816–1892
'Golden Pippin' in a Loosebox
oil on canvas 41.2 x 51.5
2010.1893

Duval, John 1816–1892
'Scot Guard', a Grey, with Jockey Up in a Landscape
oil on canvas 49.3 x 69.5
58.8

Dyck, Anthony van (after) 1599–1641
Frederick Henry, Prince of Orange (1584–1647), in Armour
oil on canvas 119.5 x 99
58.108

Dyck, Anthony van (after) 1599–1641
Countess Amalia of Solms (1602–1675), Wife of Frederick Henry, Prince of Orange
oil on canvas 117.2 x 97.8
58.11

Fielding, Anthony V. C. 1787–1855
Sailing Boat in Rough Seas off a Jetty 1831
oil on canvas 41.2 x 60.2
2009.527

Fragonard, Jean-Honoré (circle of) 1732–1806
Study of a Girl in a Brown Dress
oil on canvas 69.8 x 36.1
2009.525

Gainsborough, Thomas 1727–1788
Cattle Watering in a Stream
oil on linen 24.1 x 29.8
2009.54

Gainsborough, Thomas 1727–1788
Landscape with a Peasant Driving Cows
oil on linen 24.7 x 29.2
2009.533

Gainsborough, Thomas 1727–1788
Richard Savage Nassau de Zuylestein (1723–1780), Second Son of the 3rd Earl of Rochford
oil on canvas 124 x 98.4
58.18

Garrard, George 1760–1826
Equestrian Portrait of Douglas, 8th Duke of Hamilton and Brandon
oil on canvas 104.5 x 155
205.17

German School
Children with Sheep, Cattle and Goats Resting near a Town
oil on panel 30.3 x 39
2009.563.2

German School
Figures and Animals, with a Distant Ruined Roman Bridge
oil on panel 30 x 38.8
2009.563.1

Grant, Francis 1803–1878
Lady Susan Hamilton (d.1891), Daughter of Alexander, 10th Duke of Hamilton
oil on canvas 109.8 x 85.7
2009.565

Grant, Francis (attributed to) 1803–1878
Princess Marie of Baden (1817–1888), Daughter of Charles Louis Frederick, Prince of Baden
oil on canvas 123.8 x 98.4
58.499

Hall, Harry 1814–1896
Bay Racehorse with a Jockey on Newmarket Racecourse 1865
oil on canvas 57.2 x 75
2010.1894

Hall, Harry 1814–1896
'Lollypop' in a Loosebox
oil on canvas 41.9 x 52
2010.1887

Hanneman, Adriaen (after) 1601–1671
William Hamilton (1616–1650), KG, 2nd Duke of Hamilton
oil on canvas 127 x 101.6
2009.566

Hering, George Edwards 1805–1879
View of Brodick Bay 1857
oil on canvas 93.9 x 167.6
58.38

Herring I, John Frederick 1795–1865
The St Leger, 1826 1826
oil on canvas 34.3 x 59.7
2009.603

Herring I, John Frederick 1795–1865
'Mundig', Winner of the Derby, 1835 1835
oil on canvas 69.8 x 88.9
2009.61

Herring I, John Frederick 1795–1865
'Charles XII', Winner of the St Leger, 1839 1839
oil on canvas 59.8 x 68.7
2009.615

Herring I, John Frederick 1795–1865
Punchestown Steeplechase 1844
oil on canvas 104.1 x 210.8
2009.605 (P)

Herring I, John Frederick 1795–1865
The Derby, 1844: The Start 1844
oil on canvas 102.8 x 209.5
2009.604

Herring I, John Frederick 1795–1865
A Bay Racehorse in a Loosebox 1845
oil on canvas 36.8 x 49
2009.593

Herring I, John Frederick 1795–1865
The Race for the Emperor of Russia's Cup at Ascot, 1845 1845
oil on canvas 45.1 x 69.8
2009.612

Herring I, John Frederick 1795–1865
The Flying Dutchman' and 'Voltigeur' Running at York, 13 May 1851 1851
oil on canvas 45.1 x 69.8
2009.613

Herring I, John Frederick 1795–1865
'Mango', Winner of the St Leger, 1837
oil on canvas 53.1 x 73.4
2009.616

Herring I, John Frederick (attributed to) 1795–1865
'Fleur de Lys' Held by a Trainer on a Racecourse
oil on canvas 57.5 x 67.5
2009.594

Herring I, John Frederick (attributed to) 1795–1865
'The Baron', Winner of the St Leger, 1845
oil on canvas 33.8 x 48.7
2009.611

Herring II, John Frederick 1815–1907
A Farmyard Scene with Horses, Ducks and Poultry
oil on canvas 43.2 x 73.8
2009.537.1

Herring II, John Frederick 1815–1907
Workhorses in a Farmyard
oil on canvas 43 x 73.4
2009.537.2

Hoare, William 1707–1792
James (1703–1743), 5th Duke of Hamilton and 2nd Duke of Brandon
oil on canvas 73.6 x 61
2009.564.1

Hoare, William 1707–1792
Elizabeth Ann Spencer (d.1771), Wife of the 5th Duke of Hamilton
oil on canvas 73.6 x 61
2009.564.2

Italian (Bolognese) School
A Lady of the Pendelavi Family
oil on glass 6.5 x 5
2012.515

J., F. W.
Two Horses Finishing a Race 1891
oil on panel 17.5 x 24.8
2010.1892

Jacques, Charles Émile 1813–1894
Poultry in a Landscape 1861
oil on canvas 48.9 x 68.6
2010.1881

Jacques, Charles Émile 1813–1894
Shepherdess and Sheep in a Landscape 1871
oil on canvas 43.7 x 65.3
2010.1884

Jacques, Charles Émile 1813–1894
A Shepherd Boy and Sheep
oil on panel 16.4 x 23.2
2010.1882

Jacques, Charles Émile 1813–1894
Pigs and Poultry
oil on canvas 30.3 x 45.5
2010.1889

Jacques, Charles Émile 1813–1894
Pigs and Poultry Feeding
oil on canvas 36.8 x 53.2
2010.1888

Facing page: Neeffs the elder, Peeter, c.1578–1656/1661, *A Cathedral Interior*, 1657 (?), The National Trust for Scotland, Brodie Castle (p. 224)

Jacques, Charles Émile 1813–1894
Poultry in a Midden
oil on canvas 17 x 29.5
2010.188

Jacques, Charles Émile 1813–1894
Sheep and Poultry in a Barn
oil on panel 20.3 x 29.2
2010.1878

Jacques, Charles Émile 1813–1894
Three Sheep in a Barn
oil on canvas 21.1 x 32.4
2010.1876

Kauffmann, R.
Eleonora of Toledo (1522–1562), Grand Duchess of Tuscany, Aged 35
oil 6.5 x 6.5
2009.531

Kneller, Godfrey 1646–1723
Portrait of a Nobleman (said to be Frederick Nassau de Zuylestein, 1608–1672)
oil on canvas 123.4 x 100.3
58.114

Kneller, Godfrey (attributed to) 1646–1723
Portrait of a Nobleman (said to be Brigadier General William Nassau de Zuylestein, 1682–1710)
oil on canvas 125.4 x 100.6
58.92

László, Philip Alexius de 1869–1937
Lady Marie Louise Hamilton (1884–1957), Daughter of William, 10th Duke of Hamilton 1912
oil on canvas 213.3 x 137
2009.569

Lely, Peter (follower of) 1618–1680
Portrait of a Man in Black with a White Collar
oil on canvas 119.5 x 99
58.113

MacWhirter, John 1839–1911
River and Rocks c.1880–1900
oil on canvas
2010.1899

Maddox, Willes 1813–1853
William Beckford on His Deathbed 1844
oil on panel 28.3 x 36
58.17

Maddox, Willes 1813–1853
Alexander (1767–1852), 10th Duke of Hamilton 1852
oil on canvas 142.2 x 111.7
58.5.2

Maddox, Willes 1813–1853
Susan Euphemia Beckford (1786–1859), Duchess of Hamilton, Wife of Alexander, 10th Duke of Hamilton 1852
oil on canvas 142.2 x 111.7
58.5.1

Maganza, Alessandro (attributed to) 1556–1635
Christ Healing the Woman with an Issue of Blood 16th C
oil on copper 19.7 x 76.1
58.42

Martens, Henry 1790–1868
Glasgow Yeomanry at Exercise
oil on canvas 30.4 x 40.6
2010.1885

Master of the Female Half-Lengths active c.1525–1550
The Magdalene Reading
oil on panel 36.5 x 23.3
2009.57

Memling, Hans (after) 1430–1440
Portrait of a Young Man with His Hands Clasped in Prayer
oil on panel 27.9 x 21
58.43

Meulen, Adam Frans van der 1631–1690
Wooded Landscape with Horsemen and a Baggage Train on a Road
oil on panel 22 x 28.4
2009.554.2

Meulen, Adam Frans van der 1631–1690
Wooded Landscape with Horsemen on a Road
oil on panel 22 x 28.7
2009.554.1

Meytens, Martin van (circle of) 1695–1770
Portrait of a Young Man with a Dog
oil on canvas 74.3 x 61.5
2009.556

Morland, George 1763–1804
Lovers Observed
oil on canvas 44.5 x 55
2009.546

Moucheron, Frederick de 1633–1686
A Wooded Landscape with a Herdsman
oil on canvas 78.8 x 115.5
2009.558.2

Moucheron, Frederick de 1633–1686
A Wooded Scene with a Sportsman, His Dog and a Hawking Party
oil on canvas 78.8 x 115.5
2009.558.1

Nasmyth, Alexander 1758–1840
View of Edinburgh Castle
oil on canvas 44.5 x 60
2009.573

Neeffs the younger, Peeter 1620–1675
Interior of a Church
oil on copper 9.4 x 14.2
2009.552.2

Neeffs the younger, Peeter 1620–1675
Interior of St Bavo, Haarlem
oil on copper 8.6 x 13.3
2009.552.1

Palizzi, Giuseppe 1812–1888
A Shepherd Boy and Sheep
oil on panel 13.5 x 19
2009.542

Pickersgill, Henry William (attributed to) 1782–1875
The Marquess of Douglas (1811–1863), Later 11th Duke of Hamilton
oil on canvas 92 x 71.8
58.111

Poelenburgh, Cornelis van 1594–1667
Classical Ruins
oil on panel 8.6 x 13.3
2009.571

Poelenburgh, Cornelis van 1594–1667
Nymphs near a Pool
oil on panel 22 x 26.1
2009.553.1

Poelenburgh, Cornelis van 1594–1667
Nymphs near a Ruin
oil on panel 21.7 x 26.5
2009.553.2

Pollard, James 1792–1867
The St Albans Grand Steeplechase of 8 March, 1832 1832–1833
oil on canvas 30.1 x 62.8
58.3.1

Pollard, James 1792–1867
The St Albans Grand Steeplechase of 8 March, 1832 1832–1833
oil on canvas 29.8 x 42.3
58.3.2

Pollard, James 1792–1867
The St Albans Grand Steeplechase of 8 March, 1832 1832–1833
oil on canvas 29.9 x 43.1
58.3.3

Pollard, James 1792–1867
The St Albans Grand Steeplechase of 8 March, 1832 1832–1833
oil on canvas 30.2 x 43.1
58.3.4

Pollard, James 1792–1867
The St Albans Grand Steeplechase of 8 March, 1832 1832–1833
oil on canvas 30.1 x 42.7
58.3.5

Pollard, James 1792–1867
The St Albans Grand Steeplechase of 8 March, 1832 1832–1833
oil on canvas 30 x 42.8
58.3.6

Pratt, Hilton Lark 1838–1875
Fighting Cocks
oil on canvas 30 x 23.5
58.116.1

Pratt, Hilton Lark 1838–1875
Fighting Cocks
oil on canvas 30 x 23.5
58.116.2

Pratt, Hilton Lark 1838–1875
Fighting Cocks
oil on canvas 30 x 23.5
58.116.3

Pratt, Hilton Lark 1838–1875
Fighting Cocks
oil on canvas 30 x 23.5
58.116.4

Reinagle, H.
View on the Thames near Twickenham
oil on panel 12.7 x 16.5
2010.1895

Reinagle, H.
Wooded Landscape
oil on panel 8.8 x 12.3
2009.528

Reinagle, Ramsay Richard 1775–1862
William Warr Defeating William Wood at Navestock in Essex, 31 December, 1788 1790
oil on canvas 77.5 x 115.5
2009.597

Roberts, David 1796–1864
The Church of St Jacques, Dieppe 1826
oil on canvas 76.8 x 61
58.12

Rubens, Peter Paul (after) 1577–1640
Archduke Albert of Austria (1559–1621)
oil on panel 7.6 x 6.5
2009.538.1

Rubens, Peter Paul (after) 1577–1640
Archduchess Isabella (1566–1633)
oil on panel 7.6 x 6.5
2009.538.2

Sartorius, John Nost 1759–1828
The Oatlands Stakes, Ascot Heath, 28 June, 1791 1791
oil on canvas 38.6 x 53.3
2009.614

Sartorius, John Nost 1759–1828
The Second Year of the Derby Stakes at Epsom 1792
oil on canvas 40 x 53.4
2009.617

Sartorius, John Nost 1759–1828
A Huntsman and Three Hounds at the Edge of a Wood 1805
oil on canvas 68.7 x 87.6
58.1

Sartorius, John Nost 1759–1828
The Gold Cup, Epsom, May 1811 1811
oil on canvas 41.1 x 51.2
2009.596

Sartorius, John Nost (circle of) 1759–1828
A Fighting Cock in a Landscape
oil on canvas 56.5 x 47.5
58.119

Sartorius, John Nost (circle of) 1759–1828
Fox-Hunting
oil on panel 16 x 22.7
2010.1891

Scougall, David (attributed to) 1610–1680
Ann (1631–1716), Duchess of Hamilton, Daughter of James, 1st Duke of Hamilton
oil on canvas 111.7 x 92.7
58.44

Sell, Christian 1831–1883
Scenes in the Franco-Prussian War 1874
oil on panel 12.6 x 15.8
2010.1897.1

Sell, Christian 1831–1883
Scenes in the Franco-Prussian War 1874
oil on panel 12.6 x 15.8
2010.1897.2

Seymour, James (attributed to) 1702–1752
The Great Chaise Match, Newmarket, 1750
oil on canvas 91.4 x 135.8
2009.607

Spanish School
La marquesa de Santa Cruz (1763–1808), née Waldstein c.1800
oil on canvas 22.8 x 17.7
58.49

Stadler
Landscape
oil on porcelain or glass 11.5 x 11.5
58.57.3b

Stadler
Landscape with Cattle, Sheep and Peasants under Trees
oil on porcelain or glass
58.57.3

Stadler
Landscape with Peasant and Animals Watering
oil on porcelain or glass
58.57.1

Stadler
View of a Swiss Town (possibly Lucerne)
oil on porcelain or glass 17.2 x 21
58.56.2

Stadler
View of Geneva, with an Artist Sketching
oil on porcelain or glass 17.2 x 21
58.56.1

Steelink II, Willem 1856–1928
The Shepherd with His Flock
oil on canvas 44.4 x 33.6
2010.1903

Tasker, William H. (attributed to) 1808–1852
'Rhoda', a Bay Racehorse
oil on canvas 48 x 57.5
2009.608

Teniers II, David 1610–1690
A Landscape with Peasants before a Large Mansion
oil on panel 15.2 x 12
2009.543

Teniers II, David 1610–1690
The Temptation of Saint Anthony
oil on panel 24.8 x 18.5
58.15

Teniers II, David 1610–1690
Two Angels Holding a Shrine
oil on panel 38 x 30.5
58.45

Towne, Charles 1763–1840
Two Racehorses at a Starting Post 19th C
oil on panel 9.8 x 15
2010.1890.1

Towne, Charles (follower of) 1763–1840
Two Racehorses Neck and Neck 19th C
oil on panel 9.8 x 14.6
2010.1890.2

unknown artist
Carrisbrook Castle
oil & mother of pearl on panel
58.3079

unknown artist
Cottage Interior
oil on panel
58.174.2

unknown artist
Interior with Household Pets
oil on panel 44.5 x 44.5
58.174.1

unknown artist
'Painted', a Racehorse with Jockey Up in Harlequin Colours
oil on paper laid on card 21.9 x 33.7
58.117

Verelst, Maria 1680–1744
Elizabeth Gerrard (1682–1744)
oil on canvas 96 x 72
58.109

Vrancx, Sebastian 1573–1647
Landscape with Members of the House of Orange Returning from a Hunt
oil on canvas 113 x 232.41
58.16

Watteau, Jean-Antoine 1684–1721
L'aventurière
oil on copper 17.7 x 26
58.7018.2

Watteau, Jean-Antoine 1684–1721
L'enchanteur
oil on copper 17.7 x 26
58.7018.1

Wheatley, Francis 1747–1801
The Sportsman's Refreshment
oil on canvas 54.6 x 45.1
2009.539

Winterhalter, Franz Xaver 1805–1875
William Alexander (1845–1895), 12th Duke of Hamilton 1863
oil on canvas 62.8 x 38.7
2009.529

Wyck, Jan 1645–1700
The Battle of Larida, Spain
oil on canvas 83.7 x 119.3
58.11

Facing page: Critz the elder, John de, 1551/1552–1642, *James VI of Scotland and I of England (1566–1625)*, The National Trust for Scotland, Fyvie Castle (p. 85)

The National Trust for Scotland, Robert Burns Birthplace Museum

Robert Burns Birthplace Museum (RBBM) encompasses the birthplace of Scotland's national poet, and the setting for some of his best work, both in poetry and song. The museum is situated in the village of Alloway, two miles south of the town of Ayr in South Ayrshire. RBBM is also home to the world's most significant collection of artefacts which evoke and explain the life of Burns and the full breadth and power of his creativity; without this one collection we would know a very different Burns. In safeguarding and presenting these treasures, the museum's interpretive approach seeks to make Alloway – such a special place in the life of Burns – a place of inspiration for every visitor.

The landscape and landmarks of Alloway that shaped Burns and which he immortalised in his epic poem Tam o' Shanter, share with the collection a unique and intrinsic relationship to the person of Burns, and provide a relevant and fitting context for the interpretation of the collection and the story of Burns. With these tangible links to Burns, Alloway is the international epicentre for the interpretation of Burns's life and work, and RBBM has a major role in engaging people with Burns through heritage.

At the heart of the collection are 170 holograph letters and 140 poems in the hand of Burns; a large collection of personalia with intrinsic connections to the poet and his family; and an extensive library on the subject of Burns, including a comprehensive range of early editions of his work – the most complete set of the poet's published work known to exist. The collection covers the whole life of Burns, but is especially strong in representing the Burns family (notably the poet's mother, father and brother, Gilbert); Burns's correspondence, poems and songs composed in later life; and in the comprehensive printed commentary on, and analysis of, the poet since his death.

Having such a rich collection of manuscripts and art on display against the backdrop of landscapes and landmarks which inspired them, heightens the significance of that collection and adds visitor understanding and appreciation.

In 2007, the entire collection of the Burns Monument Trust (now the RBBM collection) was recognised by the Scottish Government as being of National Significance.

Auld, Patrick Campbell 1813–1866
The Burns Monument
oil on canvas 72.5 x 87
3.8136

Carse, Alexander 1770–1843
Poosie Nansie's Inn c.1820
oil on canvas 53.1 x 62.4
3.8037

Carse, Alexander 1770–1843
The Mauchline Holy Fair c.1830
oil on canvas 86 x 131
3.8028

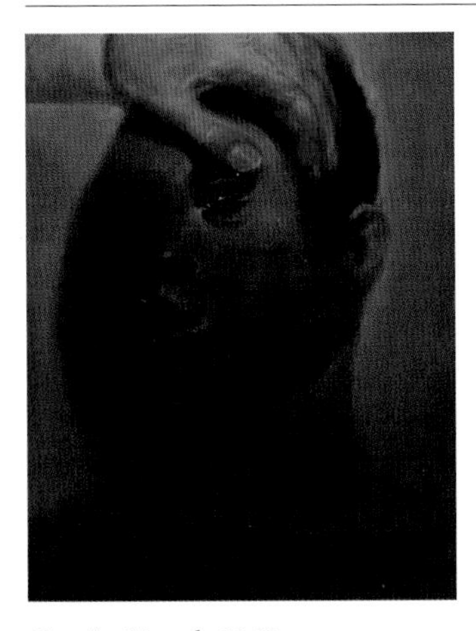

Currie, Ken b.1960
A Man's a Man
oil on board 20 x 15.5
2012.408 (P)

Drummond, John 1802–1889
Tam Pursu'd by the Witches c.1870
oil on canvas 45.6 x 56.2
3.8042

Fleming, John B. 1792–1845
Alloway Kirk from the East 1816
oil on canvas 31 x 42
3.8044

Fleming, John B. 1792–1845
Alloway Kirk from the West 1816
oil on canvas 31 x 42
3.8047

Fleming, John B. 1792–1845
Brig o' Doon 1816
oil on canvas 31 x 42
3.8046

Fleming, John B. 1792–1845
The Cottage 1816
oil on canvas 31 x 42
3.8045

Fraser, Alexander George 1786–1865
The Haggis Feast c.1840
oil on canvas 91.3 x 122
3.803

Hill, David Octavius 1802–1870
Burns Cottage, Interior
oil on board 28 x 43.5
3.8001

Lauder, Robert Scott 1803–1869
The Meeting of Burns and Captain Francis Grose
oil on canvas 40 x 60
3.8036

McIllwraith, William
Burns Cottage
oil on canvas 35.5 x 44
3.8172

McIllwraith, William
'Tam o' Shanter Inn'
oil on canvas 54.5 x 45
2011.829

Midwood, William Henry 1833–1888
The Betrothal of Burns and Highland Mary
c.1860
oil on canvas 91.8 x 71
3.8034

Nasmyth, Alexander (copy after) 1758–1840
Robert Burns (1759–1796) 19th C
oil on canvas 48 x 37.4
3.8354

Nasmyth, Alexander (copy after) 1758–1840
Robert Burns (1759–1796) 20th C
oil on canvas 36.2 x 26.6
3.8029

Nasmyth, Alexander (copy after) 1758–1840
Robert Burns (1759–1796)
oil on board 76.1 x 50.4
3.804

Nicol, Erskine 1825–1904
Tam o' Shanter
oil on canvas
3.8033 (P)

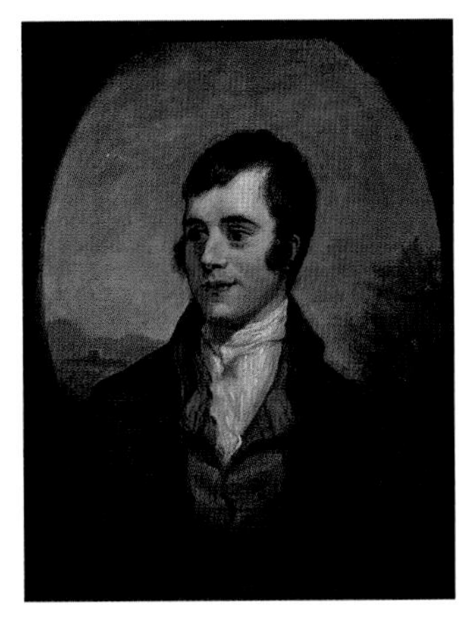

Penny, A. M.
Robert Burns (1759–1796) (after Alexander Nasmyth) 1823
oil on canvas 49.8 x 25.7
3.815

Roberts, David 1796–1864
The Brig o' Doon and Burns Monument 1862
oil on canvas 109.5 x 147.5
3.8031

Thomson, William Hill 1882–1956
Burns and His Brother
oil on canvas 60.5 x 61.2
2012.409 (P)

unknown artist
Alloway Auld Kirk with Arran in the Distance
oil on canvas 55 x 75.2
3.8342

unknown artist
Burns in a Cottage Scene
oil on board 39 x 49.5
3.8363

unknown artist
Burns in an Edinburgh Drawing Room
oil on canvas 45 x 59.5
3.8364

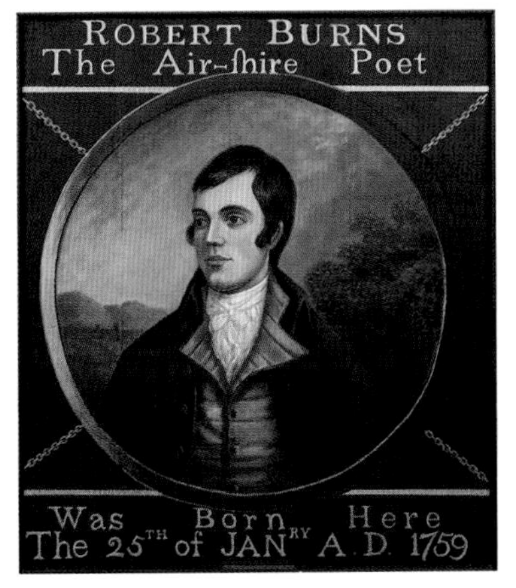

unknown artist
Robert Burns (pub sign)
oil on board 107 x 91.5
3.8617

unknown artist
Scene inside Burns Cottage
oil on canvas 45.6 x 61.1
3.8365

unknown artist
Tam o' Shanter over Brig o' Doon
oil on canvas 27 x 32
3.8171

unknown artist
The Auld Brig of Ayr
oil on canvas 44 x 60
3.8041

unknown artist
The Burns Monument and the 1844 Burns Festival Procession
oil on canvas 26.5 x 36.6
3.8032

unknown artist
The Cotter's Saturday Night
oil on canvas 39 x 59.5
3.8035

The National Trust for Scotland, Culzean Castle, Garden & Country Park

Located on the Ayrshire coast of the Firth of Clyde some 19 kilometres south of Ayr, Culzean comprises the core of the estate of the Kennedys of Cassillis. Its designed landscape surrounds the carefully selected cliff-top defensive site of a mediaeval tower that became Robert Adam's late masterwork Culzean Castle.

Culzean has long been acknowledged as the canonical Romantic Adam-style castle – its placement as well as its architectural qualities contribute to this. It is the best-known Scottish work of Scotland's most influential architect, and as such is of the highest national importance and can stand to represent the best of Scottish architecture on an international stage. The formal qualities of the design – the bravura of the seaward front, the complex geometry of the plan and elaborate Adam-designed interior – are the hallmarks of its architectural quality.

Aspects of the castle's complex developmental history remain incompletely understood. However, this does not prevent appreciation of either the significance of the pre-Adam structures, nor of Adam's brilliance in responding to the constraints of patron and site, finally overcoming both to be given a virtually free hand to complete his design. The nineteenth-century Wardrop and Reid additions are of considerable art-historical importance in a national context as the first use of an Adam revival style to adapt an Adam original.

Of the Adam interiors, the round saloon and oval stair are outstanding in terms of aesthetics and visitor experience. The subtleties of the interior fittings of original Adam work and subsequent Adam-revival phases are of great interest to architectural historians. The collections contain a few pieces surviving from the Adam castle – primarily mirrors and girandoles – which are of great importance. However, the majority of the collections acquired by the Trust date from the early nineteenth-century furnishing of the castle by the 1st Marquess of Ailsa with later introductions during the Adam-revival period of the late nineteenth century. Individual items of note among the picture collection include the long run of family portraits, the Batoni portrait, and the Nasmyth views of Culzean. The collection of flintlock pistols is now regarded as the most comprehensive outside Royal collections and is of high national importance in terms of the size of the collection and the mode of display, which makes an immediate impact upon visitors.

The 5th Marquess of Ailsa gave Culzean to the Trust in 1945, and at his request, the Trust, on behalf of a grateful nation, gave General Eisenhower lifetime use of the castle's top floor.

Alexander, Cosmo 1724–1772
John (1736–1806), 7th Earl of Galloway 1753
oil on canvas 76 x 63.5
202.88 (P)

Alexander, John 1686–1766
John (1736–1806), 7th Earl of Galloway 1755
oil on canvas 76.3 x 63.5 (E)
202.87 (P)

Batoni, Pompeo 1708–1787
Thomas Kennedy (d.1775), 9th Earl of Cassillis
oil on canvas 99 x 73.9
45.54

Boudin, Eugène Louis 1824–1898
Fishing Boats, Anvers 1871
oil on board 29 x 43
95.46

Boudin, Eugène Louis 1824–1898
Le Havre 1888
oil on board 37.5 x 48.8
73.181.1

Boudin, Eugène Louis 1824–1898
Fishing Boats
oil on board 33 x 41.5
73.181.2

Bright, Henry 1810–1873
Wolf's Crag
oil on canvas 61 x 91.5
50.1

British (English) School
A Man-of-War and Other Vessels at Sea
c.1750
oil on canvas 38.3 x 58.8
45.26 (P)

British (Scottish) School
Craigmillar Castle
oil on canvas 45.1 x 59.7
2010.2057

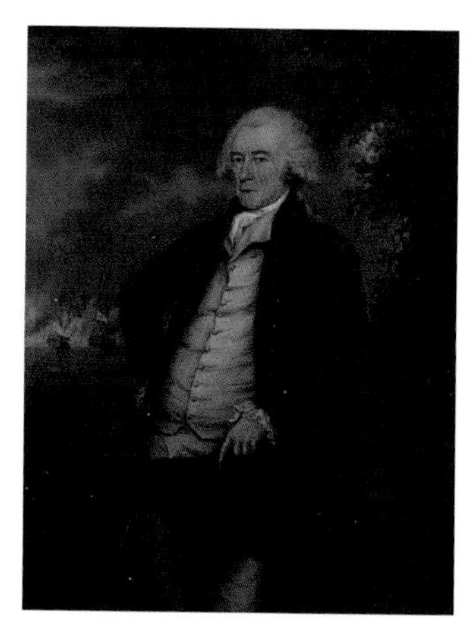

Brown, Mather 1761–1831
Captain the Honourable Archibald Kennedy (d.1794), 11th Earl of Cassillis
oil on canvas 126.4 x 101
45.50.1 (P)

Brown, Mather 1761–1831
Anne Watts (d.1793), Wife of the 11th Earl of Cassillis
oil on canvas 126.4 x 100.9
45.50.2 (P)

Callander, Adam 1750–1817
Views of Inverary 1781
oil on canvas 65.4 x 91.4
2010.2061.1

Callander, Adam 1750–1817
Views of Inverary 1781
oil on canvas 65.4 x 91.4
2010.2061.2

Cameron, David Young 1865–1945
View of Culzean Castle with Ailsa Craig in the Distance
oil on canvas 96.5 x 125.7
2010.2062

Canaletto (after) 1697–1768
A Regatta on the Grand Canal
oil on canvas 66.5 x 89.8
45.42.1 (P)

Canaletto (after) 1697–1768
The Mouth of the Grand Canal
oil on canvas 66.6 x 91.2
45.42.2 (P)

Colone, Adam de (circle of) 1572–1651
James VI and I (1566–1625) 1623
oil on canvas 77.8 x 53.4
45.57

Condy, Nicholas Matthew 1816–1851
The Queen's Barge off Osborne 1845
oil on panel 35.3 x 45.8
45.3

Dandridge, Bartholomew 1691–1754
William Cunninghame (d.1775), 13th Earl of Glencairn
oil on canvas 125.7 x 97.8
87.84.4 (P)

Daubigny, Karl 1846–1886
The Seashore
oil on canvas 31 x 64
50.11

Dayes, Edward 1763–1804
A Review on Woolwich Common 1800
oil on canvas 93.3 x 126.4
45.66

Deschamps, J.
A Patrician Family at Table
oil on canvas 108 x 139.5
45.16

Droochsloot, Cornelis 1630–1673
A Peasant Feast outside of an Inn
oil on panel 59.7 x 83.7
45.17 (P)

Dubbels, Hendrik Jacobsz. (circle of) 1621–1707
Fishing Vessels off a Beach, with a Man-of-War at Anchor
oil on panel 36.3 x 43
45.7

Dutch School
Men-of-War off a Town
oil on canvas on panel 32.8 x 47.7
45.4

Dyck, Anthony van 1599–1641
Lady Henrietta Stewart, Daughter of Alexander Stewart, 3rd Earl of Galloway, Wife of William, 12th Earl of Glencairn
oil on canvas 90.2 x 68.6
87.84.5 (P)

Dyck, Anthony van (after) 1599–1641
Portrait of a Cleric (said to be Alexander Henderson, 1583–1646)
oil on canvas 116.8 x 93.4
45.25

Eismann, Johann Anton 1608–1705
A Man-of-War and Other Vessels in a Calm
oil on canvas 18.5 x 28.5
45.59 (P)

Elliott, Thomas active c.1790–1800
HMS 'Victory' Leaving Portsmouth Harbour
oil on canvas 87.5 x 139
45.67 (P)

Ferneley I, John E. 1782–1860
Archibald (1794–1832), Lord Kennedy, Later Earl of Cassillis, on a Hunter 1819
oil on canvas 86.5 x 107
45.13

Fowles, Arthur Wellington 1815–1883
'Vanguard' and 'Foxhound' off the Longships 1870
oil on canvas 61 x 106.6
45.764

Goyen, Jan van (style of) 1596–1656
Sailing Barges and Fishermen off a Town
oil on canvas 47.4 x 62.8
2010.2041

Graves, Henry Richard 1818–1882
The Honourable Evelyn Stuart (d.1888), Daughter of the 12th Lord Blantyre and Wife of Archibald Kennedy, 3rd Marquess of Ailsa
oil on canvas 80 x 62.2
45.8 (P)

Hamilton, Gavin 1723–1798
Susanna Kennedy (1689–1780), Daughter of Sir Archibald Kennedy, 1st Bt of Culzean, 3rd Wife of Alexander Montgomery, (...)
oil on canvas 248.9 x 165.1
45.22 (P)

Hondecoeter, Melchior de (circle of) 1636–1695
Duck at a Pool and a Kingfisher on a Stump
oil on canvas 102.2 x 131.2
45.18 (P)

Huet I, Jean-Baptiste (circle of) 1745–1811
Shepherdesses with a Fortune-Teller by a Waterfall (after François Boucher)
oil on panel 38 x 29
45.6

Italian School
Putto beside a Chariot and Deer 1871–1872
oil on panel 20.3 x 27.9
45.56.11 (P)

Italian School
Putto Driving a Chariot Pulled by Deer 1871–1872
oil on panel 20.3 x 27.9
45.56.9 (P)

Italian School
Putto Falling off a Chariot Pulled by Two Swans 1871–1872
oil on panel 20.3 x 27.9
45.56.8 (P)

Italian School
Putto in a Chariot Drawn by Two Lions 1871–1872
oil on panel 20.3 x 27.9
45.56.5

Italian School
Putto in a Chariot Drawn by Two Swans 1871–1872
oil on panel 20.3 x 27.9
45.56.3

Italian School
Putto in a Chariot with Deer 1871–1872
oil on panel 20.3 x 27.9
45.56.1 (P)

Italian School
Putto Riding Goats 1871–1872
oil on panel 20.3 x 27.9
45.56.4

Italian School
Putto with a Hound Chasing a Hare 1871–1872
oil on panel 20.3 x 27.9
45.56.2

Italian School
Putto with Deer 1871–1872
oil on panel 20.3 x 27.9
45.56.10

Italian School
Winged Victory with Shield and Spear 1871–1872
oil on panel 27.9 x 20.3
45.56.7 (P)

Italian School
Woman with a Red Shawl 1871–1872
oil on panel 27.9 x 20.3
45.56.6 (P)

Lacroix, Charles François Grenier de 1700–1782
A Wreck on a Rocky Coast
oil on canvas 43.8 x 71.2
80.865

Lavery, John 1856–1941
Robert Bontine Cunninghame Graham of Ardoch (1852–1936), on His Argentinian Pony 1901
oil on canvas 45.7 x 40.6
207.2 (P)

Lefèvre, Robert 1755–1830
The Emperor Napoleon (1769–1821) 1813
oil on canvas 238.1 x 161.3
45.61 (P)

Louch, John
A Girl on a Woodland Path
oil on canvas 44.5 x 27.9
2010.2059

Luny, Thomas 1759–1837
HMS 'London', a Cutter, off Dover
oil on canvas 63.5 x 76.4
45.5 (P)

Lutyens, Charles Augustus Henry 1829–1915
Archibald Kennedy (1816–1870), 2nd Marquess of Ailsa 1864
oil on canvas 168.9 x 140
45.11 (P)

Lutyens, Charles Augustus Henry 1829–1915
Lord John Kennedy (1850–1895), Youngest Son of the 2nd Marquess of Ailsa, by the (...) 1864
oil on canvas 75 x 50 (E)
45.75

Macleay, Macneil 1806–1883
Castle Campbell
oil on panel 32.5 x 44.5
45.48

MacNee, Robert Russell 1880–1952
Bothy with Poultry
oil on canvas 40.6 x 50.8
2010.2058

Marshall, Benjamin 1768–1835
Archibald Kennedy (1770–1846), 12th Earl of Cassillis, Later 1st Marquess of Ailsa, Riding a Match from Culzean to Glasgow
oil on canvas 101.6 x 128.3
45.9

Martin, David 1736–1798
Nicol Graham of Gartmore (1695–1775) (after John Bogle) 1794
oil on canvas 127 x 101.6
87.84.3 (P)

Martin, David 1736–1798
John Cunninghame (1749–1796), 15th Earl of Glencairn
oil on canvas 83.8 x 71.7
87.84.8 (P)

Martin, David 1736–1798
Lady Margaret Cunninghame (d.1790), Eldest Daughter of William Earl of Glencairn, Wife of Nicol Graham of Gartmore
oil on canvas 121.9 x 99.1
87.84.2 (P)

Miller, William Edwards 1852–1934
Archibald Kennedy (1874–1943), 4th Marquess of Ailsa 1910
oil on canvas 157.5 x 106.7
45.12

Mitchell, William 1801–1900
A Trial Ordered by Vice Admiral Codrington, 31 July 1831, off the Dodman 1889
oil on canvas 45.5 x 65.5
45.68.1

Mitchell, William 1801–1900
A Trial Ordered by Vice Admiral Codrington, 31st July 1831, off the Dodman 1889
oil on canvas 45.3 x 65.5
45.68.2

Facing page: Hamilton, Gavin, 1723–1798, *Susanna Kennedy (1689–1780), Daughter of Sir Archibald Kennedy, 1st Bt of Culzean, 3rd Wife of Alexander Montgomery, 8th Earl of Eglinton*, The National Trust for Scotland, Culzean Castle, Garden & Country Park (p. 263)

Mosman, William 1700–1771
Thomas Kennedy (1733–1775), 9th Earl of Cassillis 1746
oil on canvas 240.5 x 147.6
45.4 (P)

Nasmyth, Alexander 1758–1840
Culzean Castle from the North with Ailsa Craig c.1816
oil on canvas 147.3 x 216.5
45.53

Nasmyth, Alexander 1758–1840
Culzean Castle from the Sea c.1816
oil on canvas 148 x 217
45.52

Nasmyth, Alexander 1758–1840
A Wooded River Landscape
oil on panel 28.7 x 40.5
45.55

Owen, William 1769–1825
Archibald Kennedy (1770–1846), 12th Earl of Cassillis, Later 1st Marquess of Ailsa 1816
oil on canvas 238.7 x 144.8
45.71.1

Owen, William 1769–1825
Margaret Erskine of Dun (c.1772–1848), Wife of the 12th Earl of Cassilis, Later 1st Marquess of Ailsa 1816
oil on canvas 238.7 x 144.8
45.71.2

Partridge, John 1789–1872
The Honourable Montgomerie Stewart (1780–1860), Fourth Son of the 7th Earl of Galloway 1847
oil on canvas 127.4 x 102
202.86 (P)

Pine, Robert Edge 1720–1788
Colonel John Graham of Kippen, Third Son of Nicol Graham of Gartmore
oil on canvas 124.5 x 97.8
87.84.6 (P)

Pine, Robert Edge 1720–1788
Simon Watson Taylor
oil on canvas 124.5 x 94.6
87.84.9 (P)

Pirman, L. E.
Daffodils in a Vase
oil on canvas 43.8 x 27.9
2010.206

Raeburn, Henry 1756–1823
Robert Graham of Gartmore (1735–1797)
oil on canvas 71.1 x 58.4
87.84.7 (P)

Ramsay, Allan 1713–1784
Queen Charlotte (1744–1818), in Her Coronation Robes
oil on canvas 254 x 177.8
201.114 (P)

Reynolds, Joshua (attributed to) 1723–1792
Robert Graham of Ardoch
oil on panel 73.7 x 60.9
207.1 (P)

Spruyt, Johannes 1627–1671
Duck and a Woodcock near Reeds, a Mere beyond
oil on canvas 87.5 x 115.7
45.19 (P)

Stannus, Anthony Carey 1830–1919
Archibald Kennedy (1847–1938), 3rd Marquess of Ailsa 1875
oil on canvas 134.6 x 96.5
45.767 (P)

unknown artist
A Swan
oil on panel 18.2 x 12.5
T4777

unknown artist
Apollo with Three Women, with a Crown, Book and Laurel Wreath
oil on panel 70 x 70 (E)
T4444

unknown artist
Female Figure with a Book, Gesturing
oil on panel 35 x 70 (E)
T4442

unknown artist
Female Figure with a Horn
oil on panel 35 x 70 (E)
T4443

unknown artist
Female Figure with a Lyre
oil on panel 35 x 70 (E)
T4441

unknown artist
Female Figure with a Lyre and Book
oil on panel 35 x 70 (E)
T4438

unknown artist
Female Figure with Compasses and an Orb
oil on panel 35 x 70 (E)
T4439

unknown artist
Female Figure with Compasses and a Tablet
oil on panel 35 x 70 (E)
T4440

unknown artist
Robert Burns (1759–1796)
oil on canvas 34.2 x 29
T4436

unknown artist
Shepherdess
oil on panel 13.5 x 10
T4437

unknown artist
Three Dancing Figures with Cymbals and Drums
oil on panel 80 x 80 (E)
T4434

unknown artist
Two Figures Dancing
oil on panel 50 x 50 (E)
T4433

unknown artist
Two Figures Dancing
oil on panel 50 x 50 (E)
T4435

unknown artist
Woman in a Hat
oil on panel 13.5 x 10
T4432

Vanson, Adrian (attributed to) 1540–1605
Sir Thomas Kennedy of Culzean (1543/1558–1602) c.1600
oil on canvas 201.2 x 89.5
45.21

Vernet, Claude-Joseph 1714–1789
A Rocky Coast with Survivors Being Retrieved from a Wreck
oil on canvas 88.9 x 132.8
88.142.1

Vos, Paul de (studio of) 1591–1678
The Lion and the Mouse
oil on canvas 160 x 228.5
45.1 (P)

Watt, George Fiddes 1873–1960
Archibald Kennedy (1847–1938), 3rd Marquess of Ailsa
oil on canvas 81.2 x 63.5
45.1 (P)

Watt, George Fiddes 1873–1960
Frances Stewart (d.1849), Wife of Archibald Kennedy, 4th Marquess of Ailsa
oil on canvas 68.6 x 55.9
45.14 (P)

Wild, Frank Percy 1861–1950
Archibald (1847–1938), 3rd Marquess of Ailsa 1901
oil on canvas 70 x 50
T4445

Wright, John Michael 1617–1694
John Kennedy (d.1701), 7th Earl of Cassillis
oil on canvas 74.9 x 59.7
45.47

Wright, John Michael (circle of) 1617–1694
Lady Susanna Hamilton (before 1638–1694), Daughter of James, 1st Duke of Hamilton, 1st Wife of John Kennedy, 7th Earl of Cassillis
oil on canvas 101.6 x 76.2
45.37

Wright, John Michael (circle of) 1617–1694
Margaret Hay (d.1695), Widow of Lord Kerr, 2nd Wife of John Kennedy, 7th Earl of Cassillis
oil on canvas 101.6 x 76.2
45.35 (P)

Wright, John Michael (circle of) 1617–1694
William Cunninghame (1610–1664), 9th Earl of Glencairn
oil on canvas 121.9 x 99
87.84.1 (P)

Zucchi, Antonio 1726–1796
Ceiling Roundel
oil on panel 100 x 100 (E)
2010.2042

Facing page: Batoni, Pompeo, 1708–1787, *Thomas Kennedy, 9th Earl of Cassillis*, The National Trust for Scotland, Culzean Castle, Garden & Country Park (p. 260)

Paintings Without Reproductions

This section lists all the paintings that have not been included in the main pages of the catalogue. They were excluded as it was not possible to photograph them for this project. Additional information relating to acquisition credit lines or loan details is also included. For this reason the information below is not repeated in the Further Information section.

The National Trust for Scotland, Falkland Palace & Garden

Crichton-Stuart, Frances b.1951, *Major Michael Crichton-Stuart Seated in the Drawing Room,* oil on canvas 90.5 x 37.5, 52.581, on loan from a private collection, image unavailable due to copyright restrictions

The National Trust for Scotland, Thomas Carlyle's Birthplace

Greaves, W. *Thomas Carlyle,* oil on canvas 30.5 x 35.6, T4476, not available at the time of photography

Millais, John Everett (copy after) 1829–1896, *Thomas Carlyle,* oil on canvas 38.1 x 33, T4477, not available at the time of photography

The National Trust for Scotland, The Georgian House

Moir, John (attributed to) 1776–1857, *James Graham of Airth,* oil on canvas 77.5 x 66.5, 203.25, bequeathed, not available at the time of photography

The National Trust for Scotland, Brodie Castle

Altenkirch, Otto 1875–1945, *Corn Stooks,* 1929, oil on canvas 66 x 78.5, 73.545, transferred, image unavailable due to copyright restrictions

The National Trust for Scotland, Castle Fraser, Garden & Estate

Miereveld, Michiel Jansz. van after 1567–1641, *Prince Maurice of Nassau,* oil on panel 25.5 x 20.25, 2012.405, stolen, 2009, not available at the time of photography

The National Trust for Scotland, Broughton House & Garden

Hornel, Edward Atkinson 1864–1933, *Sketch for 'The Butterfly',* 1897–1933, oil on canvas 101.5 x 122, 5.74, transferred, not available at the time of photography

Hornel, Edward Atkinson 1864–1933, *Two Girls Gathering Bluebells in a Woodland,* 1897–1933, oil on canvas 91.5 x 49, 5.64, transferred, not available at the time of photography

Hornel, Edward Atkinson 1864–1933, *Geisha Girls amongst Blossoms,* 1921–1925, oil on canvas 76 x 35.5, 5.52, transferred, not available at the time of photography

Hornel, Edward Atkinson 1864–1933, *Figures in a River,* c.1922, oil on canvas 56.5 x 182.9 (E), 5.136.1, transferred, not available at the time of photography

Hornel, Edward Atkinson 1864–1933, *Burmese Dancers,* 1922–1927, oil on canvas 101.5 x 76, 5.43, transferred, not available at the time of photography

Hornel, Edward Atkinson 1864–1933, *Two Burmese Maidens with a Green Parasol,* 1922–1927, oil on canvas 51 x 23, 5.5, transferred, not available at the time of photography

unknown artist *Shepherd with Cattle and Sheep on a Mountain Path,* oil on canvas 15.2 x 17.1, 5.93, transferred, not available at the time of photography

The National Trust for Scotland, Newhailes

Norie, James 1684–1757, *River Landscape with Figures,* oil on panel 96.5 x 94, 21.65, transferred, not available at the time of photography

Raeburn, Henry (follower of) 1756–1823, *Sir Adam Fergusson of Kilkerran,* 19th C, oil on canvas 76.2 x 63.5, 21.68, transferred, not available at the time of photography

Thomson, John 1778–1840, *Tantallon Castle,* oil on canvas 128.9 x 116.8, 21.1, transferred, not available at the time of photography

unknown artist *Christ Appearing in the Tomb,* oil on canvas 73.7 x 50.8, 21.69, transferred, not available at the time of photography

The National Trust for Scotland, Kellie Castle & Garden

unknown artist *Landscape,* oil on panel , 2010.2037.6, transferred, not available at the time of photography

unknown artist *Landscape,* oil on panel 49 x 126, 2010.2037.37, transferred, not available at the time of photography

unknown artist *Landscape,* oil on panel , 2010.2037.61, transferred, not available at the time of photography

Further Information

The paintings listed in this section have additional information relating to one or more of the five categories outlined below. This extra information is only provided where it is applicable and where it exists. Paintings listed in this section follow the same order as in the illustrated pages of the catalogue.

I The full name of the artist if this was too long to display in the illustrated pages of the catalogue. Such cases are marked in the catalogue with a (...).

II The full title of the painting if this was too long to display in the illustrated pages of the catalogue. Such cases are marked in the catalogue with a (...).

III Acquisition information or acquisition credit lines as well as information about loans, copied from the records of the owner collection.

IV Artist copyright credit lines where the copyright owner has been traced. Exhaustive efforts have been made to locate the copyright owners of all the images included within this catalogue and to meet their requirements. Any omissions or mistakes brought to our attention will be duly attended to and corrected in future publications.

V The credit line of the lender of the transparency if the transparency has been borrowed. Bridgeman images are available subject to any relevant copyright approvals from the Bridgeman Art Library at www.bridgemanart.com

The National Trust for Scotland, Craigievar Castle

British (Scottish) School *Sir John Forbes (1636–1703), 2nd Bt of Craigievar,* purchased
British (Scottish) School *Margaret (d.1683), Wife of Sir John Forbes, Daughter of Peter Young of Auldbar,* purchased
British (Scottish) School *Sir William Forbes (1660–1723), 3rd Bt of Craigievar,* purchased
British (Scottish) School *Portrait of an Officer,* purchased
British (Scottish) School *Dr John Forbes of Corse,* purchased
British (Scottish) School *Sir William Forbes (d.1648), 1st Bt of Craigievar,* purchased
Gordon, John Watson 1788–1864, *Charlotte Elizabeth (1801–1883), Wife of Sir John Forbes, 7th Bt of Craigievar, Daughter of the 18th Lord Forbes,* purchased
Gordon, John Watson 1788–1864, *Sir John Forbes (1785–1846), 7th Bt of Craigievar,* purchased
Jamesone, George 1588–1644, *Patrick Forbes of Corse (1564–1635), Bishop of Aberdeen,* purchased
Jamesone, George 1588–1644, *William Forbes of Menie and Craigievar (1566–1627),* purchased
Lawrence, Thomas (after) 1769–1830, *Elizabeth (1775–1830), Wife of the 17th Lord Forbes,* purchased
Lawrence, Thomas (after) 1769–1830, *James Ochonochar (1765–1843), 17th Lord Forbes (?),* purchased
Raeburn, Henry 1756–1823, *Sir William Forbes (1755–1816), 5th Bt of Craigievar,* purchased
Raeburn, Henry 1756–1823, *Sarah (1762–1799), Wife of Sir William Forbes, Daughter of John, 13th Lord Sempill,* purchased
Raeburn, Henry 1756–1823, *The Honourable Janet Sempill of Craigievar,* on loan from a private collection
Ramsay, Allan (follower of) 1713–1784, *Sir Arthur Forbes (1709–1773), 4th Bt of Craigievar,* purchased
Scougall, David 1610–1680, *Sir John Forbes (1636–1703), 2nd Bt of Craigievar,* purchased
Stuart, Gilbert 1755–1828, *Sir Arthur Forbes (1784–1823), 6th Bt of Craigievar,* purchased
unknown artist *Icon of the Virgin Mary,*
unknown artist *Icon of the Virgin Mary,*
unknown artist *Portrait of a Lady with a White Ruff,*
unknown artist *Portrait of a Man in Armour,*
unknown artist *Woman Seated on a Chair,*
Wild, Frank Percy 1861–1950, *Portrait of a Young Girl,* © the artist's estate
Wild, Frank Percy 1861–1950, *Sir John Forbes (1863–1934), 9th Bt of Craigievar and 18th Lord Sempill,* gift © the artist's estate

The National Trust for Scotland, Crathes Castle, Garden & Estate

Borsseler, Pieter (style of) style of, *active 1664–1687,* Gilbert Burnett (1643–1715), Bishop of Salisbury, on loan from the Burnett family
Brekelenkam, Quiringh van (circle of) circle of–1627, 1674, , A Girl Embroidering and a Youth Eating in an Interior, gift
British (Scottish) School , Robert (1661–1694), 3rd Viscount Arbuthnott, Brother of Dame Margaret Arbuthnott, gift
British (Scottish) School , Sir Alexander Burnett of Leys (1679–1758), 4th Bt and 16th Laird, gift
British (Scottish) School , William Burnett of Criggie (1638–1747), Son of Sir Thomas Burnett of Leys, 3rd Bt, gift
British (Scottish) School , Sir Thomas Burnett of Leys (1759–1783), 6th Bt and 18th Laird, gift
Dutch School , Topers in an Interior, bequeathed
Fraser, Alec C. , Sir Thomas Burnett (b.1586), gift
Grixoni, Mario –1879, 1946, , Sybil Crozier Smith (d.1960), Wife of Major General Sir James Lauderdale Gilbert Burnett of Leys, 13th Bt, gift, © the copyright holder
Holbein the younger, Hans (after) after–1497, 1543, , Erasmus (1466–1536), gift
Holbein the younger, Hans (after) after–1497, 1543, , Thomas Cromwell (c.1485–1540), gift
Horsburgh, John A. –1835, 1924, , Elizabeth Bannerman Burnett (1839–1877), gift
Italian School , Quartet Dancing Outside an Inn, gift
Jamesone, George –1588, 1644, , Alexander Skene of Skene (b.1590), gift
Jamesone, George –1588, 1644, , Janet Burnett, Sister of Sir Thomas Burnett of Leys, 1st Bt, and Wife of Alexander Skene of Skene, gift
Jamesone, George –1588, 1644, , Sir Thomas Burnett of Leys (1619–1653), 1st Bt and 13th Laird, gift
Jamesone, George (circle of) circle of–1588, 1644, , Jean Burnett, Daughter of Sir Thomas Burnett of Leys and Wife of Sir William Forbes of Monymusk, Bt, and Robert Comyne of Altyre, gift
Jamesone, George (circle of) circle of–1588, 1644, , Sir William Forbes of Monymusk (d.1654), Bt, Husband of Jane Burnett, gift
Kneller, Godfrey (circle of) circle of–1646, 1723, , Gilbert Burnett (1643–1715), Bishop of Salisbury, on loan from the Burnett family
Lander, John Saint-Helier –1869, 1944, , Major General Sir James Lauderdale Gilbert Burnett of Leys (1886–1953), 13th Bt, gift, © the copyright holder
Moir, John –1776, 1857, , Margaret Dalrymple Horn Elphinstone, Daughter of General Robert Dalrymple Horn Elphinstone of Logie Elphinstone and Wife of Sir Robert Burnett of Leys, gift
Scougal, John –1645, 1737, , Sir Thomas Burnett of Leys, 3rd Bt and 15th Laird, gift

The National Trust for Scotland, Mar Lodge Estate

Adams, A. Denovan active 1870s, *Homeward Bound, Glenlochy,* gift
Adams, A. Denovan active 1870s, *The Rivals,* gift
Alexander, Cosmo 1724–1772, *Elizabeth of York,* purchased
Alexander, Robert L. 1840–1923, *Head of a Deerhound,* bequeathed
Alexander, Robert L. 1840–1923, *A Bay Pony Sheltering,* bequeathed
Alexander, Robert L. 1840–1923, *A St Bernard Dog,* bequeathed
Anderson, Charles Goldsborough 1865–1936, *Portrait of a Gentleman with a Dog,*
Ashton, G. A. *A Spanish Girl,* (after Bartolomé Esteban Murillo), bequeathed
Barry, W. *A Tower House by a Loch,* bequeathed
Barry, W. *Ailsa Craig with Fishing Boats at Dusk,* bequeathed
British (English) School *Fishing Boats and Activities on Shore,* bequeathed
British (Scottish) School *A Gentleman in a Black Coat Holding an Open Letter,* gift

British (Scottish) School *Portrait of a Woman in a Black Dress Holding a Book,* gift
Craig, H. T. M. *Evening Cloud,* bequeathed © the copyright holder
Dozeman, Roelof b.1924, *The South of France,* bequeathed © the copyright holder
Dyck, Anthony van style of 1599–1641, *James Skene,* purchased
Evans, Treyer Meredith 1889–1958, *Miss D. Walker,* bequeathed © the copyright holder
Ewan, Frances 1891–1944, *Isobel (Portrait of a Young Girl),* © the copyright holder
Fergusson, D. *Cliad Beach, Isle of Coll,* bequeathed © the copyright holder
Ferneley I, John E. 1782–1860, *The Game Keeper's Larder,* purchased
Ferneley I, John E. 1782–1860, *The Game Keeper's Larder,* purchased
Ferneley I, John E. 1782–1860, *Solomon, Out of King David,* bequeathed
Giles, James 1801–1870, *The Honourable Mrs Gordon of Fyvie,* transferred
Gino *Beached Fishing Boats,* bequeathed © the copyright holder
Guarguetta possibly *Mexican Window Scene,* bequeathed
H., W. *A Lady Seated Wearing a Red Dress and Crocheting by Candlelight,* bequeathed
Hansford, Audrey Peagram active 1974–1979, *Mar Lodge Estate with the Dalvorer Ruins,* purchased © the copyright holder
Hansford, Audrey Peagram active 1974–1979, *Mar Lodge Estate with the River Lui and Derry,* purchased © the copyright holder
Hansford, Audrey Peagram active 1974–1979, *Mar Lodge Estate with the River Lui and Fairy Glen,* purchased © the copyright holder
Hansford, Audrey Peagram active 1974–1979, *Mar Lodge Estate, the River Geldie,* purchased © the copyright holder
Hansford, Audrey Peagram active 1974–1979, *Mar Lodge Estate, Bridge over the River Geldie,* purchased © the copyright holder
Hansford, Audrey Peagram active 1974–1979, *Mar Lodge Estate, the River Geldie Looking East,* purchased © the copyright holder
Hinchcliffe, P. *Culross Houses,* © the copyright holder
Inglis, R. *Landscape,* bequeathed
Italian School *Travellers Resting in a Landscape,* bequeathed
Law, Jean *Dahlias and Gladioli in a Stoneware Jug,* bequeathed
Leemput, Remi van after 1607–1675, *George Skene, of that Ilk, Aged 30,* purchased
Loose, Basile de 1809–1885, *The Connoisseur,* bequeathed
Lucas, Henry Frederick Lucas 1848–1943, *'Minting', a Bay Chaser,* bequeathed © the copyright holder
McCulloch, Horatio 1805–1867, *Landscape,*
Miereveld, Michiel Jansz. van after 1567–1641, *Alexander Skene,* purchased
Nicholson, Jim 1924–1996, *The Hills of Harris from Lusk,* bequeathed © the copyright holder
Peddie, George *A Village Landscape with Trees,* bequeathed
Pruser *Roses in a Pottery Vase,* bequeathed
Ramsay, Hugh 1877–1906, *Roses,*
Ritchie, C. S. *Lady Stewart,* gift
Robb, Lena 1891–1980, *White Rhododendrons in a Vase,* bequeathed © the copyright holder
Roe, Robert Henry attributed to 1793–1880, *Brighton Rivière, a Collie in a Highland Landscape,* purchased
Shirreff, J. B. *Portrait of a Gentleman,* (said to be Stewart of Banchory), gift
unknown artist *Beatrix Gordon,* bequeathed
unknown artist *Mrs Sayle,* gift
unknown artist *Captain Gordon, Master of the 'Queen Charlotte', off Algiers,* bequeathed
unknown artist *Portrait of a Gentleman of the Gordon of Abergeldie Family,* bequeathed
unknown artist *Portrait of a Seated Man,* (said to be Sir Stewart), gift
unknown artist *A Vase of Summer Flowers,* bequeathed
unknown artist *Lady Castlehill, Wife of Sir John, 4th Bt,* bequeathed
unknown artist *Landscape (River Estuary),* gift
unknown artist *Madonna della sedia,* (after a sixteenth-century Italian original), bequeathed
unknown artist *Portrait of a Gentleman,*
unknown artist *Portrait of a Gentleman in Morning Dress,*
unknown artist *Portrait of a Seated Man at a Desk with Papers,* gift
unknown artist *Portrait of a Woman,* (said to be Lady Stewart), gift
unknown artist *Portrait of a Woman with a Bonnet,*
unknown artist *Portrait of the Daughter of Lady Mary Kerr,* purchased
unknown artist *Sir Robert Sinclair, 9th Bt of Stevenson and Caithness,*
unknown artist *Skene of Skene,* purchased
unknown artist *The Brodie of Brodie with a Dog,*
unknown artist *The Mongols (Battlescene),* gift
unknown artist *Wooded Landscape,* gift
Weiler, Lina von 1830–1890, *William Forbes-Sempill, 17th Lord Sempill,*
Wheeler, Alfred 1851–1932, *'Bendigo' with Jockey,* bequeathed
Wheeler, John Arnold 1821–1903, *An Irish Setter, 'Dan',* bequeathed
Whiteford *Coast,* bequeathed © the copyright holder
Witz, Johannes van Pritzel *Girl with a Lace Shawl,* bequeathed
Wyllie, Aileen *Mrs Mona Grogan,* bequeathed

The National Trust for Scotland, Drum Castle, Garden & Estate

Alexander, Cosmo 1724–1772, *Alexander Irvine (d.1761), 17th Laird of Drum,* bequeathed
Alexander, Cosmo 1724–1772, *James Irvine of Altamford,* bequeathed
Alexander, Cosmo 1724–1772, *Mary Ogilvie, Wife of Alexander Irvine, 17th Laird of Drum,* bequeathed
Alexander, Cosmo 1724–1772, *Alexander Irvine,* (possibly 10th, 11th or 12th Laird of Drum), bequeathed
Alexander, Cosmo 1724–1772, *Charles Irvine, Brother of Alexander Irvine, 16th Laird of Drum,* bequeathed
Alexander, Cosmo 1724–1772, *Mrs James Irvine of Altamford,* bequeathed
Bough, Samuel 1822–1878, *Mountain Valley with a Drover,* bequeathed
Brandon, Louis E. active 1953–1958, *Henry Quentin Forbes Irvine (1908–1975), 24th Laird of Drum,* bequeathed © the copyright holder
British (Scottish) School *Portrait of a Gentleman in Armour,* (possibly one of the Campbell of Glenlyon family), bequeathed
British (Scottish) School *Portrait of a Gentleman in Armour,* (possibly John Campbell, 1636–1717, 1st Earl of Breadalbane), bequeathed
British (Scottish) School *Portrait of a Gentleman in Armour,* bequeathed
British (Scottish) School *Portrait of a Gentleman in Armour and a White Stock,* bequeathed, 1976
British (Scottish) School *Captain Robert Campbell of Glenlyon (1630–1696),* (copy after a seventeenth-century original), bequeathed
British (Scottish) School *Portrait of a Gentleman in a Dark Red Coat,* bequeathed
British (Scottish) School *Portrait of a Lady in a Red Dress,* bequeathed
British (Scottish) School *Portrait of a Lady in a Red Dress,* bequeathed
British (Scottish) School *Bathia Forbes, Wife of Gutcher,* bequeathed
British (Scottish) School *Lady Egidia Keith,* bequeathed
British (Scottish) School *Robert Campbell, 3rd Earl of Breadalbane,* bequeathed
British (Scottish) School *Jean Grant, Daughter of Sir Francis Grant,* bequeathed
British (Scottish) School *Mr Burnett of Elrick and Dalgety,* bequeathed
British School *Mrs Penelope Garden of Dalgety and Her Son,* bequeathed
British School *Margaret Hamilton (d.1855), Wife of Alexander Irvine, 19th Laird of Drum,* bequeathed
British School *A Girl with a Rake over Her Shoulder,* bequeathed
British (Scottish) School *Alexander Gordon, MP for Aberdeenshire,* bequeathed
British (Scottish) School *John Campbell of Glenlyon,* bequeathed
British (Scottish) School *View of Drum Castle with Cattle,* bequeathed
Carmichael, John Wilson (circle of) 1799–1868, *Dutch Vessels and a Man-of-War at Sea,* bequeathed
Chalmers, George 1720–1791, *Mary Irvine, Sister of Alexander Irvine, 16th Laird of Drum,* bequeathed
De Noter, Pierre-François 1779–1843, *A Canal in a Town,* bequeathed
Downes, Thomas Price active 1835–1887, *Mary Agnes Ramsay (b.1858), Daughter of John Ramsay of Banna and Wife of Francis Hugh Forbes Irvine, 21st Laird of Drum,* bequeathed
Dubois, Louis 1821–1869, *A Poser,* bequeathed
Dubois, Louis 1821–1869, *An Interesting Letter,* bequeathed
Dyck, Anthony van (circle of) 1599–1641, *Charles I (1600–1649), in Armour,* bequeathed
Giles, James (attributed to) 1801–1870, *Alexander Forbes Irvine (1777–1861), 19th Laird of Drum,* bequeathed
Graham-Gilbert, John 1794–1866, *James Irvine (d.1831),* bequeathed
Graham-Gilbert, John 1794–1866, *Ann Margaret Forbes Leslie, Wife of Alexander Forbes Irvine, 20th Laird of Drum,* bequeathed
Graham-Gilbert, John (attributed to) 1794–1866, *Alexander Forbes Irvine (1818–1892), 20th Laird of Drum,* bequeathed
Hamilton, Gavin (circle of) 1723–1798, *Woman with a Lyre,* bequeathed
Hollis, Charles T. 1855–1925, *Distant View of Windsor,* bequeathed
Howard, Henry 1769–1847, *Charles Irvine,* bequeathed
Howard, Henry 1769–1847, *Hugh Irvine, Son of Alexander Irvine, 16th Laird of Drum,* bequeathed
Irvine, Hugh 1783–1829, *Castle Gate, Aberdeen,* bequeathed
Irvine, Hugh 1783–1829, *Archangel Gabriel,* bequeathed
Irvine, James (attributed to) –1703, *Portrait of a Man,* (said to be James Irvine of Drum), bequeathed
Kettle, Tilly (circle of) 1735–1786, *Francis Garden (1721–1793), Lord Gardenstone,* bequeathed
Kettle, Tilly (circle of) 1735–1786, *Francis Garden (1721–1793), Lord Gardenstone, 5th of Troup, in His Kilt and Plaid,* bequeathed
Leslie, George Dunlop 1835–1921, *Washington Irving (1783–1859),* (after Charles Robert Leslie), bequeathed
Meder *Fruit Being Given to Children,* bequeathed
Moir, John 1776–1857, *Christina Irvine, Daughter of Alexander Irvine, 18th Laird of Drum,* bequeathed
Morland, George (style of) 1763–1804, *A Pastiche,* bequeathed
Mosman, William –1771, *Erminia after Imperiali with a View of Culter House in the Background,* on loan from James Holloway
Nasmyth, Alexander 1758–1840, *Stirling Castle,* bequeathed
Nasmyth, Alexander (circle of) 1758–1840, *Loch Katrine,* bequeathed
Nattier, Jean-Marc (after) 1685–1766, *Prince Charles Edward Stuart (1720–1788), in Armour,* bequeathed
Peters, Matthew William (circle of) 1742–1814, *Miss Bianca,* bequeathed
Raeburn, Henry 1756–1823, *James Hamilton,* bequeathed
Raeburn, Henry 1756–1823, *Mary Irvine, Daughter of Alexander Irvine, 16th Laird of Drum,* bequeathed
Raeburn, Henry (circle of) 1756–1823, *Francis Garden (1721–1793), Lord Gardenstone,* bequeathed
unknown artist *Landscape with a Large House,*
unknown artist *Portrait of a Lady,* bequeathed
unknown artist *Portrait of a Lady,* bequeathed
unknown artist *Portrait of a Man with a White Stock,*
unknown artist *Portrait of a Seated Lady,* bequeathed
unknown artist *Portrait of an Old Lady Spinning,* bequeathed
Verboeckhoven, Charles Louis 1802–1889, *Belgian Vessels in a Stiff Breeze,* bequeathed
W., F. *Woman with a Snowball,* bequeathed
Wright, John Michael (attributed to) 1617–1694, *Alexander or William, 11th Lord Forbes,* bequeathed

The National Trust for Scotland, Haddo House

Alexander, John 1686–1766, *Portrait of a Lady,* (said to be the Countess of Aberdeen, Mother of George, 4th Earl of Aberdeen), transferred
Allan, William 1782–1850, *Sir Walter Scott Dictating to His Daughter, Anne, in the Armoury at*

Abbotsford, transferred

Anglo/Dutch School & Monnoyer, Jean-Baptiste (1636-1699) *Sir William Lockhard of Lee*, transferred

Anglo/Dutch School & Monnoyer, Jean-Baptiste (1636-1699) *Lady Lockhart*, transferred

Aubrey, John 1909–1985, *June, Marchioness of Aberdeen*, on loan from a private collection © the copyright holder

Aubrey, John 1909–1985, *Saint John the Baptist with a Kneeling Knight of the Order of Saint John*, transferred © the copyright holder

Barnekow, Elizabeth *John, 1st Marquess of Aberdeen and Temair*, transferred © the copyright holder

Barnekow, Elizabeth *John, 1st Marquess of Aberdeen and Temair*, transferred © the copyright holder

Barnekow, Elizabeth *The Honourable Ishbel Marjoribanks, Later Wife of the 7th Earl of Aberdeen and 1st Marquess of Aberdeen and Temair*, (after A. E. Ellis), transferred © the copyright holder

Batoni, Pompeo 1708–1787, *George Gordon, Lord Haddo*, transferred

British (English) School *David, Earl of Devon*, transferred

British (Scottish) School *William, 2nd Earl of Aberdeen*, transferred

British (Scottish) School *Lady Anne Gordon, 3rd Wife of the 2nd Earl of Aberdeen, with Her Son, Alexander, Lord Rockville*, transferred

British (Scottish) School *Lady Anne Gordon*, on loan from a private collection

British (Scottish) School *Lady Jean Gordon, Aged 14*, on loan from a private collection

British School *Portrait of a Man, Aged 57*, (said to be James VI and I), transferred

British School *Cecile Elizabeth Gordon*, transferred

Brooke, Bryan active 1958–1979, *Stella Hamilton*, © the copyright holder

Canziani, Louisa Starr 1845–1909, *Two Little Home Rulers: The Honourable Dudley Gladstone Gordon and the Honourable Archie Gordon*, transferred

Carpenter, Margaret Sarah 1793–1872, *Lady Harriet Hamilton*, transferred

Carpenter, Margaret Sarah 1793–1872, *Mary, Lady Haddo*, transferred

Carpenter, Margaret Sarah 1793–1872, *The Honourable and Reverend Douglas Gordon*, transferred

Childers, Milly 1866–1922, *Dudley Gordon*, transferred

Custodis, Hieronymus (circle of) active c.1585–1598, *Portrait of a Gentleman, Aged 26*, transferred

Delaroche, Paul 1797–1856, *Francois-Pierre-Guillaume Guizot*, transferred

Domenichino (circle of) 1581–1641, *David with the Head of Goliath*, transferred

Donaldson, Gordon *David, 4th Marquess of Aberdeen*, transferred © the copyright holder

Dughet, Gaspard 1615–1675, *A Classical Landscape*, transferred

Dutch (The Hague) School *Portrait of an Officer*, transferred

Dutch School *Portrait of a Gentleman*, transferred

Dutch School *Portrait of a Lady*, transferred

Dyck, Anthony van 1599–1641, *Head of a Bearded Old Man*, (style of Paolo Veronese), transferred

Dyck, Anthony van (circle of) 1599–1641, *Charles I (1600–1649)*, transferred

Dyck, Anthony van (circle of) 1599–1641, *Henrietta Maria*, transferred

Eastman, Frank S. 1878–1964, *June, Marchioness of Aberdeen*, purchased © the copyright holder

Eaton, Wyatt 1849–1896, *Lady Marjorie Gordon*, transferred

Eaton, Wyatt 1849–1896, *The Honourable Archie Gordon*, transferred

Evans, Robert *Arthur Wellesley, 1st Duke of Wellington*, (after Thomas Lawrence), transferred

Fink, Wilhelm *Lady Marjorie Gordon*, transferred

Ford, Emily *Saint Christopher*, transferred © the copyright holder

Gascars, Henri 1634–1701, *Portrait of a Woman*, transferred

Giles, James 1801–1870, *The Interior of the Drawing Room at Haddo*, transferred

Giles, James 1801–1870, *Woodland Path with Figures*, transferred

Giles, James 1801–1870, *Moorland Landscape with Sportsman and Setter*, purchased, 1995

Giles, James 1801–1870, *Bridge over a River*, transferred

Giles, James 1801–1870, *Castle by a River*, transferred

Giles, James 1801–1870, *Deer Forest*, transferred

Giles, James 1801–1870, *Hagberry Pot, River Ythan*, transferred

Giles, James 1801–1870, *Stalking*, transferred

Giles, James 1801–1870, *Landscape*,

Giles, James 1801–1870, *Buchanness*, transferred

Giles, James 1801–1870, *The Monarch of the Glen*, transferred

Giles, James 1801–1870, *A Gun Room with George, 4th Earl of Aberdeen*, transferred

Giles, James 1801–1870, *A Lake at Haddo*, transferred

Giles, James 1801–1870, *Aberdeen from the South, with the Bridge of Dee*, transferred

Giles, James 1801–1870, *An Interior*, transferred

Giles, James 1801–1870, *An Interior at Haddo with George, 4th Earl of Aberdeen, Reading*, transferred

Giles, James 1801–1870, *Baillie George Hendry of Aberdeen*, gift

Giles, James 1801–1870, *Castle of Gight*, transferred

Giles, James 1801–1870, *Evening on the Findhorn*, transferred

Giles, James 1801–1870, *Gight, from below*, transferred

Giles, James 1801–1870, *Haddo: The Park Seen through the Open Drawing Room Door*, transferred

Giles, James 1801–1870, *On Deeside*, transferred

Giles, James 1801–1870, *Quarrying: Peterhead Quarry with a Lighthouse in the Background*, transferred

Giles, James 1801–1870, *The Findhorn from Heronry*, transferred

Giles, James 1801–1870, *Tolquhon Castle*, transferred

Giles, James 1801–1870, *Tolquhon Castle*, transferred

Giles, James 1801–1870, *View of a Scottish Castle*, transferred

Giles, James (after) 1801–1870, *Figures by a Palace*,

Giles, James (attributed to) 1801–1870, *A Sketch of Lord Haddo's Terrace*, transferred

Giles, James (attributed to) 1801–1870, *Landscape*,

Gordon, John Watson 1788–1864, *George, 4th Earl of Aberdeen*, transferred

Grainger *Farmyard Scene*, © the copyright holder

Haddo, George 1816–1864, *A Stormy Landscape with Classical Figures*, (after Gaspard Dughet), transferred

Haddo, George 1816–1864, *Lady Haddo*, transferred

Haddo, George 1816–1864, *View from St Leonard's Park*, transferred

Haddo, George 1816–1864, *Windsor Castle*, transferred

Haddo, George 1816–1864, *A Cathedral*, transferred

Haddo, George 1816–1864, *A Piebald Pheasant*, transferred

Haddo, George 1816–1864, *Hagar and the Angel*, (after Claude Lorrain), transferred

Haddo, George 1816–1864, *Mediterranean Coastal Landscape*, transferred

Haddo, George 1816–1864, *Sailing Barges*, transferred

Haddo, George 1816–1864, *Seascape from a Pillared Terrace*, transferred

Hambling, Harry 1902–1998, *The Blacksmith's Shop*, bequeathed © the artist's estate

Hambling, Maggi b.1945, *Archibald, 5th Marquess of Aberdeen and Temair*, bequeathed © the artist/Bridgeman Art Library

Hambling, Maggi b.1945, *River Scene*, © the artist/Bridgeman Art Library

Harris, Robert 1849–1919, *John, 7th Earl of Aberdeen, Later 1st Marquess, Montreal*, transferred

Harwood, Lucy 1893–1972, *Still Life, Fruit and Flowers on a Kitchen Table*, bequeathed © the copyright holder

Haynes, Edward Travanyon 1840–1922, *Gladstone*,

Hayter, George 1792–1871, *Ladies Alice, Jane and Caroline Gordon*, transferred

Hayter, George 1792–1871, *George John James, 5th Earl of Aberdeen*, transferred

Hayter, George 1792–1871, *Lady Alice Gordon*, transferred

Hayter, George 1792–1871, *Lady Caroline Gordon*, transferred

Hayter, George 1792–1871, *Lady Jane Gordon*, purchased, 1979

Heyl, Daniel *The Fire of London*, transferred

Hutchison, William Oliphant 1889–1970, *George, 2nd Marquis of Aberdeen*, transferred © the artist's estate

Innocenzo Francucci da Imola 1485–1548, *The Virgin*, transferred

Jangers, N. *Lady Marjorie Gordon*, transferred

Jangers, N. *'Monarch': Head of a Terrier*, transferred

Janssens van Ceulen, Cornelis (attributed to) 1593–1661, *Charles I (1600–1649)*, on loan from a private collection

Jehme, W. *A Nurse at a Sickbed*, transferred

Lawrence, Thomas (after) 1769–1830, *George, 4th Earl of Aberdeen*, transferred

Lawrence, Thomas (after) 1769–1830, *Harriet, 2nd Wife of the 4th Earl of Aberdeen*, transferred

Lawrence, Thomas (after) 1769–1830, *Lady Maria Hamilton*, transferred

Lawrence, Thomas (circle of) 1769–1830, *John James Stewart, 1st Marquess of Abercorn*, transferred

Lawrence, Thomas (circle of) 1769–1830, *Philip Kemble*, transferred

Lee, Frederick Richard 1798–1879, *On the Lochy, near Killin*, transferred

Lely, Peter (studio of) 1618–1680, *Charles II (1630–1685)*, transferred

Leslie, Charles Robert 1794–1859, *Dominie Sampson*, transferred

Lilley, E. *Country Scene*, © the copyright holder

Lockwood, Lucy active 1896–1934, *'Monarch': A Terrier*, transferred

Lorrain, Claude (attributed to) 1604–1682, *A Pastoral River Landscape with Fishermen*, transferred

Lucas, John 1807–1874, *The Honourable Arthur Gordon as a Boy*, transferred

Maratta, Carlo (circle of) 1625–1713, *Portrait of a Gentleman*, transferred

Marsh, Edward *Dudley, 3rd Marquess of Aberdeen*, transferred © the copyright holder

Medina, John (circle of) 1720–1796, *George, 1st Earl of Aberdeen*, transferred

Medina, John (circle of) 1720–1796, *John Murray, Duke of Atholl*, transferred

Miereveld, Michiel Jansz. van (circle of) 1567–1641, *Earl of Southampton*, transferred

Morales, Juan Francisco active 17th C, *Trompe L'oeil*, transferred

Morales, Juan Francisco active 17th C, *Trompe l'oeil*, purchased, 1979

Morris *Rural Cottage*,

Morris, Cedric Lockwood 1889–1982, *Coconut Gatherers*, transferred © trustees of the Cedric Lockwood Morris Estate/Foundation

Morris, Cedric Lockwood 1889–1982, *Lord Archie Gordon, Later 5th Marquess of Aberdeen*, transferred © trustees of the Cedric Lockwood Morris Estate/Foundation

Mosman, William 1700–1771, *Ann (1713–1791), Countess of Aberdeen, with Her Eldest Son, William*, transferred

Mosman, William 1700–1771, *Catherine, Wife of George, Lord Haddo, Later 3rd Earl of Aberdeen*, transferred

Mosman, William 1700–1771, *George, Lord Haddo, Later 3rd Earl of Aberdeen*, transferred

Murillo, Bartolomé Esteban (circle of) 1617–1682, *The Good Shepherd*, transferred

Neri, Pietro Martire 1596–1661, *Portrait of a Clerk*, transferred

Norie, James 1684–1757, *Landscape with a Bridge*,

Norie, James 1684–1757, *Landscape with Cattle*,

Norie, James 1684–1757, *Figures by a River**, transferred

Norie, James 1684–1757, *Fortified Building with Trees and Figures**, transferred

Norie, James 1684–1757, *Kneeling Figure by a Road**, transferred

Norie, James 1684–1757, *Landscape with a Lake and Building**,

Norie, James 1684–1757, *Landscape with a River and a Building**,

Norie, James 1684–1757, *Town by a River**, transferred

Panini, Giovanni Paolo (circle of) 1691–1765, *A Prison Interior*, transferred

Patten, George 1801–1865, *George Canning*, (after Thomas Lawrence), transferred

Patten, George 1801–1865, *Henry, 3rd Earl of Bathurst*, transferred

Patten, George 1801–1865, *Robert Stewart, Earl of Castlereagh*, transferred

Patten, George 1801–1865, *Sir Robert Peel, 2nd Bt*, (after Thomas Lawrence), transferred

Patten, George 1801–1865, *William Pitt the Younger*, (after Thomas Lawrence), transferred

Phillips, Thomas 1770–1845, *General the Honourable Sir Alexander Hamilton Gordon,* transferred
Puligo, Domenico 1492–1527, *Young Woman: La Fornarina,* transferred
R., E. T. *Landscape with Trees,*
Raeburn, Henry 1756–1823, *Jean Christie, 2nd Wife of the 4th Duke of Gordon,* on loan from a private collection
Reid, George 1841–1913, *William Cosmo Gordon of Fyvie, 2nd Earl of Aberdeen,* transferred
Reid, George 1841–1913, *Alexander Henry Gordon of Fyvie,* transferred
Reni, Guido (circle of) 1575–1642, *The Virgin Sewing,* transferred
Romagnoli, Angiolo 1826–1896, *The Visitation,* (after Mariotto Albertinelli), transferred
Rosa, Salvator 1615–1673, *Vanitas,* transferred
Russell, John Bucknell 1819–1893, *The Bear and the Beehives,* transferred
Russell, John Bucknell 1819–1893, *The Cat and the Mice,* transferred
Russell, John Bucknell 1819–1893, *The Crow and the Pot,* transferred
Russell, John Bucknell 1819–1893, *The Dog and the Piece of Flesh,* transferred
Russell, John Bucknell 1819–1893, *The Fighting Cocks and the Partridge,* transferred
Russell, John Bucknell 1819–1893, *The Fox and the Grapes,* transferred
Russell, John Bucknell 1819–1893, *The Goat and the Well,* transferred
Russell, John Bucknell 1819–1893, *The Parliament of Birds,* transferred
Russell, John Bucknell 1819–1893, *The Stag Looking into the Water,* transferred
Russell, John Bucknell 1819–1893, *The Tortoise and the Hare,* transferred
Russell, John Bucknell 1819–1893, *The Wolf and the Lamb,* transferred
Sant, George active 1856–1879, *Ishbel, Countess of Aberdeen,* transferred
Sant, George active 1856–1879, *John, 7th Earl of Aberdeen,* transferred
Smith-Burnet *Lady Catherine Gordon,* (after Henry Raeburn), on loan from a private collection
Smith-Burnet *Alexander, 4th Duke of Gordon,* (after Henry Raeburn), on loan from a private collection
Somer I, Paulus van (circle of) 1576–1621, *James VI and I (1566–1625),* transferred
Steel, Gourlay 1819–1894, *Old Pets at Haddo,* transferred
Syme, J. T. *Seascape,*
Thomson, John 1778–1840, *A Lake among Mountains with a Castle,* transferred
unknown artist *Portrait of a Woman,*
unknown artist *Corner of Terrace at Haddo,* transferred
unknown artist *Charles II (1630–1685),* on loan from a private collection
unknown artist *Cornish Coastal Scene,* bequeathed
unknown artist *Dianthus with Butterfly,* bequeathed
unknown artist *Heron Wading,* bequeathed
unknown artist *Landscape, River Scene,*
unknown artist *Parrots in a Forest Scene,*
unknown artist *Portrait of a Man,*
unknown artist *Portrait of a Priest,*
unknown artist *Rachel Emily Shaw Lefevre,* transferred
unknown artist *The Coast at Boddam,* transferred
unknown artist *Two Birds on Branches,*
unknown artist *Woman Reading by a Window,*
Veronese, Paolo (after) 1528–1588, *The Adoration of the Shepherds,* transferred
Vlieger, Simon de 1601–1653, *A Boat off Shore,* transferred
Vlieger, Simon de 1601–1653, *Fishing Boats off a Jetty,* transferred
Voet, Jakob Ferdinand (style of) 1639–1700, *Portrait of a Nobleman,* transferred
W., D. *Wood Anemones,* bequeathed
Waldorp, Antonie W. 1803–1866, *A Canal near The Hague,* transferred
Ward, Edwin Arthur 1859–1933, *John, 7th Earl of Aberdeen, 1st Marquess,* transferred
Wells, Henry Tanworth 1828–1903, *Katherine, Wife of the 6th Lord Burleigh,* transferred
Wilson, Derek *Willy Lot's Cottage, Drockwaters,* bequeathed © the copyright holder
Wissing, Willem (circle of) 1656–1687, *Queen Mary,* transferred
Wissing, Willem (studio of) 1656–1687, *Portrait of a Woman,* transferred

The National Trust for Scotland, Pitmedden Garden

Adam, Joseph Denovan 1841–1896, *Highland Cattle on a Moorland,* gift
Anrooy, Anton Abraham van 1870–1949, *An Interior with a Woman Reading,* gift © the copyright holder
Borthwick, Alfred Edward 1871–1955, *The Fugitive,* gift © the copyright holder
British (Scottish) School *Lake Scene,* gift
British (Scottish) School *Portrait of a Lady in a Black Dress,* gift
Elwell, Frederick William 1870–1958, *Beverley Minster from the Hall Garth,* gift © the copyright holder
Munro, Charles Binning 1840–1910, *Catterline from Dunnottar,* gift
Reid, Archibald David 1844–1908, *The Ythan Estuary,* gift
Reid, Stephen 1873–1948, *The Letter,* gift, 1988 © the copyright holder
unknown artist *Portrait of a Gentleman,* gift
Wright, E. *An East Coast Fishing Village,* gift

The National Trust for Scotland, The Hill House

Fergusson, John Duncan 1874–1961, *Elizabeth Dryden,* gift © The Fergusson Gallery, Perth and Kinross Council, Scotland
Henry, George 1858–1943, *Mrs Younger,* © the copyright holder
Mackintosh, Margaret Macdonald 1864–1933, *Sleeping Princess,* gift
Raeburn, Henry 1756–1823, *Walter Graham,* gift
Strain, Hilary 1884–1960, *Walter Blackie,* on loan from a private collection © the copyright holder
Torrance, James 1859–1916, *Mr Younger*

The National Trust for Scotland, Leith Hall Garden & Estate

Aiken, John MacDonald 1880–1961, *Charles O'Neill Leith-Hay of Rannes, Aged 14,* gift © the copyright holder
Aiken, John MacDonald 1880–1961, *The Honourable Henrietta O'Neill (d.1965), Wife of Charles Leith-Hay,* gift © the copyright holder
Anglo/Indian School *Nawab of Oudh,* gift
Anglo/Indian School *Sir Stapleton Cotton, Lord Combermere, Commander-in-Chief, India (1825–1830),* gift
Barclay, John MacLaren 1811–1886, *Colonel Alexander Sebastian Leith-Hay (1818–1900),* gift
Bassano II, Francesco 1549–1592, *The Element of Water,* gift
Berchem, Nicolaes Pietersz 1620–1683, *An Italianate Landscape with Herdsmen,* gift
Bird, William *Children in a Landscape,* gift
Bird, William *Children in a Landscape,* gift
Breun, John Ernest 1862–1921, *Charles Edward Norman Leith-Hay (1858–1939), of Leith Hall,* gift
British (English) School *Captain, Lord Cochrane (1775–1860), Later 10th Earl of Dundonald,* gift
British (English) School *Captain, Later Rear-Admiral, John Leith-Hay (1788–1854), RN,* gift
British (English) School *Fishing Boats in Rough Seas,* gift
British (English) School *John Leith of Leith Hall (c.1698–1736),* gift
British (English) School *Mary Hay of Rannes (c.1698–1736),* gift
British (Scottish) School *George Ross of Clachan and Colp,* gift
British (Scottish) School *Portrait of a Lady,* gift
British (Scottish) School *Chess Players,* gift
British (Scottish) School *Nicola Arbuthnot (1823–1874),* gift
British (Scottish) School *Elspeth Robertson, Wife of George Ross of Clachan and Colp,* gift
British (Scottish) School *Alexander Leith of Freefield,* gift
British (Scottish) School *Christina Howieson (d.1705),* gift
British (Scottish) School *Classical Ruins with a Rotunda,* gift
British (Scottish) School *Elizabeth Leith-Ross, Wife of David Souter Robertson, with Her Son Thomas Robertson,* gift
British (Scottish) School *Elizabeth Young of Bourtie (1782–1852),* gift
British (Scottish) School *John Ross of Arnage (1707–1789),* gift
British (Scottish) School *John Ross of Arnage (1707–1789),* gift
British (Scottish) School *John Ross of Clachan and Colp,* gift
British (Scottish) School *Lawrence Begg, a Cook,* gift
British (Scottish) School *Portrait of a Lady of Mar,* gift
British (Scottish) School *Portrait of a Man,* (said to be Lord Nisbet), gift
British (Scottish) School *Ross John Leith (1777–1839),* gift
British (Scottish) School *Walter Robertson,* gift
British (Scottish) School *William Stuart of Loanhead,* gift
British (Scottish) School *Woman with a Candle,* gift
British School *Portrait of a Gentleman,* gift
Cameron, J. D. Beauchamp *John Leith Ross,*
Cameron, J. D. Beauchamp *John Leith Ross,*
Chandler, John Westbrooke 1764–1807, *General Alexander Leith-Hay of Rannes and Leith Hay (1758–1838),* gift
Chandler, John Westbrooke 1764–1807, *Mary Forbes of Ballogie (d.1824), Wife of General Leith-Hay,* gift
Crespi, Giovanni Battista 1575–1632, *The Flight into Egypt,* gift
Dighton, Denis 1792–1827, *The Storming of San Sebastian,* gift
Dutch School *A Woman and Children in a Yard,* gift
French School *Romulus and Remus,* gift
Hay, J. E. *View of Leith Hall from the South East,* gift
Hayter, George 1792–1871, *Sir Andrew Leith-Hay, MP,* gift
Henry, John *Christian Leith-Ross,* gift
Howe, James 1780–1836, *John Anderson, Falconer to the Flemings of Barochan,* gift
Hughes, Edward Robert 1851–1914, *Charles Edward Leith-Hay Clark (1858–1939),* purchased
Italian School *Saint Peter,* gift
Italian School *The Adoration of the Shepherds,* gift
Kneller, Godfrey (circle of) 1646–1723, *Jean Ross (1683–1717), Wife of Sir David Ogilvie, 3rd Bt of Barras,* gift
Kneller, Godfrey (circle of) 1646–1723, *Portrait of a Man in Armour,* gift
Lawrence, Thomas 1769–1830, *Head of a Boy,* gift
Maes, Dirk (follower of) 1659–1717, *A Cavalry Skirmish,* gift
Medina, John 1720–1796, *John Ross (1664–1714),* gift
Moir, John 1776–1857, *Harriot Christian Leith-Hay (d.1830), Wife of Sir Harry N. Lumsden, Bt,* gift
Mosman, William 1700–1771, *Mary Hay of Rannes (d.1736), Wife of John Leith,* gift
Mura, Francesco de (circle of) 1696–1782, *Madonna and Child,* gift
Northcote, James 1746–1831, *Mary Margaret Clarke (d.1859), Wife of Sir Andrew Leith-Hay,* gift
Northern Italian School *The Holy Family with Saint Elizabeth and the Infant Saint John the Baptist,* gift
Opie, John 1761–1807, *A Girl with a Basket of Flowers,* gift
Raeburn, Henry 1756–1823, *Alexander Leith of Freeland,* gift
Ramsay, Allan 1713–1784, *Jean, Lady Banff,* gift
Ramsay, Allan 1713–1784, *Jane Nisbet, Lady Dirleton,* gift
Smith, Arthur 1814–1882, *A Frigate off a Rocky Coast,* gift
Smith, W. *Andrew Hay of Rannes (b.1713),* (after Henry Raeburn), gift
Smith, W. *John Leigh of Leith Hall (1731–1763),* gift
Smith, W. H. *Harriot Steuart of Auchlunchart, Wife of John Leith,* gift
Spanish School *A Praying Saint with Cherubim above,* gift
Stuart, Gilbert 1755–1828, *William Abercromby of Glasgow,* gift
Teniers II, David (attributed to) 1610–1690, *Peasants Merrymaking in a Courtyard,* gift
unknown artist *Portrait of a Boy,* gift
unknown artist *Admiral R. MacAlpine,* gift
unknown artist *Funerary Monument,* gift
unknown artist *Portrait of a Small Child,*
unknown artist *The Lute Player,*
unknown artist *William Leith Ross,*
Varley I, John 1778–1842, *View with Leith Hall,* bequeathed
Watson, George (after) 1767–1837, *Alexander Leith of Freefield,* gift

Weigall, Henry 1829–1925, *Christina Grace Agnes Hamilton (d.1897), Wife of Colonel Alexander Leith-Hay,* gift
Westmacott I, Richard 1775–1856, *Colonel Sir Andrew Leith-Hay (1785–1862), MP,* gift
Wouwerman, Philips 1619–1668, *Landscape with a Woodman Loading a Horse,* gift
Zuccarelli, Francesco 1702–1788, *Landscape with a Mill,* gift

The National Trust for Scotland, Castle Fraser, Garden & Estate

Anglo/Dutch School *Four Monks in an Interior,* gift
Beechey, William (after) 1753–1839, *General Francis Humberstone Mackenzie (1782–1815), 1st Lord Seaforth,* gift
Belle, Alexis-Simon (after) 1674–1734, *Prince James Edward Stuart (1688–1766),* gift
British (English) School *Portrait of a Man,* (said to be Prince Henry Frederick, 1592–1612, Prince of Orange),
British (Scottish) School *Portrait of an Officer in Armour with a Sash,*
British (Scottish) School *Portrait of a Lady in a Red Dress,*
British (Scottish) School *Portrait of an Officer in Armour with a Stock,* gift
British (Scottish) School *Portrait of an Officer in Armour,*
British (Scottish) School *Portrait of a Boy in a Brown Coat with a Pink Sash,*
British (Scottish) School *Portrait of a Man in a Black Surplice,*
British (Scottish) School *Portrait of a Man in Classical Costume,*
British (Scottish) School *Portrait of a Gentleman in a Red Coat,*
British (Scottish) School *Portrait of a Lady in a Red Dress,* gift
British (Scottish) School *James Byres of Tonley (1734–1817),* gift
British (Scottish) School *Portrait of a Lady in a Landscape,* gift
British (Scottish) School *A Girl with Two Dogs,*
British (Scottish) School *Portrait of a Gentleman in a Slashed Doublet,* gift
British (Scottish) School *Portrait of a Lady,* (said to be the wife of Andrew, 1st Lord Fraser), gift
British (Scottish) School *Portrait of a Lady in a Black Dress,* (possibly Lady Fraser, wife of the 1st Lord Fraser), gift
British (Scottish) School *Portrait of a Man Holding a Flower,*
British (Scottish) School *Portrait of the Wife of Andrew, 1st Lord Fraser,* gift
British School *Portrait of a Man in a Hat,* gift
British School *Portrait of a Man with a Ruff,* gift
British School *Portrait of a Monk,* gift
British School *Lady Blanche Drummond (d.1954),* gift
British School *Head of a Lady with a Pearl Necklace,* gift
British School *Portrait of a Lady in a White Dress and Black Gown,* gift
Bronckhorst, Arnold (after) active c.1566–1586, *George Buchanan,* gift
Chinnery, George 1774–1852, *Mary Bristow (d.1805),* gift
Colone, Adam de (after) 1572–1651, *James VI and I (1566–1625),*
Cosway, Richard (attributed to) 1742–1821, *Alexander Mackenzie (1758–1809), 9th Lord Fraser of Inverallochy,* gift
Cosway, Richard (attributed to) 1742–1821, *Helen Mackenzie (1764–1802), Wife of Alexander Mackenzie, 9th Lord Fraser of Inverallochy,* gift
Dyck, Anthony van (after) 1599–1641, *Charles I (1600–1649), in a White Lace Collar and a Blue Sash,*
Faulkner, Benjamin Rawlinson 1787–1849, *Colonel Charles Mackenzie Fraser of Inverallochy and Castle Fraser (1792–1871),* gift
Gianni, Giuseppe 1829–1885, *Harbour at Malta,* transferred
Gianni, Giuseppe 1829–1885, *Stormy Seas, Malta,* transferred
Giles, James 1801–1870, *Castle Fraser,* transferred
Gryeff, Peter de *Parrots and a Cockatiel,* bequeathed
Hay, A. *A Pug: 'Jo',* © the copyright holder
Isenbrandt, Adriaen (after) 1500–1546, *The Mystic Marriage of Saint Catherine with Four Female Saints,* gift
Jamesone, George (circle of) 1588–1644, *Andrew Fraser (1574–1636), 1st Lord Fraser of Castle Fraser,* gift
Jamesone, George (circle of) 1588–1644, *Andrew Fraser (1574–1636), 1st Lord Fraser of Castle Fraser,* gift
Jamesone, George (follower of) 1588–1644, *Portrait of a Man in a Black Slashed Coat with Lace Collar,*
Jamesone, George (follower of) 1588–1644, *Portrait of a Man in Armour,*
Jouanne, M. *Lieutenant Colonel Frederick Mackenzie Fraser (1831–1887),*
Largillière, Nicolas de (after) 1656–1746, *Prince James Frances Edward Stuart (1688–1766),* gift
Lawrence, Thomas (after) 1769–1830, *Arthur Wellesley (1769–1852), 1st Duke of Wellington,* gift
Lawrence, Thomas (after) 1769–1830, *Jane Hay (1799–1861), Daughter of Sir John Hay of Haystoun and Inverallochy, and Wife of Colonel Charles Mackenzie of Fraser and Castle Fraser,* gift
MacIvor, Maurice *Portrait of a Lady with a Cat,* gift
Mackenzie, Frederick *Mrs Frederick Mackenzie, née Theodora Lovett (d.1947),* (Frederick Mackenzie's second wife), gift
Mytens, Daniel (after) 1590–1647, *Charles I (1600–1649), in Robes of State,*
Parrocel, Pierre (after) 1670–1739, *George Keith (1693–1778), 10th Earl Marischal,* gift
Raeburn, Henry 1756–1823, *Charles Mackenzie Fraser, MP,* gift
Raeburn, Henry 1756–1823, *Eliza Fraser of Castle Fraser,*
Raeburn, Henry (after) 1756–1823, *Lieutenant-General Sir Alexander Mackenzie Fraser of Inverallochy (1758–1809),* gift
Raeburn, Henry (after) 1756–1823, *Martha Fraser of Inverallochy (1727–1803),* gift
Raeburn, Henry (after) 1756–1823, *The Hononourable William Mackenzie (1791–1814), MP,* gift
Sanders, George 1774–1846, *Lieutenant-General Sir Thomas Bradford (1777–1853),* gift
Schunemann, L. (attributed to) active 1651–1681, *Portrait of a Gentleman in a Dark Blue Mantle,* gift
unknown artist *'Laddie'*
unknown artist *Leap Castle,* gift
unknown artist *Portrait of a Woman,*
unknown artist *Portrait of a Woman in a White Dress with a Red Gown*
Webster, A. *An Oriental Harbour*

The National Trust for Scotland, Fyvie Castle

Alexander, John 1686–1766, *John Graham (1648–1689), 1st Viscount Dundee,* transferred
Allan, David 1744–1796, *Portrait of a Young Man in a Green Jacket,* transferred
Anderson, Douglas Hardinge b.1934, *Lady Ruth Forbes-Leith (1897–1973),* on loan from a a private collection © the artist
Anderson, Douglas Hardinge b.1934, *Sir Ian Forbes-Leith (1902–1973),* on loan from a private collection © the artist
Batoni, Pompeo 1708–1787, *Colonel William Gordon (1736–1816),* transferred
Beale, Mary (circle of) 1633–1699, *Portrait of a Cleric,* transferred
Beale, Mary (circle of) 1633–1699, *Portrait of a Cleric,* transferred
Beechey, William 1753–1839, *William Gordon of Fyvie,* transferred
Belle, Alexis-Simon 1674–1734, *Prince James Stuart (1688–1766), 'The Old Pretender', as a Young Man,* transferred
Bertier, Francisque-Edouard active 1888–1906, *Lady Forbes-Leith (d.1930), née Mary Louise January,* on loan from a private collection
Bertier, Francisque-Edouard active 1888–1906, *Percy Forbes-Leith (1881–1900),* on loan from a private collection
Breun, John Ernest 1862–1921, *Arthur Burn,* on loan from a private collection
Breun, John Ernest 1862–1921, *Alexander Forbes-Leith (1847–1925), Lord Leith of Fyvie,* on loan from a private collection
Breun, John Ernest (attributed to) 1862–1921, *Portrait of a Gentleman,* (possibly Sir Thomas January), transferred
British (English) School *Portrait of a Girl, Aged 10,* transferred
British (English) School *Portrait of a Young Man,* transferred
British (English) School *Portrait of a Gentleman in Red Robes,* transferred
British (English) School *Portrait of a Lady in a Green Dress and a Red Cloak,* transferred
British (English) School *Mary, Queen of Scots (1542–1587),* transferred
British (Scottish) School *Alexander Forbes of Blackford,* on loan from a private collection
British (Scottish) School *John Forbes of Blackford,* on loan from a private collection
British (Scottish) School *Portrait of a Lady of the Leith Family,* transferred
British (Scottish) School *Portrait of a Gentleman of the Leith Family,* transferred
British (Scottish) School *Portrait of a Highland Officer,* transferred
British (Scottish) School *Portrait of a Lady in a Russet Dress,* transferred
British (Scottish) School *Portrait of a Gentleman in Red Robes and a White Cravat,* (possibly John Leith), on loan from a private collection
Burnet, John 1784–1868, *The Trial of Charles I, 1st January 1649,* transferred
Chalmers, George 1720–1791, *Dr John Gregory (1724–1773),* purchased, 1984
Chalmers, George 1720–1791, *Dorothy Montagu Gregory (1755–1830),* transferred
Chandler, William (after) *General Alexander Leith-Hay (1758–1838),* on loan from a private collection
Closterman, John (circle of) 1660–1711, *Sarah Jennings (1660–1744), Duchess of Marlborough,* purchased, 1984
Critz the elder, John de (circle of) 1551–1642, *James VI of Scotland and I of England (1566–1625),* transferred
Dahl I, Michael 1656–1743, *Sir Robert Walpole (1676–1745), Later 1st Earl of Orford,* purchased, 1984
Dance-Holland, Nathaniel (circle of) 1735–1811, *Portrait of a Gentleman,* (said to be Spranger Barry, 1719–1773), transferred
Downman, John 1750–1824, *Lord Edward Conway (d.1785),* transferred
Dutch School *Portrait of a Gentleman in a Black Coat,* transferred
Dutch School *Portrait of a Lady,* transferred
Dutch School *Portrait of a Gentleman,* (said to be George Buchanan, 1506–1682), transferred
Dyck, Anthony van 1599–1641, *Charles I (1600–1649),* transferred
Dyck, Anthony van (circle of) 1599–1641, *Algernon Percy (1602–1668), 10th Earl of Northumberland,* transferred
Dyck, Anthony van (style of) 1599–1641, *Charles I (1600–1649),* transferred
Eccardt, John Giles 1720–1779, *John Monckton (1695–1751), 1st Viscount Galway,* on loan from a private collection
Eccardt, John Giles (attributed to) 1720–1779, *William Monckton (d.1772), 2nd Viscount Galway,* on loan from a private collection
Fildes, Luke 1843–1927, *The Honourable Ethel Louise Forbes-Leith (1872–1930), Lady Forbes Leith,* transferred
Flemish School *The Virgin Mary Receiving the Eucharist from Saint John the Apostle,* transferred
Franca, Manuel Joachim de 1808–1865, *Derrick January,* on loan from a private collection
Franca, Manuel Joachim de 1808–1865, *Mrs Derrick January and Her Children,* on loan from a private collection
French School *The Prince of Wales as a Child in Antique Costume,* transferred
French School *Portrait of an Officer,* transferred
Gainsborough, Thomas 1727–1788, *Major William Tennant (d.1803), of Needwood House, Staffordshire,* transferred
German School *Portrait of a Cleric,* transferred
Giles, James 1801–1870, *Anne (1713–1791), Countess of Aberdeen, and Her Son, Lord William Gordon of Fyvie (1736–1816),* transferred
Giles, James 1801–1870, *Self Portrait in a Maroon Coat and Crimson Beret,* transferred
Giles, James 1801–1870, *Deer Drinking at a Forest Stream,* transferred
Giles, James 1801–1870, *Waterfall,* transferred
Giles, James 1801–1870, *William Elphinstone (1431–1514), Bishop of Aberdeen,* (after Flemish School), transferred
Greuze, Jean-Baptiste 1725–1805, *The Young Mendicants,* transferred
Gruyter, Jacob de (attributed to) 1630–1681, *Wreck of a Dutch Fleet after Battle,* transferred
Highmore, Joseph (circle of) 1692–1780, *Portrait of a Gentleman,* transferred

Hone I, Nathaniel 1718–1784, *James Sinclair-Erskine (1762–1837), Later 2nd Earl of Rosslyn, His Brother John and His Sister Henrietta Maria,* transferred
Hoppner, John 1758–1810, *Horatio, 1st Viscount Nelson (1758–1805),* transferred
Hoppner, John 1758–1810, *Mrs Paul Le Mesurier,* transferred
Huchtenburgh, Jan van (circle of) 1647–1733, *A Cavalry Engagement between Turks and Europeans,* transferred
Huchtenburgh, Jan van (circle of) 1647–1733, *A Cavalry Engagement between Turks and Europeans in front of a Town,* transferred
Hudson, Thomas 1701–1779, *John Campbell (1696–1782), Lord Glenorchy, Later 3rd Earl of Breadalbane,* transferred
Italian School *Portrait of a Cleric,* transferred
Jamesone, George (after) 1588–1644, *David Anderson of Finzeach (b.c.1566), Known as 'Davie Do a Thing',* transferred
Jamesone, George (after) 1588–1644, *Self Portrait of the Artist, His Wife and Child,* transferred
Jamesone, George (follower of) 1588–1644, *David Gregorie of Kinairdrie,* transferred
Kettle, Tilly 1735–1786, *Robert Lovelace (d.1821), of Quiddenham Hall, Norfolk,* transferred
Kneller, Godfrey (circle of) 1646–1723, *John Leith of Leith Hall (d.1727),* on loan from a private collection
Kneller, Godfrey (circle of) 1646–1723, *Marjory, Daughter of Arthur Forbes, Wife of John Forbes of Newleslie,* transferred
Kneller, Godfrey (circle of) 1646–1723, *Portrait of a Gentleman,* (said to be John Churchill, Duke of Marlborough), transferred
Kneller, Godfrey (circle of) 1646–1723, *The Honourable Janet Ogilvie (1668–1743),* transferred
Larkin, William (circle of) 1585–1619, *Portrait of a Lady,* (said to be Elizabeth of Bohemia), transferred
László, Philip Alexius de 1869–1937, *Sir Charles Burn (1859–1930), Later Forbes-Leith, 1st Bt,* on loan from a private collection
Lawrence, Thomas 1769–1830, *Countess of Oxford, Wife of the 4th Earl of Oxford (1728–1804),* transferred
Lawrence, Thomas (after) 1769–1830, *Arthur Wellesley (1769–1852), 1st Duke of Wellington,* transferred
Leader, Benjamin Williams 1831–1923, *The Silent Evening Hour,* transferred
Lely, Peter 1618–1680, *James Scott (1648–1685),* transferred
Lely, Peter 1618–1680, *James Scott (1648–1685), Duke of Monmouth and Buccleugh,* transferred
Lely, Peter (after) 1618–1680, *Louise de Kerouaille (1649–1734), Duchess of Portsmouth,* transferred
Lely, Peter (circle of) 1618–1680, *Charles II (1630–1685),* transferred
Lely, Peter (circle of) 1618–1680, *Portrait of a Nobleman,* (said to be John Maitland, Duke of Lauderdale), transferred
Lely, Peter (style of) 1618–1680, *Frances Jennings (1647–1731), Duchess of Tyrconnel,* transferred
Maes, Nicolaes 1634–1693, *Portrait of a Gentleman,* (called the Earl of Sheffield), transferred
Maes, Nicolaes 1634–1693, *Portrait of a Lady in a Black Dress,* transferred
Maes, Nicolaes (circle of) 1634–1693, *Portrait of a Nobleman,* transferred
Mignard I, Pierre (attributed to) 1612–1695, *La duchesse de la Vallière,* transferred
Mignard I, Pierre (style of) 1612–1695, *Henrietta Maria (1609–1669),* transferred
Millais, John Everett 1829–1896, *The Sound of Many Waters,* transferred
Minderhout, Hendrik van (attributed to) 1632–1696, *Capture of the Royal Prince by Admiral de Ruyter in 1666,* transferred
More, Jacob (circle of) 1740–1793, *Bay of Pozzuoli with the Temple of Serapis,* transferred
Opie, John 1761–1807, *Courtship in the Park,* transferred
Opie, John 1761–1807, *Lady Kerrison (1738–1825), née Mary Anne Davies, Wife of Sir Roger Kerrison of Brooke, Norfolk,* transferred
Paton, Waller Hugh 1828–1895, *Outlet of Loch Achray, Perthshire,* transferred
Pettie, John 1839–1893, *The Cavalier,* transferred
Raeburn, Henry 1756–1823, *Charles Gordon of Buthlaw, Lonmay and Cairness (1747–1797),* transferred
Raeburn, Henry 1756–1823, *Thomas Reid (1710–1796), Professor of Moral Philosophy at Glasgow University,* transferred
Raeburn, Henry 1756–1823, *Professor James Gregory (1753–1821),* purchased
Raeburn, Henry 1756–1823, *Alexander Edgar (d.1820), of Auchingrammont, Lanarkshire and Wedderelie, Jamaica,* transferred
Raeburn, Henry 1756–1823, *Dr George Bell, Surgeon Extraordinary to George IV and William IV,* transferred
Raeburn, Henry 1756–1823, *George Gordon (1770–1836), 5th Duke of Gordon,* transferred
Raeburn, Henry 1756–1823, *Jane (1748–1812), Duchess of Gordon, Wife of Alexander, 4th Duke of Gordon,* (after Joshua Reynolds), transferred
Raeburn, Henry 1756–1823, *John Stirling of Kippendavie (1742–1816), and His Youngest Daughter, Jean Wilhelmina (1804–1859),* transferred
Raeburn, Henry 1756–1823, *Major, Later Lieutenant-Colonel Henry Knight Erskine of Pittodrie, Aberdeenshire,* transferred
Raeburn, Henry 1756–1823, *Mrs Charles Gordon, née Christian Forbes of Ballogie, Wife of Charles Gordon of Buthlaw, Lonmay and Cairness,* transferred
Raeburn, Henry 1756–1823, *Mrs James Gregory, née Isobella Macleod (1770–1847),* transferred
Raeburn, Henry 1756–1823, *Sir General William Maxwell (1754–1837), 6th Bt of Calderwood,* transferred
Raeburn, Henry 1756–1823, *Thomas King, Esq. (c.1772–1802), of Drums and Millbank, Renfrewshire, Aged 18,* transferred
Reynolds, Joshua 1723–1792, *Elizabeth Kerr (1745–1780), Countess of Ancrum, Later Marchioness of Lothian,* transferred
Reynolds, Joshua 1723–1792, *Mrs James Fortescue, née Mary Henrietta Hunter,* transferred
Reynolds, Joshua (after) 1723–1792, *Anne, Marchioness Townshend,* transferred
Reynolds, Joshua (circle of) 1723–1792, *Edward Gibbon (1737–1794),* transferred
Romney, George 1734–1802, *Captain Arthur Forbes of Culloden (1760–1803),* transferred
Romney, George 1734–1802, *John Richard West (1757–1783), 4th Earl de la Warr,* transferred
Romney, George 1734–1802, *Mrs Stratford Canning (1777–1831), née Mehetebel Patrick, with Her Daughter Elizabeth,* transferred
Romney, George 1734–1802, *Mrs William Marwood (1743–1807), née Mary Goulston, Wife of William Marwood of Busby, near Stokesley, Yorkshire,* transferred
Rubens, Peter Paul (after) 1577–1640, *A Tiger Hunt,* transferred
Russell, John 1745–1806, *Captain Braithwaite,* transferred
Scougal, John 1645–1737, *James Gregory (1638–1675), MA, FRS,* transferred
Seccombe, Thomas Strong 1835–1890, *The Scots Greys at Waterloo,* transferred
Serres, John Thomas 1759–1825, *Port of Leghorn with a Half Galley of the Grand Duke of Tuscany Putting Out to Sea,* transferred
Shackleton, John (studio of) 1697–1767, *George II (1683–1760),* transferred
Smith, F. Pierce *Woodland,* transferred
Somer I, Paulus van (school of) 1576–1621, *Amalia van Solms (1602–1675),* (after Michiel Jansz. van Miereveld),
Somer I, Paulus van (school of) 1576–1621, *Prince Frederik Hendrik of Orange (1584–1647),* (after Michiel Jansz. van Miereveld), transferred
Trickett, W. Wadsell active 1901–1937, *'Leap Year': A Horse in a Loose Box,* on loan from a private collection © the copyright holder
unknown artist *A Man, a Woman and a Donkey,* transferred
unknown artist *Arthur Burn in the Uniform of the Royal Dragoons,* transferred
unknown artist *Portrait of a Woman in a White Ruff,* transferred
Vigée-LeBrun, Elisabeth Louise (circle of) 1755–1842, *Self Portrait,* transferred
Wales, James 1747–1795, *Charles Leslie of Aberdeen (1677–1782),* transferred
Wassdail active from 1745, *Prince Charles Edward (1720–1788), 'The Young Pretender',* transferred
Wissing, Willem (circle of) 1656–1687, *Mrs James Leith, née Margaret Strachan, Wife of James Leith of Leith Hall,* on loan from a private collection

The National Trust for Scotland, Angus Folk Museum

unknown artist *Portrait of a Woman in a Shawl**
unknown artist *Rural Village**

The National Trust for Scotland, J. M. Barrie's Birthplace

Barrie, Sara 1854–1903, *Irises**, gift
Greig, James McGavin 1861–1941, *Elizabeth Fyffe,*
Inglis, James 1835–1904, *Near the End of the Web,* gift
unknown artist *J. M. Barrie's St Bernard Glen ('Porthos'),* on loan from Angus Council Museums

The National Trust for Scotland, House of Dun

Aikman, William 1682–1731, *Anne Erskine (1709–1735), Daughter of Lord Dun and Wife Successively of James, 9th Earl of Airlie and Sir Alexander Macdonald,* bequeathed
Aikman, William 1682–1731, *David Erskine (1672–1758), 13th of Dun, in the Robes of the Court of Session,* bequeathed
Aikman, William 1682–1731, *John Erskine (1712–1787), 14th of Dun, Son of Lord Dun, Aged 10,* bequeathed
Aikman, William (attributed to) 1682–1731, *David Erskine (1672–1758), 13th of Dun,* bequeathed
Aikman, William (circle of) 1682–1731, *Magdalene, Daughter of John Riddell of the Haining, and Wife of David Erskine, Lord Dun,* bequeathed
Baillie, William James 1923–2011, *Flowers in a Niche,* gift © the artist's estate
Barrie, Mardi 1930–2004, *Storm, Cove,* gift © the artist's estate
British (English) School *Mr Snell, in the Character of a Lawyer,* bequeathed
British (Scottish) School *Helen Erskine,* (thought to be the Daughter of John Erskine, 7th of Dun), bequeathed
British (Scottish) School *Ann Beaton, Wife of John Erskine of Dun,* bequeathed
British (Scottish) School *David Erskine (d. before 1710), 11th of Dun,* bequeathed
British (Scottish) School *Ann Ogilvie, Lady Brakie,* bequeathed
British (Scottish) School *James Carnegie of Brakie,* bequeathed
British (Scottish) School *John Carnegie, Junior, of Boysack,* bequeathed
British (Scottish) School *Elen Erskine (b.1634), Daughter of Sir John Erskine,* bequeathed
British (Scottish) School *General Lumsdaine,* bequeathed
British (Scottish) School *Margaret Erskine (b.1633), Daughter of Sir John Erskine, Wife of Sir David Ogilvie of Inverquharity, 2nd Bt,* bequeathed
British (Scottish) School *Margaret Erskine, Daughter of Sir Alexander Erskine, 11th of Dun, and Wife of Sir John Carnegie of Boysack, 1st Bt,* bequeathed
British (Scottish) School *Portrait of a Carnegie in Armour,* bequeathed
British (Scottish) School *David, 2nd Lord Cardross,* on loan from a private collection
British (Scottish) School *John Erskine (d.1572), 1st Earl of Mar, Regent of Scotland,* on loan from a private collection
Brown, Edwin (possibly) 1814–1890, *A Chestnut Held by a Lancer in a Yard,* bequeathed
Buxton, W. *'Piper',* bequeathed
Buxton, W. *'Piper',* bequeathed
Cadell, Francis Campbell Boileau 1883–1937, *Pink Roses and Teapot,* gift
Cadell, Francis Campbell Boileau 1883–1937, *Venice,* gift
Casteels, Pieter 1684–1749, *A Peacock, a Turkey and Domestic Fowl in a Garden,* bequeathed
Costello, Dudley 1803–1865, *William IV,* bequeathed
Cowie, James 1886–1956, *Schoolgirl,* gift © the artist's estate
Crosbie, William 1915–1999, *Beaune,* gift © the artist's estate
Duval, John 1816–1892, *'Akbar Khan',* bequeathed
Duval, John 1816–1892, *'Cola',* bequeathed

Duval, John 1816–1892, *'Hungerford Mare'*, bequeathed
Duval, John 1816–1892, *'Mona'*, bequeathed
Eardley, Joan Kathleen Harding 1921–1963, *Summer Landscape, Catterline*, gift © the Eardley estate. All rights reserved, DACS 2013
Eardley, Joan Kathleen Harding 1921–1963, *Village, Evening, Catterline*, gift © the Eardley estate. All rights reserved, DACS 2013
Erskine, Violet Jacob *A Florentine Spinner*, bequeathed
Faugue *Augustus John William Henry Kennedy-Erskine (1866–1908), 19th of Dun, Aged 7*, bequeathed
Flemish School *Flowers on a Ledge*, bequeathed
Gandy, John *Captain James Erskine, Brother of Lord Dun, 1690*, bequeathed by Mrs Lovett, 1980
Gillies, William George 1898–1973, *Midlothian Farm*, gift © Royal Scottish Academy
Hanneman, Adriaen (after) 1601–1671, *Charles II (1630–1685), as Prince of Wales*, bequeathed
Hayter, John 1800–1891, *A Room at Windsor Castle*, bequeathed
Hayter, John 1800–1891, *Lady Augusta FitzClarence Kennedy-Erskine (d.1860), Natural Daughter of King William IV and Wife of the Honourable John Erskine, with Her Children, Wiliam Henry, Wilhelmina and Millicent Ann Mary*, bequeathed
Hunter, George Leslie 1879–1931, *Fife Pastoral*, gift
Hunter, George Leslie 1879–1931, *Still Life with Roses*, gift
Italian School *A Moor on a Plumed Charger*, bequeathed
Italian School *A Woman Sitting Side-Saddle on a Plumed Horse*, bequeathed
Italian School *Amalfi Coast*, bequeathed
Italian School *Classical Columns in Italy*, bequeathed
Italian School *Gulf of Naples*, bequeathed
Italian School *Village near Naples*, bequeathed
M., H. *William Henry Kennedy-Erskine (1828–1870), 18th of Dun, Captain of the 17th Lancers*, bequeathed
Mann, Harrington 1864–1937, *Alice Marjorie Cunningham (d.1943), Wife of Augustus Kennedy-Erskine, 18th of Dun, with Their Daughters Marjorie and Millicent*, bequeathed
Mann, Harrington 1864–1937, *Augustus John William Henry Kennedy-Erskine (1866–1908), 19th of Dun, in Riding Costume*, bequeathed
McClure, David 1926–1998, *Toledo in Winter*, gift © the artist's estate
McClure, David 1926–1998, *Salmon Bothy, Dunbeath*, gift © the artist's estate
Milne, John Maclauchlan 1886–1957, *Red Roofs, Cassis*, gift © John Maclauchlan Milne, courtesy of Portland Gallery, London
Mosman, William 1700–1771, *John Erskine (1742–1812), 15th of Dun, as a Boy*, bequeathed
Murillo, Bartolomé Esteban (after) 1617–1682, *Children Playing a Game*, bequeathed
Murillo, Bartolomé Esteban (after) 1617–1682, *Girl, Boy and Fruit*, bequeathed
Nasmyth, Alexander 1758–1840, *A View of Culzean Castle in the Early Evening*, bequeathed
Peploe, Denis Frederic Neal 1914–1993, *Grisedale Pike*, gift © the artist's estate
Peploe, Samuel John 1871–1935, *Landscape near Calvine*, gift
Peploe, Samuel John 1871–1935, *Luxembourg Gardens, Paris*, gift
Peploe, Samuel John 1871–1935, *Still Life with Roses and Mirror*, gift
Peploe, Samuel John 1871–1935, *Street Scene, Paris*, gift
Raeburn, Henry (copy after) 1756–1823, *John Erskine of Carnock (1719–1803), DD, Son of J. Erskine*, on loan from a private collection
Raeburn, Henry (studio of) 1756–1823, *The Honourable Christian Erskine, Daughter of George, 3rd Lord Reay, Wife of J. Erskine, DD*, on loan from a private collection
Ramsay, Allan 1713–1784, *Anne Erskine (b.1740), Daughter of John Erskine, 14th of Dun and Wife of John Wauchope of Edmonstone*, bequeathed
Ramsay, Allan 1713–1784, *John Erskine (1712–1787), 14th of Dun*, bequeathed
Ramsay, Allan 1713–1784, *Margaret Inglis (1720–1747), Wife of John Erskine, Daughter of Sir John Inglis of Cramond*, bequeathed
Ramsay, Allan 1713–1784, *Magdaline Erskine (b.1744), Daughter of John Erskine, 14th of Dun, as an Infant*, bequeathed
Redfern, June b.1951, *The Grassy Beach*, gift © June Redfern. All rights reserved, DACS 2013
Redfern, June b.1951, *Kitty Eating an Apple*, bequeathed © June Redfern. All rights reserved, DACS 2013
Redpath, Anne 1895–1965, *Chapelle de la Croix*, gift © the artist's estate/Bridgeman Art Library
Redpath, Anne 1895–1965, *Landscape in Skye*, gift © the artist's estate/Bridgeman Art Library
Scougall, David (attributed to) 1610–1680, *Portrait of an Officer*, (said to be Sir Alexander Erskine, fl.1662, 11th of Dun), bequeathed
Somer I, Paulus van (after) 1576–1621, *John Erskine (d.1634), 2nd Earl of Mar*, on loan from a private collection
Steell, David George 1856–1930, *A Labrador, after a Shoot*, bequeathed
Thomson, Adam Bruce 1885–1976, *Harvesting in Galloway*, gift © the artist's estate
Thomson, Adam Bruce 1885–1976, *St Monance*, gift © the artist's estate
unknown artist *Portrait of a Girl*, bequeathed
unknown artist *Landscape*, bequeathed
unknown artist *River Scene*, bequeathed
unknown artist *River Scene with Figure*, bequeathed
unknown artist *Windmill*, bequeathed
Wheeler, John Alfred 1821–1903, *'The Abbot of St Mark'*, bequeathed
Wheeler, John Alfred 1821–1903, *'Time Keeper', the Charger of W. H. Kennedy-Erskine, 17th Lancers*, bequeathed

The National Trust for Scotland, Alloa Tower

Alison, David 1882–1955, *John Francis Ashley (Jock) (1895–1953), Lord Erskine, Governor of Madras, in the Robes of Governor*, on loan from the Earl of Mar and Kellie © the copyright holder
Alison, David 1882–1955, *William Augustus Forbes Erskine (1871–1952)*, on loan from the Earl of Mar and Kellie © the copyright holder
Allan, David 1744–1796, *Clackmann Pow and Hill with the River Forth Looking East*, on loan from the Earl of Mar and Kellie
Allan, David 1744–1796, *John Francis (1741–1825), 7th Earl of Mar, and Family*, on loan from the Earl of Mar and Kellie
Allan, David 1744–1796, *The Forth at Alloa*, on loan from the Earl of Mar and Kellie
Allan, David 1744–1796, *Thomas, Lord Erskine (1705–1766)*, on loan from the Earl of Mar and Kellie
Allan, David (attributed to) 1744–1796, *Lady Charlotte Erskine*, on loan from the Earl of Mar and Kellie
Allan, David (attributed to) 1744–1796, *Sir Hugh Patterson (c.1685–1777), Bt, MP*, on loan from the Earl of Mar and Kellie
Allan, David (attributed to) 1744–1796, *View of Linlithgow Palace*, on loan from the Earl of Mar and Kellie
British (English) School *Charles II (1630–1685), as a Boy*, on loan from the Earl of Mar and Kellie
British (Scottish) School *Alexander Erskine of Gogar (1521–1590)*, on loan from the Earl of Mar and Kellie
British (Scottish) School *John Erskine (1675–1732), 6th Earl of Mar, as a Boy*, on loan from the Earl of Mar and Kellie
British (Scottish) School *James Erskine, Lord Grange (1672–1754), Lord Justice Clerk*, on loan from the Earl of Mar and Kellie
British (Scottish) School *Anne of Denmark (1574–1619)*, on loan from the Earl of Mar and Kellie
British (Scottish) School *James Erskine (1679–1754), 2nd Lord Grange, Second Son of Charles, 5th Earl of Mar, as a Boy*, on loan from the Earl of Mar and Kellie
British (Scottish) School *John Erskine (1562–1634), 2nd Earl of Mar, KG, Lord High Treasurer of Scotland (1616–1630)*, on loan from the Earl of Mar and Kellie
British (Scottish) School *John Erskine of Mar (d.1572), 1st Earl Regent*, on loan from the Earl of Mar and Kellie
British (Scottish) School *John Francis Ashley (1895–1953), Lord Erskine*, on loan from the Earl of Mar and Kellie
British School *The Honourable Alistair Erskine, MC, Brother of John, 13th Earl of Mar and 15th Earl of Kellie*, on loan from the Earl of Mar and Kellie
Dahl I, Michael (follower of) 1656–1743, *John Erskine (d.1732), 6th Earl of Mar*, on loan from the Earl of Mar and Kellie
Davidson, Duncan 1876–1946, *Kildrummie Castle*, on loan from the Earl of Mar and Kellie © the copyright holder
Davidson, Duncan 1876–1946, *Mar Castle, Earldom of Mar*, on loan from the Earl of Mar and Kellie © the copyright holder
Edwards, John b.1940, *The Earl of Mar and Kellie*, on loan from the Earl of Mar and Kellie © the artist
Hudson, Thomas (circle of) 1701–1779, *Lady Caroline Brand*, on loan from the Earl of Mar and Kellie
Jervas, Charles (attributed to) 1675–1739, *Thomas (c.1705–1766), Lord Erskine, Son of John, 6th Earl of Mar*, on loan from the Earl of Mar and Kellie
Kneller, Godfrey 1646–1723, *Frances (1690–1761), Daughter of Evelyn Pierpont, 1st Duke of Kingston*, on loan from the Earl of Mar and Kellie
Kneller, Godfrey 1646–1723, *John Erskine, 6th Earl of Mar (1672–1732), with His Son Thomas, Lord Erskine (1705–1766)*, on loan from the Earl of Mar and Kellie
Kneller, Godfrey (circle of) 1646–1723, *The Honourable Henry Erskine (1682–1707)*, on loan from the Earl of Mar and Kellie
Laidlaw, Nicol 1886–1929, *Prince Charles Edward (1720–1789), as a Boy*, on loan from the Earl of Mar and Kellie
Laidlaw, Nicol 1886–1929, *Prince Henry Stuart (1725–1807), Cardinal of York*, on loan from the Earl of Mar and Kellie
Lorimer, John Henry 1856–1936, *Walter John Francis Erskine (1865–1955)*, on loan from the Earl of Mar and Kellie
Medina, John 1720–1796, *Colonel John Erskine*, on loan from the Earl of Mar and Kellie
Medina, John 1720–1796, *Lady Jane Erskine (d.1763), Daughter of Charles, 5th Earl of Mar, Wife of Sir Hugh Patterson*, on loan from the Earl of Mar and Kellie
Medina, John (circle of) 1720–1796, *James Erskine (1672–1754), Lord Grange*, on loan from the Earl of Mar and Kellie
Morrocco, Alberto 1917–1998, *John Francis Hervey Erskine (1921–1993), 13th Earl of Mar and 15th of Kellie*, on loan from the Earl of Mar and Kellie © the artist's estate
Nasmyth, Charlotte 1804–1884, *View of Alloa and Stirling Castle from Clackmann Hill*, on loan from the Earl of Mar and Kellie
Raeburn, Henry 1756–1823, *John Francis Erskine (1741–1825), 7th Earl of Mar*, on loan from the Earl of Mar and Kellie
Raeburn, Henry 1756–1823, *The Honourable Henry Erskine (1746–1817)*, on loan from the Earl of Mar and Kellie
Ramsay, Allan (attributed to) 1713–1784, *John Francis (1741–1825), 7th Earl of Mar, Aged 17*, on loan from the Earl of Mar and Kellie
Rigaud, Hyacinthe (follower of) 1659–1743, *John Erskine (1675–1732), 6th Earl of Mar, KT*, on loan from the Earl of Mar and Kellie
Scougal, John 1645–1737, *Charles (1650–1689), 5th Earl of Mar*, on loan from the Earl of Mar and Kellie
Scougal, John (circle of) 1645–1737, *Mary (b.c.1631), Daughter of Walter Scott, 1st Earl of Buccleuch*, on loan from the Earl of Mar and Kellie
Slaughter, Stephen 1697–1765, *Gertrude (1715–1794), Daughter of John Leveson Gower, 1st Lord Gower*, on loan from the Earl of Mar and Kellie
Trevisani, Francesco 1656–1746, *Frances (1690–1761), Wife of John, 6th Earl of Mar, Daughter of Evelyn, 1st Duke of Kingston*, on loan from the Earl of Mar and Kellie
unknown artist *John Francis Miller Erskine (1795–1868), 9th Earl of Mar and 11th of Kellie*, on loan from the Earl of Mar and Kellie
unknown artist *Philadelphia (d.1853), Wife of the 9th Earl of Mar*, on loan from the Earl of Mar and Kellie

The National Trust for Scotland, Threave Estate

Earl, J. *Kitten and Rabbits by a Hutch,* gift
Faed, John 1819–1902, *The Wappenschaw,* gift
Gilbert, C. Hersley *Preston Mill, North Berwick,* © the copyright holder
Harper, M. M. *Threave Castle**
unknown artist *Mountain Lake**
unknown artist *Rocky Pool**

The National Trust for Scotland, Thomas Carlyle's Birthplace

Herdman, Robert 1829–1888, *Thomas Carlyle,* gift

The National Trust for Scotland, Broughton House & Garden

A., W. active 19th C, *An Estuary Landscape,* transferred
Blacklock, Thomas Bromley 1863–1903, *A Red-Headed Girl in a Grey Dress in a Wood,* transferred
British (English) School *Preparing the Scarecrow,* transferred
Faed, John 1819–1902, *The Artist's Mother,* transferred
Faed, John (attributed to) 1819–1902, *The Standard Bearer and Helmeted Warrior,* transferred
Faed, Thomas 1826–1900, *A Highland Tryst,* transferred
Hewat, H. *Edward Atkinson Hornel (1864–1933),* transferred
Hornel, Edward Atkinson 1864–1933, *Portrait of a Man in a Red Tunic,* (An Antwerp or Flemish veteran), transferred
Hornel, Edward Atkinson 1864–1933, *An Elderly Gentleman,* transferred
Hornel, Edward Atkinson 1864–1933, *Two Geishas,* gift
Hornel, Edward Atkinson 1864–1933, *A Winter Wonderland,* transferred
Hornel, Edward Atkinson 1864–1933, *Apple Blossom,* transferred
Hornel, Edward Atkinson 1864–1933, *Apple Blossom, Buckland Burn,* transferred
Hornel, Edward Atkinson 1864–1933, *Balloons and Blossom, Brighouse Bay,* transferred
Hornel, Edward Atkinson 1864–1933, *Blue Flax, Brighouse Bay,* transferred
Hornel, Edward Atkinson 1864–1933, *Girl with Nesting Swans,* transferred
Hornel, Edward Atkinson 1864–1933, *Girl with Wild Flowers,* transferred
Hornel, Edward Atkinson 1864–1933, *The Bluebell Wood, Gathering Primroses,* transferred
Hornel, Edward Atkinson 1864–1933, *The Flower Princess,* transferred
Hornel, Edward Atkinson 1864–1933, *The Scent of Primrose,* transferred
Hornel, Edward Atkinson 1864–1933, *Three Girls,* transferred
Hornel, Edward Atkinson 1864–1933, *Woody Briar, Buckland Bay,* transferred
Hornel, Edward Atkinson 1864–1933, *Still Life – Mushrooms,* transferred
Hornel, Edward Atkinson 1864–1933, *Studies of a Red Waterlily,* transferred
Hornel, Edward Atkinson 1864–1933, *Study of Datura,* transferred
Hornel, Edward Atkinson 1864–1933, *Waterlilies,* transferred
Hornel, Edward Atkinson 1864–1933, *Sheep Grazing in an Autumn Landscape,* donated, 2000
Hornel, Edward Atkinson (attributed to) 1864–1933, *Still Life – Time Running Out,* transferred
Hornel, Edward Atkinson 1864–1933, *Young Girl with Primroses,* on loan from a private collection
Hornel, Edward Atkinson 1864–1933, *Studies of Autumn Leaves,* transferred
Hornel, Edward Atkinson 1864–1933, *Woodland,* (possibly Buckland Wood), transferred
Hornel, Edward Atkinson 1864–1933, *Ceylon Water Pots,* transferred
Hornel, Edward Atkinson 1864–1933, *Ceylonese Water Carriers by a River Bank,* transferred
Hornel, Edward Atkinson 1864–1933, *Lace Makers, Ceylon,* gift
Hornel, Edward Atkinson 1864–1933, *A Bamboo Forest, Ceylon,* transferred
Hornel, Edward Atkinson 1864–1933, *Girls Picking Blue Flax (Gathering Bluebells, Brighouse Bay),* transferred
Hornel, Edward Atkinson 1864–1933, *Playing in the Woods,* transferred
Hornel, Edward Atkinson 1864–1933, *A Geisha Girl,* transferred
Hornel, Edward Atkinson 1864–1933, *A Geisha Girl Holding a Fan,* transferred
Hornel, Edward Atkinson 1864–1933, *Geisha Girls,* transferred
Hornel, Edward Atkinson 1864–1933, *Japanese Dancers,* transferred
Hornel, Edward Atkinson 1864–1933, *Japanese Dancers,* transferred
Hornel, Edward Atkinson 1864–1933, *Japanese Dancers,* transferred
Hornel, Edward Atkinson 1864–1933, *Japanese Girls on a Verandah,* transferred
Hornel, Edward Atkinson 1864–1933, *Japanese Musician,* transferred
Hornel, Edward Atkinson 1864–1933, *Japanese Woman by a Flowering Tree (A Geisha Girl by a Bonsai Tree),* transferred
Hornel, Edward Atkinson 1864–1933, *Tea Ceremony with Japanese Girls,* transferred
Hornel, Edward Atkinson 1864–1933, *The Pink Kimono,* transferred
Hornel, Edward Atkinson 1864–1933, *Three Japanese Peasants (Japanese Dancers),* transferred
Hornel, Edward Atkinson 1864–1933, *Two Geisha Girls,* transferred
Hornel, Edward Atkinson 1864–1933, *Two Geisha Girls in a Japanese Garden,* transferred
Hornel, Edward Atkinson 1864–1933, *Two Japanese Girls,* transferred
Hornel, Edward Atkinson 1864–1933, *Burmese Maidens on a Terrace,* transferred
Hornel, Edward Atkinson 1864–1933, *Maiden in a Pink Kimono,* transferred
Hornel, Edward Atkinson 1864–1933, *The Green Parasol,* transferred
Hornel, Edward Atkinson 1864–1933, *A Balustrade, Mandalay,* transferred
Hornel, Edward Atkinson 1864–1933, *Burmese Maidens outside a Temple,* transferred
Hornel, Edward Atkinson 1864–1933, *A Burmese Market,* transferred
Hornel, Edward Atkinson 1864–1933, *Burmese Dancers,* transferred
Hornel, Edward Atkinson 1864–1933, *Burmese Figures by a Gateway,* transferred
Hornel, Edward Atkinson 1864–1933, *Burmese Girls and Market Stalls,* transferred
Hornel, Edward Atkinson 1864–1933, *Burmese Maidens,* transferred
Hornel, Edward Atkinson 1864–1933, *Burmese Musicians and Dancers,* transferred
Hornel, Edward Atkinson 1864–1933, *Burmese Water Carriers,* transferred
Hornel, Edward Atkinson 1864–1933, *Burmese Water Carriers on the Banks of the Irrawaddy,* transferred
Hornel, Edward Atkinson 1864–1933, *Girls Resting by the Irrawaddy,* transferred
Hornel, Edward Atkinson 1864–1933, *Sketch of a Native Girl, Burma,* transferred
Hornel, Edward Atkinson 1864–1933, *Memories of Mandalay,* transferred
Hornel, Edward Atkinson 1864–1933, *Water Carriers on the Banks of the Irrawaddy,* transferred
Hornel, Edward Atkinson 1864–1933, *The Toy Boat, Brighouse Bay,* transferred
Hornel, Edward Atkinson 1864–1933, *Balloons at Brighouse Bay,* transferred
Hornel, Edward Atkinson 1864–1933, *Brighouse Bay, Wild and Burnet Roses,* transferred
Hornel, Edward Atkinson 1864–1933, *Gathering Mushrooms,* transferred
Hornel, Edward Atkinson 1864–1933, *Wild Flax and Burnet Roses,* transferred
Hornel, Edward Atkinson 1864–1933, *Wild Flax at Brighouse,* transferred
Hornel, Edward Atkinson 1864–1933, *Burmese Dancers,* transferred
Hornel, Edward Atkinson 1864–1933, *Burmese Dancers,* transferred
Hornel, Edward Atkinson 1864–1933, *Ceylonese Tea Pickers,* transferred
Hornel, Edward Atkinson 1864–1933, *Daffodils,* transferred
Hornel, Edward Atkinson 1864–1933, *Figures,* (sketch), transferred
Hornel, Edward Atkinson 1864–1933, *Geisha Girl in an Oriental Garden,* transferred
Hornel, Edward Atkinson 1864–1933, *Geisha Girls with Screen,* transferred
Hornel, Edward Atkinson 1864–1933, *Sketch of a Bamboo Trunk,* transferred
Hornel, Edward Atkinson (circle of) 1864–1933, *Washing Day,* transferred
MacGeorge, William Stewart 1861–1931, *Captain Malcolm McLachlan Harper,* transferred
MacGeorge, William Stewart 1861–1931, *Edward Atkinson Hornel (1864–1933), Aged 17,* transferred
MacGregor, Harry 1864–1934, *A Tree-Lined Country Lane,* transferred
MacNicol, Bessie 1869–1904, *Edward Atkinson Hornel,* transferred
McCubbin, Frederick 1855–1917, *Glasgow 'Barras',* transferred
Oppenheimer, Charles 1875–1961, *The Harbour, Kirkcudbright,* on loan from a private collection © the copyright holder
Oppenheimer, Charles 1875–1961, *My Garden at Twilight (14 High Street from the Garden),* transferred © the copyright holder
Rembrandt van Rijn (after) 1606–1669, *Self Portrait,* transferred
Rink, Paulus 1861–1903, *Dutch Head, 'The Artist Painted by Himself',* transferred
unknown artist *A Victorian Gentleman,* transferred
unknown artist *Birds among Trees with Peony and Apple Blossoms,* transferred
unknown artist *Portrait of a Man,* transferred
unknown artist *Study of a Man in a Hat,* transferred
Velde II, Willem van de (style of) 1633–1707, *Dutch Schooner and Fishing Boats in Full Sail,* transferred

The National Trust for Scotland, Newhailes

Aikman, William (attributed to) 1682–1731, *Portrait of a Man,* transferred
Aikman, William (attributed to) 1682–1731, *Sir James Dalrymple, Bt, MP,* transferred
Beale, Mary (circle of) 1633–1699, *Janet Rochead, Wife of the Honourable Sir David Dalrymple, 1st Bt of Hailes,* transferred
Beale, Mary (style of) 1633–1699, *Janet Rochead, Wife of the Honourable Sir David Dalrymple, 1st Bt of Hailes,* transferred
Blackburn, Samuel active 1838–1857, *Helen Boyle, Daughter of the Honourable Patrick Boyle, Wife of Thomas Mure of Warriston,* (after Henry Raeburn), transferred
Blackburn, Samuel active 1838–1857, *Thomas Mure of Warriston,* (after Henry Raeburn), transferred
British (English) School *Landscape with Trees and Figures,* transferred
Flemish School *Coastal Scene with Sailing Ships and Rowing Boats,* transferred
Glauber, Johannes (circle of) 1646–1727, *An Italianate Landscape with a Ruined Temple, Figures and Cattle,* transferred
Glauber, Johannes (circle of) 1646–1727, *Italian Landscape with Figures and a Distant View of a Castle and Town,* transferred
Grant, Francis (follower of) 1803–1878, *Sir Charles Dalrymple Fergusson, Bt,* transferred
Hoppner, John (circle of) 1758–1810, *Sir James Dalrymple, Bt,* transferred
Hulst, Frans de 1610–1661, *Coastal Scene with Sailing Boats, a Rowing Boat and Figures Hauling Nets,* transferred
Jervas, Charles (circle of) 1675–1739, *Anne Young Pringle, Wife of John Dalrymple,* transferred
Jervas, Charles (circle of) 1675–1739, *Lady Christian, Wife of Sir James Dalrymple, Mother of Lord Hailes,* transferred
Kneller, Godfrey 1646–1723, *The Honourable Sir David Dalrymple, Bt, Youngest Son of the 1st Viscount Stair,* transferred
Martin, David 1736–1798, *John Dalrymple, Son of Sir James*

Dalrymple, Bt, Lord Provost of Edinburgh, transferred
Maskell, Christopher Mark 1846–1933, *A Waterside Inn and Ferryman,* transferred
Medina, John Baptist de 1659–1710, *The Honourable Sir David Dalrymple, Bt, Younger Son of 1st Viscount Stair, and His Son Sir James Dalrymple, Bt,* transferred
Medina, John Baptist de (circle of) 1659–1710, *John, 2nd Viscount and 1st Earl of Stair,* transferred
Medina, John Baptist de (circle of) 1659–1710, *Portrait of a Gentleman in Armour,* transferred
Medina, John Baptist de (circle of) 1659–1710, *Sir James Dalrymple of Stair, President of the Court of Session, Created 1st Viscount Stair,* transferred
Medina, John Baptist de (circle of) 1659–1710, *The Honourable Sir Hew Dalrymple, Bt, MP, President of the Court of Session (1698), Third Son of the 1st Viscount Stair,* transferred
Mitchell, E. *A Black Highland Bull in a Highland Landscape,* transferred
Nattier, Jean-Marc 1685–1766, *The Honourable General James Sinclair of Dysart,* (after Allan Ramsay), transferred
Norie, James 1684–1757, *Landscape with Castle, River and Figures,* transferred
Norie, James 1684–1757, *Landscape with Castle, River and Figures,* transferred
Norie, James 1684–1757, *Landscapes with Ruined Buildings and Figures,* transferred
Norie, James 1684–1757, *Landscapes with Ruined Buildings and Figures,* transferred
Norie, James 1684–1757, *River Landscape with Buildings and Figures,* transferred
Norie, James (attributed to) 1684–1757, *A Procession of the Gods above a Riverscape,* transferred
Ramsay, Allan 1713–1784, *Agnes Murray Kynynmond, Daughter of Hugh Dalrymple Murray Kynynmond, Wife of the Right Honourable Sir Gilbert Elliot of Minto, Bt, MP,* transferred
Ramsay, Allan 1713–1784, *Sir James Dalrymple, Bt, MP, Auditor of the Exchequer,* transferred
Ramsay, Allan 1713–1784, *Lady Christian Dalrymple,* transferred
Ramsay, Allan 1713–1784, *Janet, Daughter of the Honourable Sir David Dalrymple, Bt,* transferred
Ramsay, Allan 1713–1784, *Hew Dalrymple, Lord Drummore,* transferred
Ramsay, Allan 1713–1784, *Field Marshal John, 2nd Earl of Stair, KT,* transferred
Ramsay, Allan 1713–1784, *Sir David Dalrymple, Bt, Lord Hailes,* transferred
Ruysdael, Salomon van (attributed to) 1602–1670, *Wooded River Landscape with Cottages, a Ferry Boat, Cattle and Figures,* transferred
Seton, John Thomas 1730–1806, *Helen Ferguson, Wife of Sir David Dalrymple, Later Lord Hailes,* transferred
Smibert, John (attributed to) 1688–1751, *Lady Christian Dalrymple, Wife of Sir James Dalrymple, Bt, Daughter of Thomas, 6th Earl of Haddington,* transferred
Stewart, F. E. S. *A Brown Pony,* gift
Stewart, F. E. S. (attributed to) *A Bay Pony,* gift
Symonds, William Robert 1851–1934, *The Right Honourable Sir Charles Dalrymple, Bt,* transferred
Thomson, John 1778–1840, *Landscape with Hailes Castle and Traprain Law,* transferred
unknown artist *A Jack Russell Terrier,* transferred
unknown artist *A West Lothian Beach,* (possibly Longniddry), transferred
unknown artist *Capriccio Coastal Inlet with Classical Ruins, Figures, Cattle and Sheep,* transferred
unknown artist *Sailing Boats off a Rocky Shore,* transferred
unknown artist *A Covered Urn,* transferred
Vogelsang, Isaac (attributed to) 1688–1753, *Views around Newhailes,* transferred
Vogelsang, Isaac (attributed to) 1688–1753, *Views around Newhailes,* transferred
Vogelsang, Isaac (attributed to) 1688–1753, *Views around Newhailes,* transferred
Vogelsang, Isaac (attributed to) 1688–1753, *Views around Newhailes,* transferred
Walker, F. Hanson *Margaret, Lady Blake, Previously Lady Dalrymple, Wife of Sir Charles Dalrymple,* transferred
Walker, F. Hanson *Alice Mary Hunter Blair, Wife of Charles Dalrymple of Newhailes,* transferred
Watson, George 1767–1837, *Sir John Pringle Dalrymple, Bt,* transferred

The National Trust for Scotland, Gladstone's Land

Aikman, William 1682–1731, *Elizabeth Graham of Airth,* bequeathed
Aikman, William 1682–1731, *John Lumsden of Blanearn,* bequeathed
Aikman, William 1682–1731, *Rachel Graham, Wife of John Lumsden of Blanearn,* bequeathed
Aikman, William (attributed to) 1682–1731, *Katherine Erskine, Daughter of Sir Charles Erskine of Alva, Wife of Patrick Campbell of Monzie,* bequeathed
Belle, Alexis-Simon (circle of) 1674–1734, *James, 5th Earl of Linlithgow and 4th Earl of Callendar,* bequeathed
British (Scottish) School *Admiral Thomas Gordon,* bequeathed
Claesz. the younger, Anthony (attributed to) 1616–1652, *Spring Flowers in a Delft Vase: Iris, Rose and Lily of the Valley,* bequeathed
Claesz. the younger, Anthony (attributed to) 1616–1652, *Spring Flowers in a Delft Vase: Iris, Roses and a Tulip,* bequeathed
Kneller, Godfrey (circle of) 1646–1723, *Lady Henrietta Livingstone,* bequeathed
Kneller, Godfrey (circle of) 1646–1723, *Lady Mary Graham, née Livingstone,* bequeathed
Larkin, William (attributed to) 1585–1619, *Countess of Shirley,* gift
Mosman, William 1700–1771, *Elizabeth Graham of Airth, Wife of William MacDowall of Castle Semple and Garthland,* bequeathed
Ramsay, Allan (studio of) 1713–1784, *Judge James Graham of Airth, Dean of the Faculty and Judge of the Court of Admiralty,* bequeathed
unknown artist *Dame Margaret Lauder*
unknown artist *Sir Alexander Seton*

The National Trust for Scotland, Hermiston Quay

Annand, Louise Gibson 1915–2012, *Circe's Island,* gift © the copyright holder
Bannatyne, John James 1836–1911, *Clyde Estuary,* bequeathed
Breun, John Ernest 1862–1921, *Foreign Dispatches,* transferred
British (English) School *Chillingham Cattle by an Ancient Oak Tree,* bequeathed
British (Scottish) School *James, The 'Admirable' Crichton,* bequeathed
British School *Two Children Paddling,* bequeathed
Brodie, Alexander Kenneth active 1894–c.1898, *A Breton Interior,* on loan from a private collection
C., T. A. *Wooded Landscape,* bequeathed © the copyright holder
Cadell, Francis Campbell Boileau 1883–1937, *The Steading, Strachur,* gift
Cameron, David Young 1865–1945, *Loch Awe,* gift © the artist's estate
Cameron, David Young 1865–1945, *Loch Ness,* gift © the artist's estate
Cameron, David Young 1865–1945, *Rannoch Moor,* gift © the artist's estate
Claesz., Pieter 1597–1660, *A Silver Beaker, a Roehmer and a Peeled Lemon,* gift
Clairval, F. *Vase of Roses,* gift
Clarkson, Albert *Fraisthorpe Maid,*
Corbett, Lucy b.1980, *Professor Roger Wheater, OBE, FRSE,* © the artist
Craven, Helen *Roses,* bequeathed
Crowe, Victoria b.1945, *The Earl of Wemyss and March, KT, President of The National Trust for Scotland,* purchased, 1991 © Victoria Crowe
Donald, John Milne 1819–1866, *Rural Idyll,* bequeathed
Dujardin, Karel (attributed to) 1626–1678, *Figures outside a Building,* gift
Ellis, Edwin 1842–1895, *North Wales,* bequeathed
Faed, Thomas 1826–1900, *The Old Road round Knock Veoch,*
Faed the younger, James 1857–1920, *A Heather Burn in Galloway,*
Giordani *Bay from a Terrace Garden,* bequeathed
Godward, John William 1861–1922, *On the Terrace,* gift
Greig, James McGavin 1861–1941, *James Fyffe, Friend of Sir James Barrie,*
Gysaerts, Gualetrus Wouter 1649–1679, *Tulips, Roses and Other Flowers,* gift
Gysaerts, Gualetrus Wouter 1649–1679, *Tulips, Roses and Other Flowers,* gift
Hall, Dora M. *Rhododendrons,* bequeathed © the copyright holder
Harley, Daisy *A Steep Highland Glen,* bequeathed © the copyright holder
His, René Charles Edmond 1877–1960, *Le Sentier du Moulin,* bequeathed © the copyright holder
Hoog, Bernard de 1867–1943, *Interior with a Mother and Child (A Happy Family),* gift © the copyright holder
Hornel, Edward Atkinson 1864–1933, *Japanese Girl,*
Hornel, Edward Atkinson 1864–1933, *Unknown Fragment of a Larger Painting,* transferred
Houghton-Smith, Ann *'Found', a Bloodhound Seated beside a Cross,* gift © the copyright holder
Hunter, George Leslie 1879–1931, *Anemones and Fruit,* gift
Hunter, George Leslie 1879–1931, *The Old Mill,* gift
Hutchison, W. *Figures in an Interior,*
Kay, James 1858–1942, *View on the Clyde,* gift
Kay, James 1858–1942, *Square in Paris, 2 Clichy,* gift
Lawrence, Thomas 1769–1830, *The Countess of Aberdeen,* gift
Lawrence, Thomas (after) 1769–1830, *Prince Metternich,*
Lee-Hankey, William 1869–1952, *In My Garden,* gift © the copyright holder
Lely, Peter (circle of) 1618–1680, *John Graham, 1st Viscount Dundee,* bequeathed
MacWhirter, John 1839–1911, *Ben Blaven,* bequeathed
MacWhirter, John 1839–1911, *Broadford Bay,* bequeathed
MacWhirter, John 1839–1911, *Broadford Bay,* bequeathed, 1946
MacWhirter, John 1839–1911, *Broadford from the Mainland,* bequeathed
MacWhirter, John 1839–1911, *Skye from Lochalsh,* bequeathed
Medina, John (attributed to) 1720–1796, *Major John Forbes of Pittencrieff,*
Medina, John Baptist de (follower of) 1659–1710, *Ann, Countess of Callander,* bequeathed
Medina, John Baptist de (follower of) 1659–1710, *Alexander Livingston, Earl of Callandar,* bequeathed
Miller, William Ongley 1883–1960, *Trees,* © the copyright holder
Molenaer, Klaes 1630–1676, *Ice-Skating Scene,* gift
Molenaer, Klaes 1630–1676, *Winter Scene,* gift
Neeffs the elder, Peeter 1578–1656, *Interior of Antwerp Cathedral,* gift
Neer, Aert van der 1603–1677, *Moonlit Landscape,* gift
Nicholson, John P. active late 19th C, *Landscape with Farm,*
Noble, James Campbell 1846–1913, *Dutch Canal Scene,* bequeathed
Noble, James Campbell 1846–1913, *Waves,* bequeathed
Peploe, Samuel John 1871–1935, *Roses,* gift
Pettie, John 1839–1893, *The First Step,* gift
Ramsay, Allan 1713–1784, *John, 3rd Earl of Bute,* gift
Ruisdael, Jacob van (attributed to) 1628–1682, *A Country Scene,* gift
Scott, J. B. *A Fishing Boat Beached in a Sandy Bay,* bequeathed
Sheagreen, Lena *Bridge with Trees,* bequeathed
Sheagreen, Lena *Old Cottage, Criccieth, in Wales,* bequeathed
Smith, George A. active 1959–1961, *Morning Mist, Aberdeen Harbour,* © the copyright holder
Tol, Dominicus van 1635–1676, *An Old Woman Fleecing a Boy,* purchased
unknown artist *Mrs J. Drinkwater,* gift
unknown artist *Colonel Drinkwater,* gift
unknown artist *Mrs Drinkwater,* gift
unknown artist *Charles Drinkwater,* gift
unknown artist *Duncan Turner,* bequeathed
unknown artist *Miss Drinkwater,* gift
unknown artist *Edward Drinkwater,* gift

unknown artist *William Bethune*, gift
unknown artist *Janet Anderson (Learmonth) (d.1838)*, gift
unknown artist *A Horseman Talking to Two Villagers*, bequeathed
unknown artist *James, 1st Marquess of Montrose*, bequeathed
unknown artist *Landscape with Castle Ruins*,
unknown artist *Man with a Pipe in an Interior*,
unknown artist *Marshy Landscape*,
unknown artist *Mrs Elizabeth Turner*, bequeathed
unknown artist *Portrait of a Gentleman*, (said to be Peter the Great),
unknown artist *Portrait of a Man (A Cavalier)*,
unknown artist *Roman Soldiers about to Arrest a Woman*, transferred
unknown artist *Sir Hugh Innes (1754–1831), Bt, of Lochalsh and Coxtown*, bequeathed
unknown artist *Steps and a Balustrade*,
unknown artist *Travellers with a Covered Wagon*, bequeathed
Wells, William Page Atkinson 1872–1923, *Teignmouth from Torquay Road*, gift
Y., M. B. *Mountainous Landscape*,
Yeoman, M. B. *The Grampians*, © the copyright holder

The National Trust for Scotland, Malleny Garden

Nasmyth, Alexander 1758–1840, *John Scott (1705–1793), 3rd of Malleny*, purchased
unknown artist *Cartaret George Scott (d.1875)*, purchased
unknown artist *Charlotte Elizabeth Cunningham, Wife of Francis Cartaret Scott*, purchased
unknown artist *Francis Cartaret Scott (1754–1835), Sixth Son of John Scott, 3rd of Malleny*, purchased
unknown artist *Genre Interior (Men in a Tavern Playing Cards)**,
unknown artist *John Scott (1640–1709), 1st of Malleny*, purchased
unknown artist *Landscape*,
unknown artist *Landscape*,
unknown artist *Landscape with a Ruined Castle in the Background**,
unknown artist *Landscape with Cows and Horses*,
unknown artist *Thomas Scott (d.1729), 2nd Scott of Malleny*, purchased

The National Trust for Scotland, The Georgian House

Anglo/Flemish School *James Graham, Marquis of Montrose*,
Balen I, Hendrik van (circle of) 1575–1632, *The Virgin and Child with a Female Martyr*, on loan from a private collection
Barber *William Henry Wayne, Esq.*, on loan from a private collection
Barclay, John MacLaren 1811–1886, *Thomas Graham-Stirling of Strowan*, bequeathed
Barker II, Benjamin (attributed to) 1776–1838, *A View of a Wooded Mountainous Landscape*, on loan from a private collection
Beechey, William 1753–1839, *Portrait of a Gentleman in a Black Coat*,
Bentley, Joseph Clayton 1809–1851, *A Wooded Landscape with a Mill and Peasants*, on loan from a private collection
Bonington, Richard Parkes 1802–1828, *River Scene with Gondolas, Rouen*, (after Joseph Mallord William Turner), on loan from a private collection
British (English) School *Anne Salmon*, on loan from a private collection
British (English) School *Lord Curzon*, on loan from a private collection
British (Scottish) School *Captain Thomas Graham of Airth, in Old Age*, bequeathed
British (Scottish) School *Helen Colt of Auldhame, Later Lady Rae*, bequeathed
Burton, Mungo 1799–1882, *John Hamilton Colt II of Gartsherrie*, bequeathed
Burton, Mungo 1799–1882, *Jane Colt*, bequeathed
Carse, Alexander 1770–1843, *A Seated Man Holding a Chanter and Family in an Interior*,
Chalmers, George 1720–1791, *Oliver Colt of Auldhame and Inveresk (1708–1782)*, bequeathed
Clovio, Giulio 1498–1578, *Marriage of the Virgin*, on loan from a private collection
Duncombe, Thomas *Mrs Morris*, gift
Dutch School *Portrait of a Bearded Man in a Hat*, on loan from a private collection
Dutch School *Shipping Offshore, a Dutch Seascape*, on loan from a private collection
Gordon, John Watson 1788–1864, *An Extensive View of Elliock, Dumfriesshire*, bequeathed
Goyen, Jan van 1596–1656, *A Town Wall by a River with Figures*, on loan from a private collection
Hondecoeter, Melchior de (circle of) 1636–1695, *A White Cockatoo and Other Birds in a Wooded Landscape*, on loan from a private collection
Italian School *Landscape with a Classical Building, Town, Lake and Mountains*,
Kneller, Godfrey 1646–1723, *Portrait of a Gentleman in a Grey Robe*, on loan from a private collection
Knox, John 1778–1845, *View of Glasgow Green and a Passing Storm*, gift
Labruzzi, Carlo (circle of) 1747–1817, *View of Lake Albano with the Alban Hills and Peasants*, on loan from a private collection
Luny, Thomas 1759–1837, *An Estuary with Shipping*, on loan from a private collection
Luny, Thomas 1759–1837, *Mouth of the River Teign*, on loan from a private collection
Martin, David 1736–1798, *Elizabeth Holt (d.1803)*, bequeathed
Martin, David 1736–1798, *Helen Stewart (1729/1730–1828), Later Mrs Colt of Auldhame, and Her Son, Adam*, bequeathed
Martin, David 1736–1798, *The Honourable Helen Colt of Auldhame (1729/1730–1828), and Her Granddaughter, Grace (1781–1802)*, bequeathed
McInnes, Robert 1801–1886, *Carolus Graham of Airth*, bequeathed
Moir, John (attributed to) 1776–1857, *Captain Thomas Graham of Airth, Later Graham-Stirling of Airth and Strowan*, bequeathed
Morland, George (attributed to) 1763–1804, *'Jack Ashore', an Inn Scene with Sailors*, on loan from a private collection
Morland, George (circle of) 1763–1804, *A Barn with Three Men and a Calf*, on loan from a private collection
Morland, George (circle of) 1763–1804, *Gypsies in a Wood*, on loan from a private collection
Müller, William James 1812–1845, *Landscape with a Woman in a Quarry*, on loan from a private collection
Müller, William James (style of) 1812–1845, *Street Scenes in Cairo*, on loan from a private collection
Muziano, Girolamo 1528–1592, *The Flight into Egypt*, on loan from a private collection
Nasmyth, Alexander 1758–1840, *Jane Ross of Shandwick*, gift
Nasmyth, Alexander 1758–1840, *Landscape with a Bridge and Ruined Castle*, gift
Nasmyth, Alexander 1758–1840, *St Bernard's Well and the Water of Leith*, purchased
Niccolò dell'Abate (circle of) 1509–1571, *Head of a Woman*, on loan from a private collection
Northcote, James 1746–1831, *Miss Lydia Hobson, Lady Grant*, on loan from a private collection
Patel, Pierre I 1605–1676, *Italianate Landscape with a Ruined Temple*, on loan from a private collection
Raeburn, Henry 1756–1823, *Alexander Keith*, on loan from Allan and Carol Murray, since 2004
Raeburn, Henry 1756–1823, *Mrs Walter Buchanan*, gift
Ramsay, Allan 1713–1784, *Portrait of a Lady*, on loan from a private collection
Ramsay, Allan (circle of) 1713–1784, *Elizabeth Fullerton of Carberry, née Colt*, bequeathed
Reni, Guido (follower of) 1575–1642, *Madonna and Child*, on loan from a private collection
Riley, John 1646–1691, *Sir Christopher Wren*, bequeathed
Teniers II, David (after) 1610–1690, *Tavern Interior*, on loan from a private collection
Teniers II, David (style of) 1610–1690, *Four Monkeys Smoking and Drinking*, on loan from a private collection
unknown artist *Dugald Gilchrist*, bequeathed
unknown artist *Elanor Middleton*, bequeathed
unknown artist *Family Group*, gift
unknown artist *'Man of Feeling', Henry Mackenzie*, gift
unknown artist *St Bernard's Well and the Water of Leith*,
Watson, William Smellie 1796–1874, *Thomas Philip Graham of Airth*, bequeathed
Wright of Derby, Joseph 1734–1797, *Captain Edward Salmon*, on loan from a private collection

The National Trust for Scotland, Royal Burgh of Culross

British (Scottish) School *Lilias Stirling, Daughter of Stirling of Keir and Wife of Colonel John Erskine*, on loan from a private collection
De Wett *The Honourable C. John Erskine, Son of David, 2nd Lord Cardross*, on loan from a private collection
Jamesone, George 1588–1644, *Sir George Bruce of Carnock*, gift
unknown artist *'Black' Sir John of Erskine of Cardross*, on loan from a private collection
unknown artist *Ships at Sea*

The National Trust for Scotland, Falkland Palace & Garden

Belle, Alexis-Simon (circle of) 1674–1734, *Prince James Edward Stuart (1720–1788), 'The Old Pretender', as a Boy*, bequeathed
British (English) School *Anne of Denmark (1574–1619)*, gift
British (English) School *Mary, Queen of Scots (1542–1587)*, gift
British (English) School *Prince Henry, Duke of Gloucester*, gift
British School *Lord Ninian Crichton-Stuart (1883–1915), and His Mother, the Marchioness of Bute (1854–1932)*, on loan from a private collection
British School *Lord Ninian Crichton-Stuart (1883–1915)*, on loan from a private collection
British School *James V (1512–1542), and Queen Mary of Guise (1515–1560)*, gift
Dujardin, Karel 1626–1678, *The Halt*, purchased
Dutch School *Portrait of an Old Woman*, bequeathed
Hanneman, Adriaen (circle of) 1601–1671, *Charles II (1630–1685)*, gift
Huysmans, Jacob (studio of) 1628–1696, *Queen Catherine (1638–1705)*, gift
Kneller, Godfrey (after) 1646–1723, *Lady Mary Pierrepont (1689–1762), Later Wortley Montagu*, gift
Kneller, Godfrey (after) 1646–1723, *The 4th Earl of Moray (c.1611–1653)*, on loan from a private collection
Larkin, William (circle of) 1585–1619, *Henry, Prince of Wales (1594–1612)*, gift
Lauder, John Ettrick *The Ten Virgins*, gift
Lely, Peter (circle of) 1618–1680, *Charles II (1630–1685)*, gift
Lorimer, John Henry 1856–1936, *Ninian Patrick (1907–1910), Son of Lady and Lord Crichton-Stuart*, on loan from a private source (?)
Sánchez Coello, Alonso (circle of) 1531–1588, *James VI (1566–1625)*, gift
Somer I, Paulus van (after) 1576–1621, *James VI and I (1566–1625), with the Collar of the Order of the Garter*, unknown acquisition method
Somer I, Paulus van (attributed to) 1576–1621, *James I (1566–1625)*, gift
Spanish School *Queen Margaret of Scotland (c.1045–1093)*, gift
Thomson, John 1778–1840, *Conway Castle*,
Troy, François de (after) 1645–1730, *Prince of Wales with His Sister, Louise Marie*, (after a portrait by Largillière), gift
unknown artist *Charlotte Jane Windsor, Viscountess Mountstuart, Baroness Cardiff of Cardiff Castle*, on loan from a private collection
unknown artist *Adoration of the Magi*,
unknown artist *Christ*,
unknown artist *Landscape*,
unknown artist *Madonna and Child*, bequeathed
unknown artist *Madonna and Child*,
unknown artist *Madonna and Child*,
unknown artist *Mary, Queen of Scots (1542–1587)*, on loan from a private collection
unknown artist *Our Lady of Ostrobrama*,
unknown artist *Saint Michael and the Dragon (?)*
unknown artist *Scenes from the Life of Christ*

The National Trust for Scotland, Hill of Tarvit Mansionhouse & Garden

Abbott, Lemuel Francis (after) 1760–1803, *The Golf Players*, bequeathed

Anglo/Dutch School *Hawking Party on Horseback by a Ruin*, bequeathed

Avercamp, Barent Petersz. 1612–1679, *Winter Landscape with Skaters on a River*, bequeathed

Avercamp, Barent Petersz. (follower of) 1612–1679, *Winter Landscape with Skaters on a River near a Town*, bequeathed

Avercamp, Hendrick (follower of) 1585–1634, *A Winter Landscape with Figures around a Bridge*, bequeathed

Beecq, Jan Karel Donatus van 1638–1722, *A Naval Engagement*, bequeathed

Beerstraten, Anthonie active c.1635–c.1665, *Winter Landscape with Figures by a Bridge to a Church*, bequeathed

Berckheyde, Gerrit Adriaensz. (circle of) 1638–1698, *Winter Landscape with Men Playing Kolf*, bequeathed

Beyeren, Abraham van 1620–1690, *Still Life with a Lobster*, bequeathed

Bogdany, Jakob 1660–1724, *Peacocks and Other Exotic Birds*, bequeathed

Bogdany, Jakob (style of) 1660–1724, *Still Life of Fruit and Birds*, bequeathed

Bogdany, Jakob (style of) 1660–1724, *Still Life of Fruit and Birds*, bequeathed

British (Scottish) School *Frederick Sharp*, bequeathed

Brueghel the younger, Pieter 1564–1638, *The Bird Trap (Winter Landscape)*, bequeathed

Claesz., Pieter (follower of) 1597–1660, *Still Life*, bequeathed

Constable, John (follower of) 1776–1837, *Hampstead Heath*, bequeathed

Cuyp, Aelbert (style of) 1620–1691, *A Ferry Boat*, bequeathed

Cuyp, Jacob Gerritsz. 1594–1651, *Portrait of a Girl in Red and White*, bequeathed

Dubbels, Hendrik Jacobsz. (follower of) 1621–1707, *Winter Landscape with a Frozen River*, bequeathed

Dutch School *A Pronk Still Life*, bequeathed

Dutch School *Portrait of a Gentleman*, bequeathed

Dutch School *Still Life with Flowers in a Vase*, bequeathed

Fantin-Latour, Henri 1836–1904, *Flowerpiece*, bequeathed

Fantin-Latour, Henri 1836–1904, *Les violettes et les giroflées*, bequeathed

German School *Portrait of a Lady in Black and Red*, bequeathed

Gordon, John Watson 1788–1864, *Mrs Brown of Newhall, Penicuik, and Her Daughter*, bequeathed

Heda, Willem Claesz. (circle of) 1594–1680, *Still Life*, bequeathed

Heem, Jan Davidsz. de (follower of) 1606–1684, *Still Life*, bequeathed

Heeremans, Thomas 1640–1697, *Winter Landscape with Skaters on a Canal*, bequeathed

Heeremans, Thomas (follower of) 1640–1697, *Winter Landscape with Figures on a River*, bequeathed

Herring I, John Frederick 1795–1865, *The Fresh Team*, bequeathed

Herring I, John Frederick 1795–1865, *The Forge*, bequeathed

Highmore, Joseph 1692–1780, *Peg Woffington*, bequeathed

Hondecoeter, Melchior de (follower of) 1636–1695, *Fighting Cocks*, bequeathed

Ibbetson, Julius Caesar 1759–1817, *Waiting for the Coach*, bequeathed

Ibbetson, Julius Caesar (circle of) 1759–1817, *A Wooded Landscape with Cattle Watering*, bequeathed

Italo/Dutch School *Landscape with a Villa*, bequeathed

Italo/Dutch School *River Landscape with a Tower*, bequeathed

Maddersteeg, Michiel 1659–1714, *Dutch Shipping in a Breeze*, bequeathed

Martin, David (attributed to) 1736–1798, *Jean, Daughter of John Bernie of Broomhall and Wife of Alexander Chancellor of Shieldhall*, bequeathed

Monamy, Peter 1681–1749, *The Evening Gun*, bequeathed

Moreelse, Paulus 1571–1638, *Portrait of a Lady*, bequeathed

Morland, George 1763–1804, *Winter Landscape with Peasants and Donkeys*, bequeathed

Muir, Anne Davidson 1875–1951, *Carnations in a Vase*, © the copyright holder

Neer, Aert van der (attributed to) 1603–1677, *Winter Landscape with a River, Cottage and Village Beyond*, bequeathed

Noble, John Sargeant 1848–1896, *Still Life with a Dead Swan*, bequeathed

Peeters I, Bonaventura 1614–1652, *A Vessel Wrecked beneath a Fort in a Storm*, bequeathed

Pickenoy, Nicolaes Eliasz. 1588–1655, *Vrouw Elizabeth Coreboult*, bequeathed

Raeburn, Henry 1756–1823, *John Tait of Harvieston*, bequeathed

Raeburn, Henry 1756–1823, *Mrs Tyndall Bruce*, bequeathed

Ramsay, Allan 1713–1784, *Captain Thomas Wallace*, bequeathed

Ramsay, Allan 1713–1784, *Mrs William Mure of Caldwell*, bequeathed as part of the Sharp Collection, 1949

Ramsay, Allan (circle of) 1713–1784, *The Honourable Mrs Young, Daughter of the 1st Lord Holland*, bequeathed

Ravesteyn, Jan Anthonisz. van (attributed to) 1570–1657, *Portrait of a Gentleman with a White Ruff*, bequeathed

Rolzhoven, Julius 1858–1930, *Hugh Sharp (1897–1937), as a Boy in Highland Dress*, bequeathed

Rolzhoven, Julius 1858–1930, *Mrs Frederick Sharp*, bequeathed

Ruysdael, Salomon van 1602–1670, *Wooded River Landscape*, bequeathed

Schotanus, Petrus active c.1663–1687, *Vanitas Still Life*, bequeathed

Shields, Robert Gordon *Frederick Sharp*, bequeathed

Shields, Robert Gordon *Still Life with a Vase of Flowers*, bequeathed

Storck, Abraham Jansz. 1644–1708, *Seaport*, bequeathed

Stralen, Antoni van (attributed to) 1594–1641, *Winter Landscape*, bequeathed

Teniers I, David 1582–1649, *River Landscape with Peasants and Cattle*, bequeathed

Towne, Charles 1763–1840, *A Gentleman Shooting with a Spaniel*, bequeathed

Turner, Daniel active 1782–c.1828, *Southwark Bridge*, bequeathed

Turner, Daniel (circle of) active 1782–c.1828, *Westminster Bridge*, bequeathed

Weenix, Jan Baptist (attributed to) 1621–1661, *Hounds and an Owl with Dead Birds and Sculptures in a Landscape*, bequeathed

Weenix, Jan Baptist (attributed to) 1621–1661, *Still Life with Dead Birds*, bequeathed

Wheatley, Francis (style of) 1747–1801, *The Love Letter*, bequeathed

Wilkie, David 1785–1841, *The Reading of the Will*, bequeathed

Wyck, Jan 1645–1700, *A Pointer in a Landscape*, bequeathed

Zuylen, Hendrick van active 1613–1646, *Still Life*, bequeathed

The National Trust for Scotland, Kellie Castle & Garden

Boyter, Ian Hugh b.1943, *Crail*, © the artist

British (Scottish) School *Kellie Castle, Fife*, purchased

Chalmers, A. J. *St Andrews Harbour*, gift

de Wet, Jacob Jacobsz. 1640–1697, *Classical Scene of Gods*, transferred

Droochsloot, Joost Cornelisz. 1586–1666, *The Market Place at Amersfoort*, purchased

L'Espinasse (Comtesse), Marie *A Peasant in a Field*, gift

Lorimer, Hannah active late 19th C, *Portrait of a Man*, (copy after Henry Raeburn),

Lorimer, Hannah active late 19th C, *The Madonna of the Magnificat*, (after Sandro Botticelli), purchased

Lorimer, John Henry 1856–1936, *San Giovanni Crisogono Altarpiece*, (after Giovanni Bellini), gift

Lorimer, John Henry 1856–1936, *A Beech Tree at Kellie*, purchased

Lorimer, John Henry 1856–1936, *Hannah Lorimer Embroidering a Bedcover*, transferred

Lorimer, John Henry 1856–1936, *T. W. Lorimer*, gift

Lorimer, John Henry 1856–1936, *Sunlight in the South Room, Kellie*, on loan from the Astronomical Society of Edinburgh

Lorimer, John Henry 1856–1936, *The Long Shadows*, on loan from the Astronomical Society of Edinburgh

Lorimer, John Henry 1856–1936, *A Gentleman Holding a Glove*, (after Titian), purchased

Lorimer, John Henry 1856–1936, *A Still Life with a Vase of Flowers*, gift

Lorimer, John Henry 1856–1936, *Any Port in a Storm*, purchased

Lorimer, John Henry 1856–1936, *December Roses*, gift

Lorimer, John Henry 1856–1936, *Le peintre des fleurs*, purchased

Lorimer, John Henry 1856–1936, *Sir David Chalmers*, gift

Lorimer, John Henry 1856–1936, *Striped Roses in a Ship Mug*, gift

Lorimer, John Henry 1856–1936, *The Finding of Moses*, (after Giovanni Battista Tiepolo), gift

Lorimer, John Henry 1856–1936, *The Madonna and Child with Two Musical Angels*, purchased

Lorimer, John Henry 1856–1936, *View through a Window*,

Lorimer, Mary *Monica, Aged 7*, on loan from a private collection

Lorimer, Robert Stodart 1864–1929, *Church Spire*, gift

Lorimer, Robert Stodart 1864–1929, *A Cock and Hens*, purchased

Os, Jan van circle of 1744–1808, *Still Life with Fruit and Flowers*, purchased

Raeburn, Henry after 1756–1823, *Robert Stodart*, purchased

Sellon, William active 1882–1887, *A Bedroom in Holyrood Palace*, bequeathed

Sellon, William active 1882–1887, *A Drawing Room in Holyrood Palace*, bequeathed

Traquair, Phoebe Anna 1852–1936, *Cupid's Darts*, transferred

unknown artist *Landscape*, transferred

unknown artist *Landscape*, transferred

unknown artist *Landscape*, transferred

unknown artist *Landscape*, transferred

unknown artist *Landscape*, transferred

unknown artist *Landscape*, transferred

unknown artist *Landscape*, transferred

unknown artist *Landscape*, transferred

unknown artist *Landscape*, transferred

unknown artist *Landscape*, transferred

unknown artist *Landscape*, transferred

unknown artist *Landscape*, transferred

unknown artist *Landscape*, transferred

unknown artist *Landscape*, transferred

unknown artist *Landscape*, transferred

unknown artist *Landscape*, transferred

unknown artist *Landscape*, transferred

unknown artist *Landscape*, transferred

unknown artist *Landscape*, transferred

unknown artist *Landscape*, transferred

unknown artist *Landscape*, transferred

unknown artist *Landscape*, transferred

unknown artist *Landscape*, transferred

unknown artist *Landscape*, transferred

unknown artist *Landscape*, transferred

unknown artist *Landscape*, transferred

unknown artist *Landscape*, transferred

unknown artist *Landscape*, transferred

unknown artist *Landscape*, transferred

unknown artist *Landscape*, transferred

unknown artist *Landscape*, transferred

unknown artist *Landscape*, transferred

unknown artist *Landscape*, transferred

unknown artist *Landscape*, transferred

unknown artist *Landscape*, transferred

unknown artist *Landscape*, transferred

unknown artist *Landscape*, transferred

unknown artist *Landscape*, transferred

unknown artist *Landscape*, transferred

unknown artist *Landscape*, transferred

unknown artist *Landscape*, transferred

unknown artist *Landscape*, transferred

unknown artist *Landscape*, transferred

unknown artist *Landscape*, transferred

unknown artist *Landscape*, transferred

unknown artist *Landscape*, transferred

unknown artist *Landscape*, transferred

unknown artist *Landscape*, transferred
unknown artist *Landscape*, transferred
unknown artist *Landscape*, transferred
unknown artist *Landscape*, transferred
unknown artist *Landscape*, transferred
unknown artist *Landscape*, transferred
unknown artist *Landscape*, transferred
unknown artist *Landscape*, transferred
unknown artist *Landscape*, transferred
unknown artist *Landscape*, purchased, 1970
unknown artist *Landscape*, transferred
unknown artist *Landscape*, transferred
unknown artist *Landscape*, transferred
unknown artist *Landscape*, transferred
unknown artist *Landscape*, transferred
unknown artist *Landscape*, transferred
unknown artist *Landscape*, transferred
unknown artist *Study of a Corner of a Room*, purchased
unknown artist *Thomas, 6th Earl of Kellie*, on loan from the Earl of Mar and Kellie
unknown artist *Vanitas*,
Wylie, Mary *Monica with a Blenheim Cavalier King Charles Spaniel*, purchased © the copyright holder

The National Trust for Scotland, Greenbank Garden

Peploe, Samuel John 1871–1935, *Anemones in a Brown Jar*, bequeathed
Turner, Joseph Mallord William (after) 1775–1851, *Venice*, bequeathed
unknown artist *Helen Wilson, née Primrose, Wife of James Wilson*, gift
unknown artist *James Wilson (1794–1863), Soap Maker and Candlemaker, Glasgow*, gift
unknown artist *Margaret Wilson, née Blackburn, Wife of James Wilson*, gift
unknown artist *James Wilson, Cooper of Pollockshaws, Glasgow*, gift

The National Trust for Scotland, Hugh Miller Museum & Birthplace Cottage

Bonner *Hugh Miller and Harriet*, gift
Kay, William *Lydia, Hugh Miller's Wife*, purchased
Taylor, Mike *Sundial Carved by Hugh Miller*, gift © the copyright holder
unknown artist *Hugh Miller*, gift

The National Trust for Scotland, Culloden Battlefield & Visitor Centre

Alexander, Cosmo (attributed to) 1724–1772, *Portrait of a Jacobite Lady*, on loan from a private collection
Hamilton, Hugh Douglas 1739–1808, *Prince Charles Edward Stuart (1720–1788)*, on loan from the National Portrait Gallery, London
unknown artist *Prince Charles Edward Stuart (1720–1788)*, on loan from a private collection

The National Trust for Scotland, Brodie Castle

Abbott, Lemuel Francis (attributed to) 1760–1803, *Alexander Brodie of Armhall and the Burn*, transferred
Alexander, Robert L. 1840–1923, *Mr Wu – A Pekingese*, transferred
Anderson, Douglas Hardinge b.1934, *Ninian Brodie of Brodie, 25th Brodie of Brodie*, purchased © the artist
Barclay, John MacLaren 1811–1886, *Hugh Brodie, 23rd Laird*, transferred
Barker II, Benjamin 1776–1838, *A Wooded River Landscape with a Bridge*, transferred
Barraud, Henry 1811–1874, *Black Horse in a Loose Box*, transferred
Barret the elder, George (circle of) 1728–1784, *Wooded Landscape*, transferred
Berchem, Nicolaes Pietersz (style of) 1620–1683, *A Ford*, transferred
Blanche, Jacques-Emile 1861–1942, *Racing Yachts on the Seine*, transferred
Bloemaert, Abraham 1566–1651, *Boy with a Flute*, transferred
Bol, Ferdinand 1616–1680, *Portrait of a Man*, transferred
Brangwyn, Frank 1867–1956, *Two Bridges, Perugia (The Viaduct)*, transferred © the artist's estate/ Bridgeman Art Library
British (English) School *Maidservant*, transferred
British (Norwich) School *Farm among Trees*, transferred
British (Scottish) School *Portrait of a Lady in a Red Wrap*, (said to be Mary Sleigh), transferred
British (Scottish) School *Elizabeth Baillie, Wife of William Brodie, 22nd Laird*, transferred
British School *Portrait of a Nobleman*, (said to be King James VI and I), transferred
British School *Anne, Wife of James Brodie*, transferred
British School *William Douglas Brodie, Son of James Brodie, 21st Laird*, transferred
British School *Oliver Cromwell*, transferred
Brodie, H. *A Woodland Path with Children*, (possibly at Osterley), transferred
Brodie, Joseph *James Brodie of Spynie*, transferred
Brown, John Alfred Arnesby 1866–1955, *A Norfolk Landscape with Potato Pickers*, transferred © the copyright holder
Brown, William Beattie 1831–1909, *Trees in Perthshire at Dusk*, transferred
Brueghel, Abraham (1631–1690) & Courtois, Guillaume (1628–1679) *Putti with Fruit and an Urn of Flowers*, transferred
Brundrit, Reginald Grange 1883–1960, *Stainforth, A Welsh Valley Farm*, purchased, 1980 © the copyright holder
Cadell, Francis Campbell Boileau 1883–1937, *Still Life with Blue Jug, Fan and an Apple*, purchased, 1980
Cameron, Hugh 1835–1918, *Among the Olives*, purchased, 1980
Camphuysen, Govert Dircksz. (attributed to) 1623–1672, *A Herdsman with Cattle, Sheep and Goats*, purchased, 1980
Carracci, Annibale (after) 1560–1609, *The Lamentation (Pietà)*, transferred
Chalon, Alfred Edward (attributed to) 1780–1860, *Elizabeth Brodie, Wife of the 5th Duke of Gordon*, transferred
Chalon, Alfred Edward (attributed to) 1780–1860, *George, 5th Duke of Gordon*, transferred
Ciardi, Emma 1879–1933, *Venice from the Lagoon*, transferred
Clérisseau, Charles Louis (circle of) 1722–1820, *A Classical Capriccio*, transferred
Coello, Claudio (after) 1642–1693, *Portrait of a Prince of the House of Spain, in Armour*, transferred
Cossiers, Jan (attributed to) 1600–1671, *The Concert*, transferred
Coypel, Antoine 1661–1722, *Leda and the Swan*, transferred
Craddock, Luke *Birds in a Landscape*, transferred
Craddock, Luke *Birds in a Landscape*, transferred
Crosbie, William 1915–1999, *Inlet*, transferred © the artist's estate
Currie, James active from 1846, *Caithness and William Brodie as Children in a Nursery*, transferred
Currie, James active from 1846, *Elizabeth Baillie, Wife of William Brodie*, transferred
Currie, James active from 1846, *George and Hugh Brodie as Children in Highland Dress on a Moor*, transferred
Currie, James active from 1846, *Family of William Brodie, 22nd Laird*, transferred
Currie, James active from 1846, *William Brodie, 22nd Laird*, transferred
Cuyp, Jacob Gerritsz. (after) 1594–1651, *Portrait of a Lady*, transferred
Cuyp, Jacob Gerritsz. (after) 1594–1651, *Portrait of a Man*, transferred
Delorme, Anthonie de 1610–1673, *Interior of the Church of Saint Bavo, Haarlem*, transferred
Dickson, Thomas Francis *The Penitent Magdalen*, transferred
Douglas, Andrew 1871–1935, *Highland Cattle in a Landscape*, transferred
Douglas, Phoebe Sholto b.1906, *Ian Brodie, 24th Brodie of Brodie*, transferred © the copyright holder
Downman, John 1750–1824, *Lady Margaret Duff, Daughter of the 1st Earl of Fife and Wife of James Brodie, 21st Laird*, transferred
Duck, Jacob 1600–1667, *Soldiers and Women Revelling in an Interior*, transferred
Dupré, Jules 1811–1889, *Cattle at a Woodland Pond*, transferred
Dutch School *A Footbridge across a River*, transferred
Dutch School *Riverscape with a Castle*, transferred
Dyck, Anthony van (after) 1599–1641, *Charles I (1600–1649)*, transferred
Dyck, Anthony van (follower of) 1599–1641, *The Penitent Magdalen*, transferred
Ewbank, John Wilson 1799–1847, *Edinburgh*, transferred
Ewbank, John Wilson (circle of) 1799–1847, *Shipping off Dover*, transferred
Faed, Thomas 1826–1900, *Old Woman Reading*, transferred
Ferguson, William Gouw 1632–1695, *Still Life with Game Birds*, transferred
Ferrari, Luca 1605–1654, *Herod and Mariamne*, transferred
Franco/German School *Landscape with a Herdsman and Women*, transferred
Frazer, William Miller 1864–1961, *Kings Lynn, Norfolk*, transferred © the artist's estate
G., D. C. *Fruit on a Salver on a Marble Ledge*, transferred
Gaultier, A. M. *Flowers and Fruit on a Marble Ledge*, transferred
Gaultier, A. M. *Fruit and a Wedgwood Vase*, transferred
Gibbon, Benjamin b.1914, *Spring Flowers in a Silver Mug*, transferred © the copyright holder
Goltzius, Hendrick (circle of) 1558–1617, *Saint John the Evangelist*, transferred
Goltzius, Hendrick (circle of) 1558–1617, *Saint Luke*, transferred
Gordon, John Watson 1788–1864, *William Brodie, 23rd Laird*, transferred
Gordon, John Watson (circle of) 1788–1864, *Elizabeth Duchess of Gordon*, transferred
Gordon, John Watson (circle of) 1788–1864, *Earl of Caithness in Highland Dress*, transferred
Guardi, Francesco (circle of) 1712–1793, *Venetian Fondamenta*, transferred
Guillaumin, Armand 1841–1927, *The Jetty*, transferred
H., J. A. *Military Scene in a Landscape*, transferred
H., J. A. *Military Scene in a Landscape*, transferred
Hardie, Charles Martin 1858–1916, *Old Church, Whittinghame*, transferred
Haupt, Zygmunt 1907–1975, *The Street of Lapalud*, transferred © the copyright holder
Hayter, George 1792–1871, *The Honourable Mrs William Ashley*, transferred
Hendriks, Gerardus 1804–1859, *A Dutch River Scene*, transferred
Hickey, Thomas 1741–1824, *James Brodie (d.1802)*, transferred
Holland, James 1799–1870, *Entrance to the Grand Canal, Venice*, transferred
Hondecoeter, Melchior de (circle of) 1636–1695, *Birds in a Landscape*, transferred
Hope, Robert 1869–1936, *The Vanity Glass*, transferred
Huet I, Jean-Baptiste (style of) 1745–1811, *Pastoral Scene*, trnsferred
Huet I, Jean-Baptiste (style of) 1745–1811, *Pastoral Scene*, transferred
Hughes-Stanton, Herbert Edwin Pelham 1870–1937, *The Path to the Village*, transferred
Hunter, George Leslie 1879–1931, *Still Life with Wine Bottle, Glass, Fruit and Flowers*, transferred
Hutchison, Robert Gemmell 1855–1936, *Interior with Old Woman at a Hearth*, transferred
Hutchison, Robert Gemmell 1855–1936, *On the Bents, Carnoustie*, transferred
Hutchison, Robert Gemmell 1855–1936, *The Goldfish Bowl*, transferred
Italian (Florentine) School *Angel of the Annunciation*, transferred
Italian (Venetian) School *Grand Canal, Venice*, transferred
Jurnet, F. active 1850–1857, *A Donkey and Cattle at a Pool*, transferred
Jurnet, F. (attributed to) active 1850–1857, *Cattle and Sheep*, transferred
Keyser, Thomas de (attributed to) 1596–1667, *Portrait of a Man*, transferred
Knoop, M. *An Old Woman Reading*, transferred
Lambinet, Emile Charles 1815–1877, *French River Landscape with Cattle Grazing*, transferred
Lamorinière, Jean Pierre François 1828–1911, *The Pools, near Antwerp*, transferred
Lampi, Giuseppe *Czarina Catherine the Great*, transferred
Landseer, Edwin Henry 1802–1873, *Head of 'Driver', a Deerhound Owned by the 5th Duke of Gordon*, transferred

Loiseau, Gustave 1865–1935, *Snow at Saint Auen d'Aumone,* transferred

Loiseau, Gustave 1865–1935, *Printemps à Vaudreuil,* transferred

Luce, Maximilien 1858–1941, *Spring, Trees in a Landscape,* transferred

MacTaggart, William 1903–1981, *Evening, Oslofjord,* transferred © by permission of the artist's family

Marquet, Albert 1875–1947, *Toits à Venise,* transferred © ADAGP, Paris and DACS, London 2013

Martin, David 1736–1798, *James Brodie, 21st Laird,* transferred

Martin, David (circle of) 1736–1798, *Portrait of a Woman and Her Child,* transferred

McCulloch, Horatio 1805–1867, *Coastal Landscape with a Castle at Sunset,* transferred

McKay, William Darling 1844–1924, *Landscape, Harrowing,* transferred

Medina, John (circle of) 1720–1796, *David Petty,* transferred

Michel, Georges 1763–1843, *The Gathering Storm (Landscape with Quarry and Figures),* transferred

Mieris the elder, Frans van (after) 1635–1681, *Violinist,* transferred

Munro, Mary *A Highland Estuary,* gift © the copyright holder

Musscher, Michiel van (circle of) 1645–1705, *Portrait of a Lady,* transferred

Musscher, Michiel van (circle of) 1645–1705, *Portrait of a Man,* transferred

Nash, John Northcote 1893–1977, *The Farm,* transferred © the artist's estate/Bridgeman Art Library

Neeffs the elder, Peeter 1578–1656, *A Cathedral Interior,* transferred

Nevinson, Christopher 1889–1946, *Fishermen on the Seine,* transferred © the artist's estate/ Bridgeman Art Library

Nicholls, Bertram 1883–1974, *Pitigliano,* transferred © the copyright holder

Nicholls, Bertram 1883–1974, *A Mountain Village,* transferred © the copyright holder

Nicholls, Bertram 1883–1974, *Philippe le Bel's Tower,* transferred © the copyright holder

Nicholson, William 1872–1949, *The Paper Poppies,* transferred © Elizabeth Banks

Northcote, James (attributed to) 1746–1831, *Ann, Wife of James Brodie, and Her Son, presumably William, Later 22nd Laird,* transferred

O'Connor, James Arthur (attributed to) 1792–1841, *A Classical Landscape,* transferred

Olsson, Albert Julius 1864–1942, *Moonlight on the Coast,* transferred

Opie, John 1761–1807, *James Brodie, Son of the 21st Laird,* transferred

Opie, John 1761–1807, *William Brodie, Later 22nd Laird, with His Brothers, Sisters and a Dog,* transferred

Ostade, Adriaen van (circle of) 1610–1685, *A Toper,* transferred

Padwick, Philip Hugh 1876–1958, *Distant Hills,* transferred © the copyright holder

Pavy, Philippe 1860–1930, *A Street Scene in Malaga with Child and Donkeys,* transferred

Peploe, Samuel John 1871–1935, *Douglas Hall,* transferred

Phillips, Charles (attributed to) 1708–1748, *Alexander (Sandy) Brodie, Later 20th Laird, as a Child with a Dog,* transferred

Pickenoy, Nicolaes Eliasz. 1588–1655, *Portrait of a Lady,* transferred

Pickenoy, Nicolaes Eliasz. 1588–1655, *Portrait of a Man,* transferred

Poelenburgh, Cornelis van 1594–1667, *Tobias with the Angel,* transferred

Poelenburgh, Cornelis van (circle of) 1594–1667, *Nymphs Bathing in a Classical Landscape,* transferred

Poelenburgh, Cornelis van (circle of) 1594–1667, *The Crucifixion, with Castel Sant'Angelo,* transferred

Pritchett, Edward active c.1828–1879, *The Dogana and Santa Maria della Salute, Venice,* transferred

Quinn, James Peter 1869–1951, *Fish Market at Étaples, France,* transferred © the copyright holder

Ramsay, Allan (after) 1713–1784, *Alexander Brodie, 19th Laird, Lord Lyon,* transferred

Reid, George 1841–1913, *Loch Spynie with a Figure Wildfowling,* transferred

Richardson the elder, Jonathan (attributed to) 1664–1745, *Portrait of a Lady,* transferred

Roberts, David (follower of) 1796–1864, *The Cathedral, Mainz,* transferred

Romney, George (after) 1734–1802, *Jane, Duchess of Gordon, and Her Son, George,* transferred

Rosa, Salvator (circle of) 1615–1673, *Figures in an Upland Classical Landscape,* transferred

S., R. *Daffodils,* © the copyright holder

Saedeleer, Valerius de 1867–1941, *Printemps,* transferred

Schoevaerdts, Mathys 1665–1723, *An Extensive River Landscape with Travelling Theatrical Troupe,* transferred

Schutz, J. A. H. *Banditti Attacking a Coach,* transferred

Schutz, J. A. H. *Banditti Dividing Their Spoil,* transferred

Serres, John Thomas 1759–1825, *Fishing Boat at Fulham,* transferred

Shields, Harry Gordon 1859–1935, *Still Life, Pompom Dahlias,* transferred

Smart, John 1838–1899, *Highland Cattle in Cornfield,* transferred

Smith, Colvin (circle of) 1795–1875, *George, 5th Duke of Gordon,* transferred

Spanish School *Saint Lawrence,* transferred

Steelink II, Willem 1856–1928, *Changing Pastures,* transferred

Stevens, Alfred Emile Léopold Joseph Victor 1823–1906, *Fishing Boats at Dusk,* transferred

Sustermans, Justus (circle of) 1597–1681, *Portrait of a Woman,* transferred

Teniers II, David (after) 1610–1690, *The Alchemist,* transferred

Teniers II, David (after) 1610–1690, *The Dentist,* transferred

Thaulow, Fritz (attributed to) 1847–1906, *Watermill,* transferred

Thomson, John 1778–1840, *Gorge with a Bridge (Bridge over a Ravine),* transferred

Thornton, Robert John 1763–1837, *Project for a Ceiling,* transferred

unknown artist *Caricature,* transferred

unknown artist *Portrait of a Lady in a Feigned Oval,*

unknown artist *Portrait of a Woman in White,*

Vaillant, Wallerand 1623–1677, *Young Artist,* transferred

Vincent, George 1796–1831, *Woodland Road with Horseman and Sheep,* transferred

Vliet, Willem van der 1583–1642, *Philosopher and His Pupils,* transferred

Vollon, Antoine 1833–1900, *A Bowl of Fruit and Silver on a Table,* transferred

Walker, Robert (style of) 1599–1658, *Portrait of a Gentleman in Armour,* transferred

Walls, William 1860–1942, *A Leopard,* transferred

Walls, William 1860–1942, *Lion Cubs,* transferred

Ward, James 1769–1859, *A Grey in a Stable,* transferred

Watteau, Jean-Antoine (follower of) 1684–1721, *Fête Champêtre: Music Party under an Awning,* transferred

Watts, Frederick W. (circle of) 1800–1870, *In the Meadows,* transferred

Weiss, José 1859–1919, *In Hampshire, a Landscape with Cottages,* transferred

Weiss, José (attributed to) 1859–1919, *A Wooded River Landscape in Winter,* transferred

Wilkie, David 1785–1841, *The Village School,* transferred

Wintour, John Crawford 1825–1882, *Wooded Riverscape at Sunset,* transferred

Wood, Christopher 1901–1930, *Gates in Paris,* transferred

Wouwerman, Philips (circle of) 1619–1668, *Figures under a Tree,* transferred

The National Trust for Scotland, Brodick Castle, Garden & Country Park

Alken, Henry Thomas 1785–1851, *The Dead Heat for the Doncaster St Leger, with 'Voltigeur' and 'Russborough',* gift

Alken, Henry Thomas 1785–1851, *A Chestnut Racing with a Jockey Up, with Red Colours,* gift

Alken, Henry Thomas 1785–1851, *A Chestnut with the Jockey Up, with Green Colours,* gift

Alken, Henry Thomas 1785–1851, *Cockfighting,* gift

Alken, Henry Thomas 1785–1851, *Cockfighting,* gift

Alken, Henry Thomas 1785–1851, *Fighting Cock in a Landscape,* gift

Alken, Henry Thomas 1785–1851, *The Doncaster Cup, 1858, with 'Voltigeur' and 'The Flying Dutchman',* gift

Alken, Henry Thomas 1785–1851, *The Meet,* gift

Alken, Samuel Henry 1810–1894, *'Ossian', Winner of the Doncaster St Leger,* gift

Balmer, George 1805–1846, *On the Coast of Fife,* gift

Bardwell, Thomas 1704–1767, *Portrait of a Lady,* (possibly of the Nassau de Zuylestein family), gift

Bardwell, Thomas 1704–1767, *William Henry Nassau de Zuylestein (1717–1781), 4th Earl of Rochford,* gift

Bell, Edward *On the Road to Port Patrick, near Maybole,* gift

Bellangé, Hippolyte 1800–1866, *Comrades,* gift

Berchem, Nicolaes Pietersz. (follower of) 1620–1683, *A Woman with Cattle and Sheep,* gift

Beul, Henri de 1845–1900, *Chickens in a Farmyard,* gift

Bravell, Rospar *Michael McCarfrae (1820–1876), Piper to the 11th Duke of Hamilton,* on loan from a great-great-granddaughter of the sitter (?)

Breenbergh, Bartholomeus (circle of) 1598–1657, *Classical Ruins with Figures,* gift

British (English) School *The Fight between Jackson and Mendoza at Hornchurch, 1795,* gift

British (English) School *'Nimrod' in at the Death,* gift

British (English) School *The Old Front Door, Brodick Castle,* gift

Buckner, Richard 1812–1883, *William (1845–1893), 12th Duke of Hamilton, as a Boy,* gift

Buckner, Richard 1812–1883, *William Alexander (1811–1863), 11th Duke of Hamilton,* gift

Buckner, Richard (attributed to) 1812–1883, *William Alexander (1811–1863), 11th Duke of Hamilton,* gift

Chalon, Henry Bernard 1771–1849, *Boy with Three Bullmastiffs,* gift

Chalon, Henry Bernard 1771–1849, *Three Terriers with Two Dead Rats,* gift

Clouet, François 1515–1572, *Charles IX of France (1550–1574),* on loan from the National Galleries of Scotland

Cordrey, John 1765–1825, *'Darnock' Beating 'Ledongheds' for the King's Plate at Newmarket,* gift

Cordrey, John 1765–1825, *'Gimcrack' Beating Two Other Horses at Epsom,* gift

Dandridge, Bartholomew 1691–1754, *William Henry Nassau de Zuylestein (1717–1781), 4th Earl of Rochford,* gift

Dou, Gerrit 1613–1675, *Portrait of an Old Lady (The Painter's Aunt),* gift

Duval, John 1816–1892, *'Friday' with Jockey on a Racecourse,* gift

Duval, John 1816–1892, *'Golden Pippin' in a Loosebox,* gift

Duval, John 1816–1892, *'Scot Guard', a Grey, with Jockey Up in a Landscape,* gift

Dyck, Anthony van (after) 1599–1641, *Frederick Henry, Prince of Orange (1584–1647), in Armour,* gift

Dyck, Anthony van (after) 1599–1641, *Countess Amalia of Solms (1602–1675), Wife of Frederick Henry, Prince of Orange,* gift

Fielding, Anthony V. C. 1787–1855, *Sailing Boat in Rough Seas off a Jetty,* gift

Fragonard, Jean-Honoré (circle of) 1732–1806, *Study of a Girl in a Brown Dress,* gift

Gainsborough, Thomas 1727–1788, *Cattle Watering in a Stream,* gift

Gainsborough, Thomas 1727–1788, *Landscape with a Peasant Driving Cows,* gift

Gainsborough, Thomas 1727–1788, *Richard Savage Nassau de Zuylestein (1723–1780), Second Son of the 3rd Earl of Rochford,* purchased

Garrard, George 1760–1826, *Equestrian Portrait of Douglas, 8th Duke of Hamilton and Brandon,* gift

German School *Children with Sheep, Cattle and Goats Resting near a Town,* gift

German School *Figures and Animals, with a Distant Ruined Roman Bridge,* gift

Grant, Francis 1803–1878, *Lady Susan Hamilton (d.1891), Daughter of Alexander, 10th Duke of Hamilton,* gift

Grant, Francis (attributed to) 1803–1878, *Princess Marie of Baden (1817–1888), Daughter of Charles Louis Frederick, Prince of Baden,* gift

Hall, Harry 1814–1896, *Bay Racehorse with a Jockey on*

Newmarket Racecourse, gift

Hall, Harry 1814–1896, *'Lollypop' in a Loosebox*, gift

Hanneman, Adriaen (after) 1601–1671, *William Hamilton (1616–1650), KG, 2nd Duke of Hamilton*, gift

Hering, George Edwards 1805–1879, *View of Brodick Bay*, gift

Herring I, John Frederick 1795–1865, *The St Leger, 1826*, gift

Herring I, John Frederick 1795–1865, *'Mundig', Winner of the Derby, 1835*, gift

Herring I, John Frederick 1795–1865, *'Charles XII', Winner of the St Leger, 1839*, gift

Herring I, John Frederick 1795–1865, *Punchestown Steeplechase*, on loan from a private collection

Herring I, John Frederick 1795–1865, *The Derby, 1844: The Start*, gift

Herring I, John Frederick 1795–1865, *A Bay Racehorse in a Loosebox*, gift

Herring I, John Frederick 1795–1865, *The Race for the Emperor of Russia's Cup at Ascot, 1845*, gift

Herring I, John Frederick 1795–1865, *The Flying Dutchman' and 'Voltigeur' Running at York, 13 May 1851*, gift

Herring I, John Frederick 1795–1865, *'Mango', Winner of the St Leger, 1837*, gift

Herring I, John Frederick (attributed to) 1795–1865, *'Fleur de Lys' Held by a Trainer on a Racecourse*, gift

Herring I, John Frederick (attributed to) 1795–1865, *'The Baron', Winner of the St Leger, 1845*, gift

Herring II, John Frederick 1815–1907, *A Farmyard Scene with Horses, Ducks and Poultry*, gift

Herring II, John Frederick 1815–1907, *Workhorses in a Farmyard*, gift

Hoare, William 1707–1792, *James (1703–1743), 5th Duke of Hamilton and 2nd Duke of Brandon*, gift

Hoare, William 1707–1792, *Elizabeth Ann Spencer (d.1771), Wife of the 5th Duke of Hamilton*, gift

Italian (Bolognese) School *A Lady of the Pendelavi Family*, gift

J., F. W. *Two Horses Finishing a Race*, gift

Jacques, Charles Émile 1813–1894, *Poultry in a Landscape*, gift

Jacques, Charles Émile 1813–1894, *Shepherdess and Sheep in a Landscape*, gift

Jacques, Charles Émile 1813–1894, *A Shepherd Boy and Sheep*, gift

Jacques, Charles Émile 1813–1894, *Pigs and Poultry*, gift, 1957

Jacques, Charles Émile 1813–1894, *Pigs and Poultry Feeding*, gift

Jacques, Charles Émile 1813–1894, *Poultry in a Midden*, gift

Jacques, Charles Émile 1813–1894, *Sheep and Poultry in a Barn*, gift

Jacques, Charles Émile 1813–1894, *Three Sheep in a Barn*, gift

Kauffmann, R. *Eleonora of Toledo (1522–1562), Grand Duchess of Tuscany, Aged 35*, gift, 1957

Kneller, Godfrey 1646–1723, *Portrait of a Nobleman*, (said to be Frederick Nassau de Zuylestein, 1608–1672), gift

Kneller, Godfrey (attributed to) 1646–1723, *Portrait of a Nobleman*, (said to be Brigadier General William Nassau de Zuylestein, 1682–1710), gift

László, Philip Alexius de 1869–1937, *Lady Marie Louise Hamilton (1884–1957), Daughter of William, 10th Duke of Hamilton*, gift

Lely, Peter (follower of) 1618–1680, *Portrait of a Man in Black with a White Collar*, gift

MacWhirter, John 1839–1911, *River and Rocks*,

Maddox, Willes 1813–1853, *William Beckford on His Deathbed*, gift

Maddox, Willes 1813–1853, *Alexander (1767–1852), 10th Duke of Hamilton*, gift

Maddox, Willes 1813–1853, *Susan Euphemia Beckford (1786–1859), Duchess of Hamilton, Wife of Alexander, 10th Duke of Hamilton*, gift

Maganza, Alessandro (attributed to) 1556–1635, *Christ Healing the Woman with an Issue of Blood*, gift

Martens, Henry 1790–1868, *Glasgow Yeomanry at Exercise*, gift

Master of the Female Half-Lengths active c.1525–1550, *The Magdalene Reading*, on loan from the National Galleries of Scotland

Memling, Hans (after) 1430–1440, *Portrait of a Young Man with His Hands Clasped in Prayer*, gift

Meulen, Adam Frans van der 1631–1690, *Wooded Landscape with Horsemen and a Baggage Train on a Road*, gift

Meulen, Adam Frans van der 1631–1690, *Wooded Landscape with Horsemen on a Road*, gift

Meytens, Martin van (circle of) 1695–1770, *Portrait of a Young Man with a Dog*, gift

Morland, George 1763–1804, *Lovers Observed*, gift

Moucheron, Frederick de 1633–1686, *A Wooded Landscape with a Herdsman*, gift

Moucheron, Frederick de 1633–1686, *A Wooded Scene with a Sportsman, His Dog and a Hawking Party*, gift

Nasmyth, Alexander 1758–1840, *View of Edinburgh Castle*, gift

Neeffs the younger, Peeter 1620–1675, *Interior of a Church*, gift

Neeffs the younger, Peeter 1620–1675, *Interior of St Bavo, Haarlem*, gift

Palizzi, Giuseppe 1812–1888, *A Shepherd Boy and Sheep*, gift

Pickersgill, Henry William (attributed to) 1782–1875, *The Marquess of Douglas (1811–1863), Later 11th Duke of Hamilton*, gift

Poelenburgh, Cornelis van 1594–1667, *Classical Ruins*, gift

Poelenburgh, Cornelis van 1594–1667, *Nymphs near a Pool*, gift

Poelenburgh, Cornelis van 1594–1667, *Nymphs near a Ruin*, gift

Pollard, James 1792–1867, *The St Albans Grand Steeplechase of 8 March, 1832*, gift

Pollard, James 1792–1867, *The St Albans Grand Steeplechase of 8 March, 1832*, gift

Pollard, James 1792–1867, *The St Albans Grand Steeplechase of 8 March, 1832*, gift

Pollard, James 1792–1867, *The St Albans Grand Steeplechase of 8 March, 1832*, gift

Pollard, James 1792–1867, *The St Albans Grand Steeplechase of 8 March, 1832*, gift

Pollard, James 1792–1867, *The St Albans Grand Steeplechase of 8 March, 1832*, gift

Pratt, Hilton Lark 1838–1875, *Fighting Cocks*, gift

Pratt, Hilton Lark 1838–1875, *Fighting Cocks*, gift

Pratt, Hilton Lark 1838–1875, *Fighting Cocks*, gift

Pratt, Hilton Lark 1838–1875, *Fighting Cocks*, gift, 1957

Reinagle, H. *View on the Thames near Twickenham*, gift, 1957

Reinagle, H. *Wooded Landscape*, gift

Reinagle, Ramsay Richard 1775–1862, *William Warr Defeating William Wood at Navestock in Essex, 31 December, 1788*, gift

Roberts, David 1796–1864, *The Church of St Jacques, Dieppe*, gift

Rubens, Peter Paul (after) 1577–1640, *Archduke Albert of Austria (1559–1621)*, gift

Rubens, Peter Paul (after) 1577–1640, *Archduchess Isabella (1566–1633)*, gift

Sartorius, John Nost 1759–1828, *The Oatlands Stakes, Ascot Heath, 28 June, 1791*, gift

Sartorius, John Nost 1759–1828, *The Second Year of the Derby Stakes at Epsom*, gift

Sartorius, John Nost 1759–1828, *A Huntsman and Three Hounds at the Edge of a Wood*, gift

Sartorius, John Nost 1759–1828, *The Gold Cup, Epsom, May 1811*, gift

Sartorius, John Nost (circle of) 1759–1828, *A Fighting Cock in a Landscape*, gift

Sartorius, John Nost (circle of) 1759–1828, *Fox-Hunting*, gift

Scougall, David (attributed to) 1610–1680, *Ann (1631–1716), Duchess of Hamilton, Daughter of James, 1st Duke of Hamilton*, gift

Sell, Christian 1831–1883, *Scenes in the Franco-Prussian War*, gift

Sell, Christian 1831–1883, *Scenes in the Franco-Prussian War*, gift

Seymour, James (attributed to) 1702–1752, *The Great Chaise Match, Newmarket, 1750*, gift

Spanish School *La marquesa de Santa Cruz (1763–1808), née Waldstein*, gift

Stadler *Landscape*, gift, 1957

Stadler *Landscape with Cattle, Sheep and Peasants under Trees*, gift

Stadler *Landscape with Peasant and Animals Watering*, gift

Stadler *View of a Swiss Town*, (possibly Lucerne), gift

Stadler *View of Geneva, with an Artist Sketching*, gift, 1957

Steelink II, Willem 1856–1928, *The Shepherd with His Flock*, gift

Tasker, William H. (attributed to) 1808–1852, *'Rhoda', a Bay Racehorse*, gift

Teniers II, David 1610–1690, *A Landscape with Peasants before a Large Mansion*, gift

Teniers II, David 1610–1690, *The Temptation of Saint Anthony*, gift

Teniers II, David 1610–1690, *Two Angels Holding a Shrine*, gift

Towne, Charles 1763–1840, *Two Racehorses at a Starting Post*, gift

Towne, Charles (follower of) 1763–1840, *Two Racehorses Neck and Neck*, gift

unknown artist *Carrisbrook Castle*, gift

unknown artist *Cottage Interior*, gift

unknown artist *Interior with Household Pets*, gift

unknown artist *'Painted', a Racehorse with Jockey Up in Harlequin Colours*, gift

Verelst, Maria 1680–1744, *Elizabeth Gerrard (1682–1744)*, gift

Vrancx, Sebastian 1573–1647, *Landscape with Members of the House of Orange Returning from a Hunt*, gift

Watteau, Jean-Antoine 1684–1721, *L'aventurière*, gift

Watteau, Jean-Antoine 1684–1721, *L'enchanteur*, gift

Wheatley, Francis 1747–1801, *The Sportsman's Refreshment*, gift

Winterhalter, Franz Xaver 1805–1875, *William Alexander (1845–1895), 12th Duke of Hamilton*, gift

Wyck, Jan 1645–1700, *The Battle of Larida, Spain*, gift

The National Trust for Scotland, Robert Burns Birthplace Museum

Auld, Patrick Campbell 1813–1866, *The Burns Monument*, purchased

Carse, Alexander 1770–1843, *Poosie Nansie's Inn*, gift

Carse, Alexander 1770–1843, *The Mauchline Holy Fair*, gift

Currie, Ken b.1960, *A Man's a Man*, on loan from a private collection © the artist/courtesy Flowers Gallery, London

Drummond, John 1802–1889, *Tam Pursu'd by the Witches*, purchased

Fleming, John B. 1792–1845, *Alloway Kirk from the East*, purchased

Fleming, John B. 1792–1845, *Alloway Kirk from the West*, purchased

Fleming, John B. 1792–1845, *Brig o' Doon*, purchased

Fleming, John B. 1792–1845, *The Cottage*, purchased

Fraser, Alexander George 1786–1865, *The Haggis Feast*, gift

Hill, David Octavius 1802–1870, *Burns Cottage, Interior*, gift

Lauder, Robert Scott 1803–1869, *The Meeting of Burns and Captain Francis Grose*, gift

McIllwraith, William *Burns Cottage*, gift

McIllwraith, William *'Tam o' Shanter Inn'*, gift

Midwood, William Henry 1833–1888, *The Betrothal of Burns and Highland Mary*, gift

Nasmyth, Alexander (copy after) 1758–1840, *Robert Burns (1759–1796)*, purchased

Nasmyth, Alexander (copy after) 1758–1840, *Robert Burns (1759–1796)*, purchased

Nasmyth, Alexander (copy after) 1758–1840, *Robert Burns (1759–1796)*, purchased

Nicol, Erskine 1825–1904, *Tam o' Shanter*, on loan from a private collection

Penny, A. M. *Robert Burns (1759–1796)*, (after Alexander Nasmyth), gift

Roberts, David 1796–1864, *The Brig o' Doon and Burns Monument*, purchased

Thomson, William Hill 1882–1956, *Burns and His Brother*, gift © the copyright holder

unknown artist *Alloway Auld Kirk with Arran in the Distance*, purchased

unknown artist *Burns in a Cottage Scene*, gift

unknown artist *Burns in an Edinburgh Drawing Room*, purchased

unknown artist *Robert Burns*, (pub sign), gift

unknown artist *Scene inside Burns Cottage*, gift

unknown artist *Tam o' Shanter over Brig o' Doon*, gift

unknown artist *The Auld Brig of Ayr*, purchased

unknown artist *The Burns Monument and the 1844 Burns Festival Procession*, gift

unknown artist *The Cotter's Saturday Night*, gift

The National Trust for Scotland, Culzean Castle, Garden & Country Park

Alexander, Cosmo 1724–1772, *John (1736–1806), 7th Earl of Galloway,* on loan from a private collection
Alexander, John 1686–1766, *John (1736–1806), 7th Earl of Galloway,* on loan from a private collection
Batoni, Pompeo 1708–1787, *Thomas Kennedy (d.1775), 9th Earl of Cassillis,*
Boudin, Eugène Louis 1824–1898, *Fishing Boats, Anvers,* bequeathed
Boudin, Eugène Louis 1824–1898, *Le Havre,* gift, 1978
Boudin, Eugène Louis 1824–1898, *Fishing Boats,* gift, 1979
Bright, Henry 1810–1873, *Wolf's Crag,* gift
British (English) School *A Man-of-War and Other Vessels at Sea,* on loan from the Kennedy family
British (Scottish) School *Craigmillar Castle,* gift
Brown, Mather 1761–1831, *Captain the Honourable Archibald Kennedy (d.1794), 11th Earl of Cassillis,* on loan from the Kennedy family
Brown, Mather 1761–1831, *Anne Watts (d.1793), Wife of the 11th Earl of Cassillis,* on loan from the Kennedy family
Callander, Adam 1750–1817, *Views of Inverary,*
Callander, Adam 1750–1817, *Views of Inverary,* gift
Cameron, David Young 1865–1945, *View of Culzean Castle with Ailsa Craig in the Distance,* gift the artist's estate
Canaletto (after) 1697–1768, *A Regatta on the Grand Canal,* on loan from the Kennedy family
Canaletto (after) 1697–1768, *The Mouth of the Grand Canal,* on loan from the Kennedy family
Colone, Adam de (circle of) 1572–1651, *James VI and I (1566–1625),* gift
Condy, Nicholas Matthew 1816–1851, *The Queen's Barge off Osborne,* gift
Dandridge, Bartholomew 1691–1754, *William Cunninghame (d.1775), 13th Earl of Glencairn,* on loan from a private collection
Daubigny, Karl 1846–1886, *The Seashore,* gift
Dayes, Edward 1763–1804, *A Review on Woolwich Common,*
Deschamps, J. *A Patrician Family at Table,*
Droochsloot, Cornelis 1630–1673, *A Peasant Feast outside of an Inn,* on loan from the Kennedy family
Dubbels, Hendrik Jacobsz. (circle of) 1621–1707, *Fishing Vessels off a Beach, with a Man-of-War at Anchor,* gift
Dutch School *Men-of-War off a Town,* gift
Dyck, Anthony van 1599–1641, *Lady Henrietta Stewart, Daughter of Alexander Stewart, 3rd Earl of Galloway, Wife of William, 12th Earl of Glencairn,* on loan from a private collection
Dyck, Anthony van (after) 1599–1641, *Portrait of a Cleric,* (said to be Alexander Henderson, 1583–1646), gift
Eismann, Johann Anton 1608–1705, *A Man-of-War and Other Vessels in a Calm,* on loan from the Kennedy family
Elliott, Thomas active c.1790–1800, *HMS 'Victory' Leaving Portsmouth Harbour,* on loan from the Kennedy family
Ferneley I, John E. 1782–1860, *Archibald (1794–1832), Lord Kennedy, Later Earl of Cassillis, on a Hunter,* gift
Fowles, Arthur Wellington 1815–1883, *'Vanguard' and 'Foxhound' off the Longships,* gift
Goyen, Jan van (style of) 1596–1656, *Sailing Barges and Fishermen off a Town,* gift
Graves, Henry Richard 1818–1882, *The Honourable Evelyn Stuart (d.1888), Daughter of the 12th Lord Blantyre and Wife of Archibald Kennedy, 3rd Marquess of Ailsa,* on loan from the Kennedy family
Hamilton, Gavin 1723–1798, *Susanna Kennedy (1689–1780), Daughter of Sir Archibald Kennedy, 1st Bt of Culzean, 3rd Wife of Alexander Montgomery, 8th Earl of Eglinton,* on loan from the Kennedy family
Hondecoeter, Melchior de (circle of) 1636–1695, *Duck at a Pool and a Kingfisher on a Stump,* on loan from the Kennedy family
Huet I, Jean-Baptiste (circle of) 1745–1811, *Shepherdesses with a Fortune-Teller by a Waterfall,* (after François Boucher),
Italian School *Putto beside a Chariot and Deer,* on loan from the Kennedy family
Italian School *Putto Driving a Chariot Pulled by Deer,* on loan from the Kennedy family
Italian School *Putto Falling off a Chariot Pulled by Two Swans,* on loan from the Kennedy family
Italian School *Putto in a Chariot Drawn by Two Lions,* gift
Italian School *Putto in a Chariot Drawn by Two Swans,* gift
Italian School *Putto in a Chariot with Deer,* on loan from the Kennedy family
Italian School *Putto Riding Goats,* gift
Italian School *Putto with a Hound Chasing a Hare,* gift
Italian School *Putto with Deer,* gift
Italian School *Winged Victory with Shield and Spear,* on loan from the Kennedy family
Italian School *Woman with a Red Shawl,* on loan from the Kennedy family
Lacroix, Charles François Grenier de 1700–1782, *A Wreck on a Rocky Coast,* bequeathed
Lavery, John 1856–1941, *Robert Bontine Cunninghame Graham of Ardoch (1852–1936), on His Argentinian Pony,* on loan from a private collection
Lefèvre, Robert 1755–1830, *The Emperor Napoleon (1769–1821),* on loan from the Kennedy family
Louch, John *A Girl on a Woodland Path,* gift
Luny, Thomas 1759–1837, *HMS 'London', a Cutter, off Dover,* on loan from the Kennedy family
Lutyens, Charles Augustus Henry 1829–1915, *Archibald Kennedy (1816–1870), 2nd Marquess of Ailsa,* on loan from the Kennedy family
Lutyens, Charles Augustus Henry 1829–1915, *Lord John Kennedy (1850–1895), Youngest Son of the 2nd Marquess of Ailsa, by the Swan Pond,* gift
Macleay, Macneil 1806–1883, *Castle Campbell,* on loan from the Kennedy family
MacNee, Robert Russell 1880–1952, *Bothy with Poultry,* gift the copyright holder
Marshall, Benjamin 1768–1835, *Archibald Kennedy (1770–1846), 12th Earl of Cassillis, Later 1st Marquess of Ailsa, Riding a Match from Culzean to Glasgow,* on loan from the Kennedy family
Martin, David 1736–1798, *Nicol Graham of Gartmore (1695–1775),* (after John Bogle), on loan from a private collection
Martin, David 1736–1798, *John Cunninghame (1749–1796), 15th Earl of Glencairn,* on loan from a private collection
Martin, David 1736–1798, *Lady Margaret Cunninghame (d.1790), Eldest Daughter of William Earl of Glencairn, Wife of Nicol Graham of Gartmore,* on loan from a private collection
Miller, William Edwards 1852–1934, *Archibald Kennedy (1874–1943), 4th Marquess of Ailsa,* bequeathed
Mitchell, William 1801–1900, *A Trial Ordered by Vice Admiral Codrington, 31 July 1831, off the Dodman,* gift
Mitchell, William 1801–1900, *A Trial Ordered by Vice Admiral Codrington, 31st July 1831, off the Dodman,* gift, 1945
Mosman, William 1700–1771, *Thomas Kennedy (1733–1775), 9th Earl of Cassillis,* on loan from the Kennedy family
Nasmyth, Alexander 1758–1840, *Culzean Castle from the North with Ailsa Craig,*
Nasmyth, Alexander 1758–1840, *Culzean Castle from the Sea,* on loan from the Kennedy family
Nasmyth, Alexander 1758–1840, *A Wooded River Landscape,* gift
Owen, William 1769–1825, *Archibald Kennedy (1770–1846), 12th Earl of Cassillis, Later 1st Marquess of Ailsa,*
Owen, William 1769–1825, *Margaret Erskine of Dun (c.1772–1848), Wife of the 12th Earl of Cassilis, Later 1st Marquess of Ailsa,*
Partridge, John 1789–1872, *The Honourable Montgomerie Stewart (1780–1860), Fourth Son of the 7th Earl of Galloway,* on loan from a private collection
Pine, Robert Edge 1720–1788, *Colonel John Graham of Kippen, Third Son of Nicol Graham of Gartmore,* on loan from a private collection
Pine, Robert Edge 1720–1788, *Simon Watson Taylor,* on loan from a private collection
Pirman, L. E. *Daffodils in a Vase,* gift
Raeburn, Henry 1756–1823, *Robert Graham of Gartmore (1735–1797),* on loan from a private collection
Ramsay, Allan 1713–1784, *Queen Charlotte (1744–1818), in Her Coronation Robes,* on loan from Allan and Carol Murray, since 2001
Reynolds, Joshua (attributed to) 1723–1792, *Robert Graham of Ardoch,* on loan from a private collection
Spruyt, Johannes 1627–1671, *Duck and a Woodcock near Reeds, a Mere beyond,* on loan from the Kennedy family
Stannus, Anthony Carey 1830–1919, *Archibald Kennedy (1847–1938), 3rd Marquess of Ailsa,* on loan from the Kennedy family
unknown artist *A Swan,*
unknown artist *Apollo with Three Women, with a Crown, Book and Laurel Wreath,* transferred
unknown artist *Female Figure with a Book, Gesturing,* transferred
unknown artist *Female Figure with a Horn,* transferred
unknown artist *Female Figure with a Lyre,* transferred
unknown artist *Female Figure with a Lyre and Book,* transferred
unknown artist *Female Figure with Compasses and an Orb,* transferred
unknown artist *Female Figure with Compasses and a Tablet,* transferred
unknown artist *Robert Burns (1759–1796),* gift
unknown artist *Shepherdess,* gift
unknown artist *Three Dancing Figures with Cymbals and Drums,* transferred
unknown artist *Two Figures Dancing,* transferred
unknown artist *Two Figures Dancing,* transferred
unknown artist *Woman in a Hat,*
Vanson, Adrian (attributed to) 1540–1605, *Sir Thomas Kennedy of Culzean (1543/1558–1602),* gift
Vernet, Claude-Joseph 1714–1789, *A Rocky Coast with Survivors Being Retrieved from a Wreck,* bequeathed
Vos, Paul de (studio of) 1591–1678, *The Lion and the Mouse,* on loan from the Kennedy family
Watt, George Fiddes 1873–1960, *Archibald Kennedy (1847–1938), 3rd Marquess of Ailsa,* on loan from the Kennedy family the artist's estate
Watt, George Fiddes 1873–1960, *Frances Stewart (d.1849), Wife of Archibald Kennedy, 4th Marquess of Ailsa,* on loan from the Kennedy family the artist's estate
Wild, Frank Percy 1861–1950, *Archibald (1847–1938), 3rd Marquess of Ailsa,* the artist's estate
Wright, John Michael 1617–1694, *John Kennedy (d.1701), 7th Earl of Cassillis,* gift
Wright, John Michael (circle of) 1617–1694, *Lady Susanna Hamilton (before 1638–1694), Daughter of James, 1st Duke of Hamilton, 1st Wife of John Kennedy, 7th Earl of Cassillis,* gift
Wright, John Michael (circle of) 1617–1694, *Margaret Hay (d.1695), Widow of Lord Kerr, 2nd Wife of John Kennedy, 7th Earl of Cassillis,* on loan from the Kennedy family
Wright, John Michael (circle of) 1617–1694, *William Cunninghame (1610–1664), 9th Earl of Glencairn,* on loan from a private collection
Zucchi, Antonio 1726–1796, *Ceiling Roundel,* transferred

Acknowledgements

The Public Catalogue Foundation would like to thank the individual artists and copyright holders for their permission to reproduce for free the paintings in this catalogue. Exhaustive efforts have been made to locate the copyright owners of all the images included within this catalogue and to meet their requirements. Copyright credit lines for copyright owners who have been traced are listed in the Further Information section.

The Public Catalogue Foundation would like to express its great appreciation to the following organisations for their kind assistance in the preparation of this catalogue:

Bridgeman Art Library
Flowers East
Marlborough Fine Art
National Association of Decorative & Fine Arts Societies (NADFAS)
National Gallery, London
National Portrait Gallery, London
Royal Academy of Arts, London
Tate

Collection Addresses

Aberdeenshire

Alford
Craigievar Castle
Alford, Aberdeenshire, Scotland, AB33 8JF

Argyll and Bute

Banchory
Crathes Castle, Garden & Estate
Banchory, Aberdeenshire, Scotland, AB31 5QJ

Braemar
Mar Lodge Estate
Braemar, Aberdeenshire, AB35 5YJ

By Banchory
Drum Castle, Garden & Estate
Drumoak, By Banchory, Aberdeenshire,
Scotland, AB31 5EY

Ellon
Haddo House
Methlick, Ellon, Aberdeenshire,
Scotland, AB41 7EQ

Pitmedden Garden
Ellon, Aberdeenshire AB41 7PD

Helensburgh
The Hill House
Upper Colquhoun Street, Helensburgh,
Argyll and Bute, Scotland, G84 9AJ

Huntly
Leith Hall Garden & Estate
Kennethmont, Huntly, Aberdeenshire, AB54 4NQ

Inverurie
Castle Fraser, Garden & Estate
Sauchen, Inverurie, Aberdeenshire,
Scotland, AB51 7LD

Turriff
Fyvie Castle
Turriff, Aberdeenshire, Scotland, AB53 8JS

Angus

Forfar
Angus Folk Museum
Kirkwynd Glamis, Forfar, Angus, Scotland, DD8 1RT

Kirriemuir
J. M. Barrie's Birthplace
9 Brechin Road, Kirriemuir, Angus, Scotland, DD8 4BX

Montrose
House of Dun
Montrose, Angus, Scotland, DD10 9LQ

Clackmannanshire

Alloa
Alloa Tower
Alloa Park, Alloa, Clackmannanshire, Scotland, FK10 1PP

Dumfries and Galloway

Castle Douglas
Threave Estate
Castle Douglas, Dumfries and Galloway,
Scotland, DG7 1RX

Ecclefechan
Thomas Carlyle's Birthplace
The Arched House, Ecclefechan,
Dumfries and Galloway, Scotland,
DG11 3DG

Kirkcudbright
Broughton House & Garden
12 High Street, Kirkcudbright,
Dumfries and Galloway, Scotland, DG6 4JX

East Lothian

Musselburgh
Newhailes
Newhailes Road, Musselburgh, East Lothian,
Scotland, EH21 6RY

Edinburgh

Gladstone's Land
Hermiston Quay
5 Cultins Road, Edinburgh EH11 4DF

Malleny Garden
The Georgian House
7 Charlotte Square, Edinburgh,
Scotland, EH2 4DR

Fife

Culross
Royal Burgh of Culross
Culross, Fife, Scotland, KY12 8JH

Cupar
Falkland Palace & Garden
Cupar, Fife, Scotland, KY15 7BU

Hill of Tarvit Mansionhouse & Garden
Cupar, Fife, Scotland, KY15 5PB

Pittenweem
Kellie Castle & Garden
Pittenweem, Fife, Scotland, KY10 2RF

Glasgow

Clarkston
Greenbank Garden
Flenders Road, Glasgow G76 8RB

Highland

Cromarty
Hugh Miller Museum & Birthplace Cottage
Church Street, Cromarty, Highland,
Scotland, IV11 8XA

Inverness
Culloden Battlefield & Visitor Centre
Culloden Moor, Inverness, Highland,
Scotland, IV2 5EU

Moray

Forres
Brodie Castle
Forres, Moray, Scotland, IV36 2TE

North Ayrshire

Brodick
Brodick Castle, Garden & Country Park
Brodick, North Ayrshire, Scotland, KA27 8HY

South Ayrshire

Ayr
Robert Burns Birthplace Museum

Maybole
Culzean Castle, Garden & Country Park
Murdoch's Lone Alloway, Ayr, South Ayrshire, Scotland,
KA7 4PQ

Index of Artists

In this catalogue, artists' names and the spelling of their names follow the preferred presentation of the name in the Getty Union List of Artist Names (ULAN) as of February 2004, if the artist is listed in ULAN.

The page numbers next to each artist's name below direct readers to paintings that are by the artist; are attributed to the artist; or, in a few cases, are more loosely related to the artist being, for example, 'after', 'the circle of' or copies of a painting by the artist. The precise relationship between the artist and the painting is listed in the catalogue.

Minderhout, Hendrik van (1632–1696) 93
Mitchell, E. 142
Mitchell, William (c.1806–1900) 267
Moir, John (c.1776–1857) 9, 28, 67, 170
Molenaer, Klaes (c.1630–1676) 157
Monamy, Peter (1681–1749) 187
Monnoyer, Jean-Baptiste (1636–1699) 32
Morales, Juan Francisco (active 17th C) 46
More, Jacob (1740–1793) 93
Moreelse, Paulus (1571–1638) 187
Morland, George (1763–1804) 28, 170, 187, 246
Morris 46
Morris, Cedric Lockwood (1889–1982) 46
Morrocco, Alberto (1917–1998) 119
Mosman, William (c.1700–1771) 28, 46, 69, 110, 150, 268
Moucheron, Frederick de (1633–1686) 246
Muir, Anne Davidson (1875–1951) 187
Müller, William James (1812–1845) 170
Munro, Charles Binning (d.1910) 58
Munro, Mary 223
Mura, Francesco de (1696–1782) 69
Murillo, Bartolomé Esteban (1617–1682) 47, 110
Musscher, Michiel van (1645–1705) 223, 224
Muziano, Girolamo (1528/1532–1592) 171
Mytens, Daniel (c.1590–1647) 79
Nash, John Northcote (1893–1977) 224
Nasmyth, Alexander (1758–1840) 28, 110, 163, 171, 246, 256, 268
Nasmyth, Charlotte (1804–1884) 119
Nattier, Jean-Marc (1685–1766) 28, 143
Neeffs the elder, Peeter (c.1578–1656/1661) 157, 224
Neeffs the younger, Peeter (1620–1675) 246
Neer, Aert van der (1603–1677) 157, 187
Neri, Pietro Martire (c.1601–1661) 47
Nevinson, Christopher (1889–1946) 224
Niccolò dell'Abate (c.1509–1571) 171
Nicholls, Bertram (1883–1974) 224
Nicholson, Jim (1924–1996) 17
Nicholson, John P. (active late 19th C) 157
Nicholson, William (1872–1949) 224
Nicol, Erskine (1825–1904) 257
Noble, James Campbell (1846–1913) 157
Noble, John Sargeant (1848–1896) 188
Norie, James (1684–1757) 47, 49, 143
Northcote, James (1746–1831) 69, 171, 224
Northern Italian School 69
O'Connor, James Arthur (1792–1841) 226
Olsson, Albert Julius (1864–1942) 226
Opie, John (1761–1807) 69, 93, 226
Oppenheimer, Charles (1875–1961) 136, 137
Os, Jan van (1744–1808) 195
Ostade, Adriaen van (1610–1685) 226
Owen, William (1769–1825) 268
Padwick, Philip Hugh (1876–1958) 226
Palizzi, Giuseppe (1812–1888) 246
Panini, Giovanni Paolo (1691–1765) 49
Parrocel, Pierre (1670–1739) 79
Partridge, John (1789–1872) 268
Patel, Pierre I (c.1605–1676) 171
Paton, Waller Hugh (1828–1895) 93
Patten, George (1801–1865) 49
Pavy, Philippe (b.1860) 226
Peddie, George 17
Peeters I, Bonaventura (1614–1652) 188
Penny, A. M. 257
Peploe, Denis Frederic Neal (1914–1993) 110, 111, 205
Peploe, Samuel John (1871–1935) 157, 226
Peters, Matthew William (1742–1814) 28
Pettie, John (1839–1893) 94, 157
Phillips, Charles (1708–1748) 226
Phillips, Thomas (1770–1845) 49
Pickenoy, Nicolaes Eliasz. (c.1588–c.1655) 188, 227
Pickersgill, Henry William (1782–1875) 246
Pine, Robert Edge (c.1720/1730–1788) 268
Pirman, L. E. 269
Poelenburgh, Cornelis van (1594/1595–1667) 227, 247
Pollard, James (1792–1867) 247
Pratt, Hilton Lark (1838–1875) 248
Pritchett, Edward (active c.1828–1879) 227
Pruser 17
Puligo, Domenico (1492–1527) 49
Quinn, James Peter (1869–1951) 227
R., E. T. 50
Raeburn, Henry (1756–1823) 5, 28, 29, 50, 60, 69, 79, 80, 94, 96, 111, 120, 171, 188, 195, 269
Ramsay, Allan (1713–1784) 5, 69, 111, 112, 143, 144, 150, 159, 172, 188, 227
Ramsay, Hugh (1877–1906) 17
Ravesteyn, Jan Anthonisz. van (c.1570–1657) 188
Redfern, June (b.1951) 112
Redpath, Anne (1895–1965) 112
Reid, Archibald David (1844–1908) 58
Reid, George (1841–1913) 50, 227
Reid, Stephen (1873–1948) 58
Reinagle, H. 248
Reinagle, Ramsay Richard (1775–1862) 248
Rembrandt van Rijn (1606–1669) 137
Reni, Guido (1575–1642) 50, 172
Reynolds, Joshua (1723–1792) 96, 269
Richardson the elder, Jonathan (c.1664–1667–1745) 228
Rigaud, Hyacinthe (1659–1743) 120
Riley, John (1646–1691) 172
Rink, Paulus (1861–1903) 137
Ritchie, C. S. 17
Robb, Lena (1891–1980) 17
Roberts, David (1796–1864) 228, 248, 257
Roe, Robert Henry (1793–1880) 17
Rolzhoven, Julius (1858–1930) 189
Romagnoli, Angiolo (d.1896) 50
Romney, George (1734–1802) 97, 228
Rosa, Salvator (1615–1673) 50, 228
Rubens, Peter Paul (1577–1640) 97, 248, 249
Ruisdael, Jacob van (1628/1629–1682) 144, 159
Russell, John (1745–1806) 97
Russell, John Bucknell (1819–1893) 50, 51
Ruysdael, Salomon van (c.1602–1670) 144, 189
S., R. 228
Saedeleer, Valerius de (1867–1941) 228
Sánchez Coello, Alonso (c.1531–1588) 179
Sanders, George (1774–1846) 80

The Public Catalogue Foundation

The Public Catalogue Foundation is a registered charity. It was launched in 2003 to create a photographic record of the entire national collection of oil, tempera and acrylic paintings in public ownership in the United Kingdom.

Whilst our public galleries and civic buildings hold arguably the greatest collection of oil paintings in the world, over 80 per cent of these are not on view. Few collections have a complete photographic record of their paintings let alone a comprehensive illustrated catalogue. What is publicly owned is not publicly accessible.

The Foundation is publishing a series of fully illustrated, county-by-county catalogues that will cover, eventually, the entire national UK collection. To date, it has published over 30 volumes, presenting over 72,000 paintings.

In partnership with the BBC, the Foundation will make its database of the entire UK collection of 200,000 oil paintings available online through a new website called *Your Paintings*. The website was launched in the summer of 2011.

Your Paintings (*www.bbc.co.uk/arts/yourpaintings*) offers a variety of ways of searching for paintings as well as further information about the paintings and artists, including links to the participating collections' websites. For those interested in paintings and the subjects they portray *Your Paintings* is an unparalleled learning resource.

Collections benefit substantially from the work of the Foundation, not least from the digital images that are given to them for free following photography, and from the increased recognition that the project brings. These substantial benefits come at no financial cost to the collections.

The Foundation is funded by a combination of support from individuals, charitable trusts, companies and the public sector although the latter provides less than 20 per cent of the Foundation's financial support.

Supporters

Master Patrons

The Public Catalogue Foundation is greatly indebted to the following Master Patrons who have helped it in the past or are currently working with it to raise funds for the publication of their county catalogues. All of them have given freely of their time and have made an enormous contribution to the work of the Foundation.

Peter Andreae *(Hampshire)*
Sir Henry Aubrey-Fletcher, Bt, Lord Lieutenant of Buckinghamshire *(Buckinghamshire)*
Sir Nicholas Bacon, DL, High Sheriff of Norfolk *(Norfolk)*
Sir John Bather, Lord Lieutenant of Derbyshire *(Derbyshire)*
The Hon. Mrs Bayliss, JP, Lord Lieutenant of Berkshire *(Berkshire)*
Ian Bonas *(County Durham)*
Peter Bretherton *(West Yorkshire: Leeds)*
Michael Brinton, Lord Lieutenant of Worcestershire *(Worcestershire)*
Sir Hugo Brunner, KCVO, JP *(Oxfordshire)*
Mr John Bush, OBE, Lord-Lieutenant of Wiltshire *(Wiltshire)*
Lady Butler *(Warwickshire)*
Richard Compton *(North Yorkshire)*
George Courtauld, DL, Vice Lord Lieutenant of Essex *(Essex)*

The Countess of Darnley, Lord Lieutenant of Herefordshire *(Herefordshire)*
The Marquess of Downshire *(North Yorkshire)*
Martin Dunne, Lord Lieutenant of Warwickshire *(Warwickshire)*
Sir Henry Elwes, KCVO, Lord-Lieutenant of Gloucestershire *(Gloucestershire)*
Jenny Farr, MBE, DL *(Nottinghamshire)*
John Fenwick *(Tyne & Wear Museums)*
Mark Fisher, MP *(Staffordshire)*
Patricia Grayburn, MBE, DL *(Surrey)*
The Earl of Halifax, KStJ, JP, DL *(East Riding of Yorkshire)*
Lord Roy Hattersley, PC *(South Yorkshire: Sheffield*
Algy Heber-Percy, Lord Lieutenant of Shropshire *(Shropshire)*
The Lady Mary Holborow, Lord Lieutenant of Cornwall *(Cornwall)*
Sarah Holman *(Warwickshire)*
Tommy Jowitt *(West Yorkshire)*
Alderman Sir David Lewis, The Rt Hon. The Lord Mayor of London, 2007–2008 *(The City of London)*
Sir Michael Lickiss *(Cornwall)*
Magnus Linklater *(Scotland)*
Lord Marlesford, DL *(Suffolk)*
Dr Bridget McConnell *(Glasgow)*
Lady Sarah Nicholson *(County Durham)*
Malcolm V. L. Pearce, MP *(Somerset)*
Sir John Riddell, Lord Lieutenant of Northumberland *(Northumberland)*
Venetia Ross Skinner *(Dorset)*
The Most Hon. The Marquess of Salisbury, PC, DL *(Hertfordshire)*
Julia Somerville *(Government Art Collection)*
Tim Stevenson, OBE, Lord Lieutenant of Oxfordshire *(Oxfordshire)*
Phyllida Stewart-Roberts, OBE *(East Sussex)*
Lady Juliet Townsend, Lord Lieutenant of Northamptonshire *(Northamptonshire)*
Leslie Weller, DL *(West Sussex)*
Sir Samuel C. Whitbread, KCVO, Lord Lieutenant of Bedfordshire *(Bedfordshire)*

Financial support

The Public Catalogue Foundation is particularly grateful to the following organisations and individuals who have given it generous financial support since the project started in 2003.

National Sponsor

Christie's

Benefactors (£10,000–£50,000)

The 29th May 1961 Charitable Trust
Arts Council England
The Barbour Trust
Binks Trust
City of Bradford Metropolitan District Council
Deborah Loeb Brice Foundation
The Bulldog Trust
A. & S. Burton 1960 Charitable Trust
Christie's
City of London Corporation
The John S. Cohen Foundation
Covent Garden London
Creative Scotland
Department for Culture, Media and Sport
Sir Harry Djanogly, CBE
Mr Lloyd Dorfman
Dunard Fund
The Elmley Foundation
Fenwick Ltd
Fidelity UK Foundation
Marc Fitch Fund
The Foyle Foundation
J. Paul Getty Jr Trust
Hampshire County Council
The Charles Hayward Foundation
Peter Harrison Foundation
Mr Robert Hiscox
Hiscox plc
David Hockney, CH, RA
ICAP plc

The Jordan Charitable Foundation
Kent County Council
The Linbury Trust
The Manifold Trust
Paul Mellon Centre for Studies in British Art
The Mercers' Company
Robert Warren Miller
Mr & Mrs A. Mittal
The Monument Trust
Miles Morland
Allan and Carol Murray
National Gallery Trust
Stavros Niarchos Foundation
Norfolk County Council
Northern Rock Foundation
Nottingham City Council
Malcolm V. L. Pearce, MP
P. F. Charitable Trust
The Pilgrim Trust
Provident Financial
RAB Capital plc
The Radcliffe Trust
Renaissance East Midlands
Renaissance West Midlands
Renaissance Yorkshire
Saga Group Ltd
Scottish Government
The Bernard Sunley Charitable Foundation
Townsend Family Trust
University College, London
University of Leeds
The Walker Trust
The Wolfson Foundation
Sir Siegmund Warburg's Voluntary Settlement
Garfield Weston Foundation
Mr & Mrs A. H. Wilkinson
The Wixamtree Trust

Series Patrons
(Minimum donation of £2,500)

James & Lindsay Adam
Sir John Bather
Harry Bott
Janey Buchan
Mrs Rhona Callander
Dr Peter Cannon-Brookes
The John S. Cohen Foundation
Bushey Museum in memory of Lavender Watson
Mr Lloyd Dorfman
Lord Douro
Jenny Farr, MBE, DL
Mrs Greta Fenston
The FIRS Trust
Glasgow Museums
Patricia Grayburn, MBE, DL
G. Laurence Harbottle
R. K. Harrison Insurance Services Limited
Paul & Fiona Hart
Paul & Kathrine Haworth
Lord & Lady Heseltine
Patrik Holden & Lin Hinds
Neil Honebon
Michael Jacobson
Grace Jenkins
Dr David Johnson, DL
The Keatley Trust
John Kendall, Esq.
Michael A. Lambert, CBE
David & Amanda Leathers
Miles Morland
Allan & Carol Murray
North East Regional Museums Hub
The University of Northampton
Nottingham Civic Society
Richard & Amika Oldfield
The Roper Family Charitable Trust
Adam Sedgwick
Sir Harry & Lady Soloman
Stuart M. Southall
Simon Still
Chloe Teacher
University of Surrey
David & Cissy Walker
Tony Wilkinson
Mr & Mrs Jo Windsor
Mr & Mrs Charles Wyvill

Catalogue Patrons
(£1,000–£10,000)

The 29th May 1961 Charitable Trust
ACE Study Tours
Adams & Remers
Marcus & Kate Agius
The AIM Foundation
D. C. R. Allen
John Alston, CBE
Amberley Castle
The Astor Foundation
The Aylesford Family Charitable Trust
Chairman of Cornwall County Council, Mrs Doris Anson, OBE, JP
Archant Ltd

G. F. Armitage Family Charitable Trust
Mr Ian Askew
Aurelius Charitable Trust
The Bacon Charitable Trust
Lawrence Banks, CBE, DL
Barlow Robbins LLP
Mr James & Lady Emma Barnard
Basingstoke and Deane Borough Council
Bath & North East Somerset District Council Heritage Services
Robert Baxter, DL
Birmingham Common Good Trust
Sir Christopher Bland
Johnnie Boden
The Charlotte Bonham-Carter Charitable Trust
H. R. Pratt Boorman Family Foundation
A. J. H. du Boulay Charitable Trust
The Bowerman Charitable Trust
Viscountess Boyd Charitable Trust
Lord & Lady Bradbury
Bramdean Asset Management LLP
Peter Bretherton
Brewin Dolphin
J. & M. Britton Charitable Trust
Mrs T. Brotherton-Ratcliffe
Janey Buchan
Mr & Mrs Patrick Burgess
Mr & Mrs Mark Burrell
Arnold J. Burton Charitable Trust
Bushey Museum in Memory of Lavender Watson
Mrs Anne Cadbury, OBE, JP, DL
Roger Cadbury
C. J. R. & Mrs C. L. Calderwood
Sir Ralph Carr-Ellison
Mr & Mrs J. Chambers
Chichester District Council
His Honour Richard Cole, DL & Mrs Sheila Cole
The Timothy Colman Charitable Trust
Mr & Mrs Derek Coombs
The Helen Jean Cope Trust
Mr & Mrs Ian Copesteak
Cornwall County Council
Mr S. J. D. Corsan
Graeme Cottam & Gloriana Marks de Chabris
Coutts Charitable Trust
David Crane Trust
Elaine Craven, Earl Street Employment Consultants Ltd
Harriett Cullen
Culture North East
Rt Hon. Viscount Daventry
N. Davie-Thornhill
Brigadier Mike Dauncey, DSO, DL
De La Rue Charitable Trust
Mr Robert Dean
Deborah Gage (Works of Art) Ltd
Derek Johns Ltd, London
Derby City Council
Derby High School Trust Ltd
Derbyshire Building Society
Derbyshire Community Foundation (The Ashby Fund)
J. N. Derbyshire Trust
The Duke of Devonshire's Charitable Trust
S. Dewhirst Charitable Trust
Sir Harry Djanogly, CBE
Dorset County Council
Lord Douro
Professor Patrick & Dr Grace Dowling
Dunn Family Charitable Trust
East Sussex County Council
Eastbourne Borough Council
EEMLAC, through the Association for Suffolk Museums
Lord & Lady Egremont
Sir John & Lady Elliott
Andrew & Lucy Ellis
Peter & Judy Ellwood
Essex County Council
John & Felicity Fairbairn
Fairfield Charitable Trust
Jenny Farr, MBE, DL
John Feeney Charitable Trust
The Trustees of the Finnis Scott Foundation
The Fishmongers' Company
David & Ann FitzWilliam-Lay
Elizabeth & Val Fleming
The Follett Trust
Richard & Elizabeth Fothergill

Christopher & Catherine Foyle
Freemasons of Derbyshire
The Friends of Historic Essex
The Friends of the Laing Art Gallery
The Friends of the Royal Pavilion, Art Gallery & Museums, Brighton
The Friends of Southampton's Museums, Archives and Galleries
The Friends of Sunderland Museums
The Friends of York Art Gallery (E. J. Swift Bequest)
Philip Gibbs
The Hon. H. M. T. Gibson's Charity Trust
Lewis & Jacqueline Golden
The Goldsmiths' Company
Gorringes
Charles Gregson
The Grocers' Company
The Gulland Family
David Gurney
Philip Gwyn
Sir Ernest Hall
The Earl of Halifax, KStJ, JP, DL
The W. A. Handley Charity Trust
The Hartnett Charitable Trust
Hazlitt, Gooden & Fox Ltd
Heartwood Wealth Management Ltd
The Trustees of the King Henry VIII Endowed Trust, Warwick
The Rt Hon. the Lord Heseltine, CH, PC & Lady Heseltine
The Lady Hind Trust
Hobart Charitable Trust
Edward and Anna Hocknell
David Hockney CH, RA
Patrick Holden & Lin Hinds
Mrs Michael Hollingbery
The Holman Family
Mr & Mrs A. Holman-West
The Honourable Company of Gloucestershire
The Hope Scott Trust
David & Prue Hopkinson
Major & Mrs Bill Hutchinson
His Honour Gabriel Hutton
Isle of Wight Council
The J. and S. B. Charitable Trust
Alan & Penny Jerome
James & Lucilla Joll Charitable Trust
Mr & Mrs Peter Jones
Tommy Jowitt
The Keatley Trust
Kent Messenger Group
Garrett Kirk, Jr
Mr John Kirkland, OBE & Mrs Sheila Kirkland
Robert Kirkland
Kirklees Council
The David Laing Foundation
Landau Foundation
Lord Lea of Crondall, OBE
The Leche Trust
Leeds Art Collections Fund
Leeds City Council
Leeds Philosophical and Literary Society
The Hon. David Legh, DL
Lord Leverhulme's Charitable Trust
Mr & Mrs John Lewis
Mark & Sophie Lewisohn
Tom Lugg & the Lane Family
The Orr Mackintosh Foundation
The MacRobert Trust
Maidstone Borough Council
John Manser
Mr & Mrs Derek Mapp
Walter & Barbara Marais
The Marlay Group
Marshall Charitable Trust
Stephen & Carolyn Martin
Tom & Anne Martin
The Medlock Charitable Trust
The Piet Mendels Foundation
MLA East of England
MLA North East of England
Museums Galleries Scotland
Mr Paul Myners
Rupert Nabarro
Nancie Massey Charitable Trust
Newcastle City Council
Bryan Norman
Lord & Lady Northampton
The University of Northampton
NP Aerospace Ltd
Oakmoor Trust
Jasper & Virginia Olivier
The Orr Mackintosh Foundation
Mr Christopher Oughtred
The Owen Family Trust

Sir Idris Pearce
Roger Neville Russ Peers
The Pennycress Trust
Perkins Family
The Lord & Lady Phillimore
Mrs Margaret Pollett
Simon & Ursula Pomeroy
The Portland Family
Portsmouth City Council
George Pragnell Ltd
The Prince Philip Trust Fund for the Royal Borough of Windsor and Maidenhead
Provident Financial plc
Mr John Rank
Rathbone Investment Management Ltd
The Hans and Märit Rausing Charitable Trust
Roger & Jane Reed
Renaissance North East
Renaissance South East
Renaissance South West
Michael Renshall, CBE, MA, FCA
Sir John Riddell
Sir Miles & Lady Rivett-Carnac
Rockley Charitable Trust
Rolls-Royce plc
The Roper Family Charitable Trust
Rothschild Foundation
Royal Cornwall Museum
Graham & Ann Rudd
Sir Nigel Rudd
Russell New
The J. S. & E. C. Rymer Charitable Trust
The Earl St Aldwyn
The Sammermar Trust
Scarfe Charitable Trust
Andrew & Belinda Scott
The Trustees of the Finnis Scott Foundation
Shaftesbury PLC
Mr W. Sharpe
The Shears Foundation
Robert Shields, DL
Smith & Williamson
South West of England Regional Development Agency
Caroline M. Southall
Stuart M. Southall
Southampton City Council
The Jessie Spencer Trust
Hugh & Catherine Stevenson
Mrs Andrew Stewart-Roberts, OBE
Mr Michael Stone
Mr Peter Stormonth Darling
The Stratford-upon-Avon Town Trust
Strutt and Parker
Suffolk County Council, through the Association for Suffolk Museums
Surrey County Council
The John Swire 1989 Charitable Trust
The Tanner Trust
Tennants Auctioneers
Tesco Charity Trust
The Thistle Trust
Prof. Caroline Tisdall
Trusthouse Charitable Foundation
Gladwyn Turbutt
TWM Business Partners
Tyne & Wear Museums
University College Falmouth
University of Derby
University of Essex
David & Grizelda Vermont
Wakefield Metropolitan District Council
Robert & Felicity Waley-Cohen
The Peggy Walker Charitable Trust
The Walland Trust Fund
John Wates Charitable Trust
Leslie Weller, DL
The Welton Foundation
West Sussex County Council
Mr & Mrs David Wigglesworth
Wilkin & Sons Ltd
Mr & Mrs Jo Windsor
Peter Wolton Charitable Trust
Michael J. Woodhall, FRICS
Sir Philip Wroughton
Mrs Angela Yeoman

First published in 2013 by The Public Catalogue Foundation, Printed Catalogue Division,
8 Frederick's Place, London, EC2R 8AB

The responsibility for the accuracy of the information presented in this catalogue lies solely with the holding collections. Suggestions that might improve the accuracy of the information contained in this catalogue should be sent to the relevant collection and emailed to info@thepcf.org.uk.

978-1-909475-28-1

Designed by Sally Jeffery

Printed in the UK by Gomer Press Ltd on paper sourced from sustainable forests